To Charles Day Dilks
with best wishes for good fossil collecting

Horace G. Richards

Philadelphia   December 11, 1953

RECORD OF THE ROCKS

The Geological Story of Eastern North America

By

HORACE G. RICHARDS

ASSOCIATE CURATOR OF GEOLOGY AND PALEONTOLOGY
ACADEMY OF NATURAL SCIENCES, PHILADELPHIA

LECTURER IN GEOLOGY
UNIVERSITY OF PENNSYLVANIA

THE RONALD PRESS COMPANY ⟩ NEW YORK

Library of Congress Catalog Card Number: 52-10825

PRINTED IN THE UNITED STATES OF AMERICA

PREFACE

In attempting to interpret the record of the rocks and construct a history of our physical world, the historical geologist realizes that the record is never complete in any one place. Certain parts of the world, particularly those which have been inundated frequently in the course of many millennia, contain more fossils than do others, and their history, consequently, can be recorded more completely. In his long specialization in the eastern part of North America, the author has found that region to be particularly rich in source materials for the study of general geology. This textbook, therefore, has been organized to show the geological development of the earth by an examination of the formations which are found in the Atlantic Coastal Plain and the Appalachian Mountain area. It is believed that this regional emphasis will provide a richer content for the student of general geology, and will prove particularly valuable, also, to students taking courses in local and field geology.

The introductory chapters are given over to a summary of the principles of geology, a general classification of plants and animals, and a review of various theories concerning the origin of the earth. More attention is devoted to the Mesozoic and Cenozoic periods than is usual in textbooks on historical geology to capitalize on the fact that fossils dating from these periods are particularly abundant in the Atlantic Coastal Plain region. This special emphasis, together with new interpretations based on the author's original field studies, will make this book valuable as a reference work.

Many geologists and institutions have assisted in the preparation of this book. The preliminary manuscript was read by Dr. B. F. Howell (Princeton University), Dr. Robert Nichols (Tufts College), and Mr. Eugene Richardson (Chicago Natural History Museum). Furthermore, certain sections were read by Dr. E. H. Colbert (American Museum of Natural History), Dr. Helgi Johnson (Rutgers University), Mr. Meredith E. Johnson (New Jersey Geological Survey), Dr. R. W. Stone (retired State Geologist of Pennsylvania), and Mr. Paul Dike (University of Pennsylvania). All of these individuals offered valuable suggestions.

The majority of the fossils illustrated are from the collections of the Academy of Natural Sciences of Philadelphia, while a few were borrowed from Princeton University, the United States National

Museum, or elsewhere. Among the institutions which supplied illustrative material are: The Academy of Natural Sciences of Philadelphia, The American Museum of Natural History, The Chicago Natural History Museum, The Colorado Natural History Museum, The New Jersey State Museum, The New York State Museum, The Pennsylvania Topographic and Geologic Survey, and The University of Kansas Natural History Museum. Specific acknowledgment of these contributions is given under the respective pictures. Those illustrations which are not credited to other sources are the author's.

Special acknowledgment must be given to the Hughes Tool Company of Houston, Texas, for permission to reproduce the series of paintings of J. P. Cowan of restorations of various periods in the earth's history, and to Dr. Thornton Page of the Yerkes Observatory of the University of Chicago for permission to reproduce the series of sketches illustrating the various theories of the origin of the earth. Mr. Wilhelm Bock kindly allowed the use of some illustrations from several forthcoming papers on the Triassic fauna and flora of Pennsylvania.

A special word of appreciation must be given to Dr. Carl O. Dunbar, of Yale University, and to his publisher, John Wiley and Sons, for very kindly giving permission to base some of the paleogeographic maps of this book on the series published in his *Historical Geology*. While many of the present maps are based on those of Dr. Dunbar, they have been entirely redrawn with changes or additions based on recent literature and suggestions by various colleagues of the author. The maps of the Cretaceous and Cenozoic shore lines of the Coastal Plain, although based on various published reports, are original with this work. The drawings of many of the maps and sketches in this book were done by Alexander Phillips and James Ruhle.

Finally, the author wishes to thank the members of his family as well as his many friends and students who have offered suggestions or given helpful criticism during the writing of this book.

HORACE G. RICHARDS

Philadelphia
November, 1952

CONTENTS

ILLUSTRATIONS

ILLUSTRATIONS

CHARTS

RECORD OF THE ROCKS

GEOLOGICAL TIME TABLE

Era		Period or Epoch	Years Ago (to beginning of period)	Popular Name
CENO-ZOIC	"Quater-nary"	RECENT	12,000	AGE OF MAN
		PLEISTOCENE	1,000,000	ICE AGE
	"Ter-tiary"	PLIOCENE	12,000,000	AGE OF MAMMALS
		MIOCENE	28,000,000	
		OLIGOCENE	40,000,000	
		EOCENE	60,000,000	
		PALEOCENE	70,000,000	
MESOZOIC		CRETACEOUS	130,000,000	AGE OF REPTILES
		JURASSIC	155,000,000	
		TRIASSIC	185,000,000	
PALEOZOIC		PERMIAN	210,000,000	AGE OF COAL
		PENNSYLVANIAN	250,000,000	
		MISSISSIPPIAN	265,000,000	
		DEVONIAN	320,000,000	AGE OF FISHES
		SILURIAN	360,000,000	
		ORDOVICIAN	440,000,000	AGE OF INVERTEBRATES
		CAMBRIAN	520,000,000	
PROTEROZOIC / ARCHEOZOIC		PRE-CAMBRIAN	2,000,000,000+	

INTRODUCTION

I do not know what I may appear to the world; but to myself I seem
to have been only like a boy playing on the seashore, and diverting myself in now and then finding a smoother pebble or a prettier shell than
ordinary, whilst the great ocean of truth lay all undiscovered before me.
—Isaac Newton

Not so many years ago, in attempting to determine the age of the
earth, theologians added together the ages of the various people mentioned in the Old Testament and deduced that the world was created
in the year 4004 b.c. Scientists were, of course, not satisfied with this
interpretation. In the words of the well-known physicist Sir William
Thomson (Lord Kelvin), in an address given at Glasgow in 1868,
"a very earnest effort was made by geologists at the end of the last
century, to bring geology within the region of physical science, to
emancipate it from the dictation of authority and from dogmatic hypotheses. The necessity for more time to account for geological phenomena than was generally supposed to be necessary became apparent to all who studied with candor and with accuracy the phenomena
presented by the surface of the earth." And thus the science of historical geology was born.

It is assumed that the natural forces and physical laws which are in
operation today have existed throughout geological time. The task of
interpreting the history of the earth in the light of these laws and on
the basis of the evidence of the rocks on the surface of, and buried
within, the outer crust of the earth, falls to the student of historical
geology. What geologists do try to do is to seek an explanation of the
many changes that have taken place to bring about the present conditions of the earth's surface.

The Law of Superposition tells us that the oldest rocks were laid
down at the bottom, with successively younger rocks deposited on top.
But this assumes that there were no disturbances and, as we shall see
in the chapters of this book, disturbances frequently took place which
caused lower (older) rocks to be folded or thrust on top of higher
(younger) deposits. Furthermore, in few if any places on the earth
has deposition been continuous throughout geologic time. There are
many missing links.

Nowhere is the record of the past entirely complete. At best, the
geologist can decipher only a very sketchy and "tabloid" history, and

3

to do this it is necessary for him to make comparative studies in a great many different parts of the world. Layers that are missing in one part of the world may well be present in another. Thus, by a process of correlation of a great many sections, over wide areas, it is frequently possible to fill in a few of the important missing links. Even the Grand Canyon of the Colorado, with its tremendous section covering most of geologic time, has important gaps in the record.

The record of the past geologic events is best told by those rocks that were deposited in ancient oceans, partly because of the greater abundance of fossils in such rocks. For this reason, our story is most complete in those areas which have frequently been covered by the sea. For example, the reader will note that many of the details of geologic history are told from studies of the region of the present Appalachian Mountains because this area was almost continuously covered by a sea for more than 300,000,000 years (during the Paleozoic era). The later uplift of this area, causing many of the ancient sea-deposited rocks to be exposed, has made it possible to decipher many—but by no means all—of the events of that past era. Similarly, many of our examples will be drawn from the Atlantic Coastal Plain because this region has been covered intermittently by the sea during the past 125,000,000 years (Cretaceous and Cenozoic periods). The partial emergence of the Coastal Plain has made it possible to decipher the history of the various submergences in this region.

On the other hand, fewer details can be worked out regarding the geological history of parts of New England. This region was above water during much of the geologic past and consequently fewer sediments were formed which could be used to interpret the past. Furthermore, many of the sediments that were formed in New England were obscured and complicated by volcanic action which has made their interpretation considerably more difficult.

The history of the plant and animal life throughout geologic time is also a part of historical geology. In fact, the fossil remains of ancient plants and animals are frequently of great help in determining the age of rocks in which they are preserved. Similar species of fossils in rocks that are widely separated usually indicate that the rocks are of the same geologic age. Furthermore, it is frequently possible to work out the evolutionary history of a group of plants or animals by studying the successive stages in a series of fossiliferous strata. Conversely, it is sometimes possible to determine the relative ages of different rocks by a study of the evolutionary development of groups of fossil organisms preserved in them.

Just as the record of the rocks is far from complete, so is the evolutionary history of fossils beset with many gaps. The historical geologist must interpret the record and fill in these gaps to the best of his ability. However, in view of the fact that the chances of an organism being preserved as a fossil are infinitesimal, some of the gaps in our record will probably always be present.

The story of historical geology to be told is not an exact chronicle, as would be the case of a well-documented history of our time. New information may well come to light and prove that there have been certain errors of interpretation of the record. With this thought in mind let us first examine the origins of some of the rocks that make up the earth's surface, and the ways in which geologic history may be interpreted from them. We shall then be in a better position to understand what is now known about the various chapters of the earth's history.

CHAPTER 1

HOW ROCKS ARE FORMED

Rocks are part of the language of geology, and one must become familiar with them in order to decipher the geological history of the earth. It is therefore necessary that we learn something about the kinds of rocks and the methods by which they are formed before we attempt to interpret the various chapters of geological history.

The Origin of Rocks.—In popular usage, the word "rock" means a hard, stony material. However, to a geologist the term refers to all materials composing the earth's shell. A rock may be hard or consolidated, such as sandstone, granite, and shale; it may also be loose and unconsolidated, such as sand, clay, gravel, and ash. Rocks fall into three natural classes according to their method of origin:

Sedimentary rocks are formed by the deposition of sediments by water or, less frequently, by the deposition of air-borne material. This class of rocks includes sandstone, limestone, shale, sand, and clay.

Igneous rocks (from the Latin *ignis* = fire) are formed by the solidification of hot liquid rock material, or magma, that comes from below the surface of the earth. This class includes granite, basalt, and diorite.

Metamorphic rocks (from the Greek *meta* = after, and *morphe* = form) have been derived from either of the other two classes by the recrystallization of the constituents of the rock. Thus, limestone becomes marble, sandstone becomes quartzite, and granite becomes gneiss.

Sedimentary Rocks

Sedimentary rocks are those which have been formed in layers, beds, or strata. Accumulations of soft material such as mud, sand, or clay are considered to be rock because they are composed of rock materials or fragments of rocks that have been naturally deposited. In time, and frequently under great pressure, these loose, unconsolidated sediments are cemented into hard rocks, which in turn are eventually weathered and transported by rivers to the sea, thus completing a cycle in sedimentation.

The time required for consolidation of the sediments varies greatly, under different conditions. In eastern North America, we find that

7

the majority of the Pre-Cretaceous sediments, those formed more than 100,000,000 years ago, are completely consolidated, while the younger deposits, those formed during and since the Cretaceous period, are predominantly loose and unconsolidated. However, this generalization cannot be applied to all rocks. Loose sands and clays are occasionally found in deposits as old as the Cambrian. For example, the Trempeleau sandstones of Cambrian age in Wisconsin are exceedingly soft and in some places weather to dune sand. On the other hand, late Pleistocene deposits in Florida and the West Indies, probably less than 25,000 years old, are completely consolidated limestones. In fact, even sediments of historically recent age are consolidated. Wind-blown limestones near Nassau on New Providence Island in the Bahamas, which have all the appearances of geologic age, contain coins and fragments of bottles that can date back only one or two hundred years (Figure 1).

Sedimentary rocks can be formed in ocean waters, in fresh water, or on land. Most sedimentary rocks, however, are laid down in the sea, a fact that can be demonstrated by the presence of fossil sea shells or the remains of other marine animals in most sedimentary rocks. In some cases, however, when fossils are absent, the marine origin of the rocks can be determined by the chemical nature of the material.

Sedimentary rocks whose origin has been fresh-water lakes are far less common than marine sediments. Still less common are aeolian or wind-blown sedimentaries. Again, proof of the origin can be found either in the presence of fresh-water or terrestrial types of fossils, in the occurrence of certain minerals, in the type of bedding, or in other geological evidence. For instance, certain characteristic cross-beddings indicate former deltas, while the presence of certain kinds of layers known as varves indicates deposition in glacial lakes. The characteristic red color of many Permian, Triassic, and Cretaceous deposits is often taken as an indication, although not proof, of their nonmarine origin, probably along the shores of lakes or rivers. This coloring is due to the oxidation of iron compounds in the rock and to the lack of vegetation. Decaying vegetation, had it been present, would have reduced or deoxidized the iron compounds in the rock and therefore bleached them.

There is no sharp distinction between marine and fresh-water sedimentary rocks, nor between water-laid and continental formations. The brackish water deposits of the Raritan formation of New Jersey could fall into either of the first two categories, while the great delta deposits of the Devonian of Pennsylvania indicate an ever-moving boundary between the land and the sea.

True continental deposits often contain the remains of land plants or animals, or they may give an indication of the former existence of land animals by the presence of fossil footprints. It should be pointed out, however, that the mere presence of fossils of land animals or plants

Fig. 1.   Aeolian limestone at "Queen's Staircase," Nassau, Bahamas. The recent age of some of this limestone can be demonstrated by the finding of old coins and broken bottles embedded therein.

does not prove the continental origin of a formation. It frequently happens that bones and wood are carried out to sea and deposited in a truly marine formation. Other evidence of a continental origin, although not necessarily positive proof, is the presence of "fossil" mud cracks in the rocks, similar to those now forming on river flats in hot climates. Such mud cracks are common in the Triassic rocks of Pennsylvania and New Jersey.

The wind is responsible for the deposition of certain continental formations. Sand dunes, such as those in deserts and along the shores of lakes and the ocean, are examples of wind-blown deposits. Fine silt is frequently transported considerable distances by wind, and in many parts of the world forms extensive deposits known as loess. Loess is frequently, but not always, associated with glaciers.

Unconsolidated Sedimentary Rocks

Gravel.—Unconsolidated sediments consisting of particles larger than 2 mm. (approximately the size of a pea) are called gravel. Qualifying adjectives such as "fine," "medium," and "coarse" are frequently used, depending upon the size of the particles. Individual pieces less than 64 mm. in diameter are usually called pebbles, while the larger ones are known as cobbles or boulders. Pebbles that have been carried great distances in streams or the ocean have usually been rounded by the action of currents, while the pebbles that have been carried only short distances by water, or which have been transported by glacial ice, usually have sharp or angular edges. The mineral quartz is a common constituent of the pebbles and boulders that occur in gravel deposits.

Sand.—Loose sediments composed of particles less than 2 mm. in diameter, and yet larger than $\frac{1}{16}$ mm., are known as sand. As in the case of gravel, qualifying adjectives such as "fine," "medium," and "coarse" are frequently used to describe a particular sand. While quartz is the most common constituent of sand, various other kinds are known. The coral sands of tropical beaches and the glauconitic (green) sands deposited on the ocean floor are two examples.

Silt and Clay.—These are sediments composed of particles smaller than $\frac{1}{16}$ mm. In addition to their smaller size, these materials also differ from sand in that they usually cohere when wet. While quartz is the chief mineral found in sands, clays and silts are largely made up of the mineral kaolin, which is formed from the decomposition of the feldspar of igneous rocks. Quartz grains formed by rock decomposition are larger and therefore heavier than those of kaolin. As a consequence, a separation takes place when they are transported by moving waters, the heavier sands being carried shorter distances than the lighter silts and clays. Hence, the presence of clay deposits usually indicates that they were laid down in quiet and possibly deeper water. Sand deposits usually indicate that they were laid down in shallower, more swiftly moving water.

The dividing line between silt and clay is arbitrary. Sediments composed of particles between $\frac{1}{256}$ mm. and $\frac{1}{16}$ mm. are usually considered silts, while those containing smaller particles are clays. With a little practice, silts can be distinguished from clays by their slightly gritty feel, due to the larger size of the grains.

Consolidated Sedimentary Rocks

Sandstone.—As implied by the name, this rock is consolidated sand. It is formed by the natural cementing of sand grains to make a solid mass or rock. One cementing agent is calcium carbonate, which may have (a) been present in small quantities in the water in which the original sand was laid down; (b) been dissolved from shells or other organic matter in the water; or (c) been added by ground water. Other usual cementing agents are silica, clay, iron oxide, and iron hydroxide (limonite).

Various kinds of sandstones derive their names from the other materials present in the rock. For example, *micaceous sandstones* contain considerable quantities of the mineral muscovite or mica. *Ferruginous sandstone,* often locally called "ironstone," contains conspicuous quantities of iron compounds. *Calcareous sandstone* contains calcium carbonate or lime, while *argillaceous sandstone* contains clay. Similarly, sandstone in which numerous grains of feldspar are mingled with the quartz is called *arkosic sandstone* or *arkose.* The presence of feldspar and mica usually indicates that the material forming the rock was derived from mechanically weathered and rapidly eroded granites or other igneous rocks in the general vicinity.

Conglomerate.—A rock composed largely of cemented pebbles, with sand filling the interspaces, is called conglomerate. There are many grades between a coarse sandstone and a conglomerate; the dividing line is indistinct, but is usually considered to be about 2 mm. in diameter. This is the same size distinction used in separating sand from gravel.

Shale.—Clay or mud, when hardened, becomes shale or mudstone. It usually occurs in beds composed of very thin layers that peel off when exposed to the air. The color varies, depending upon that of the original clay. Black shale may indicate the presence of iron sulphide, or possibly that the clay or mud was mixed with decomposing organic matter, while red shale implies the presence of iron oxide. As in the case of sandstone, there are numerous kinds of shale, depending upon its purity. The two most common varieties are calcareous or arenaceous (sandy) shale. Various intergrades are found between shale and sandstone and between shale and limestone.

Argillite is a compact mud rock without lamination. It is harder than true shale, weathers irregularly on exposure, and breaks with a curved (conchoidal) fracture when struck with a hammer. Argillite is common in the Triassic of New Jersey, where it has been quarried extensively as building stone. *Baked shale* is shale that has been in contact with an igneous intrusion. This rock is much harder than ordinary shale and is frequently difficult to distinguish from igneous rock.

Limestone.—This is a compact rock made up of calcium carbonate or a combination of calcium and magnesium carbonates. The main source of limestone is a limy ooze formed in the ocean by small particles of shells, corals, and other calcareous animals and plants. In some cases this rock is formed primarily of fragments of corals and is called *coralline limestone;* when shell fragments are dominant, it is termed *coquina.* Coquina is common in Pleistocene deposits of the South Atlantic coast and is now forming off the coast of Florida. Calcium carbonate is occasionally precipitated in the form of small spherules, usually less than ⅛ inch in diameter. These are called *oolites* because of their resemblance to fish eggs. Because of this resemblance to organic material, they are frequently mistaken for fossils. *Oolitic limestone* frequently occurs in the Pleistocene rocks of Florida, certain Paleozoic rocks of Pennsylvania, and elsewhere. Although limestone usually originates in sea water, fresh-water limestones are present in some formations, particularly in Wyoming and Michigan.

Siliceous limestone contains silica, either in the form of sand grains or as particles of sponge skeletons or other siliceous animals that lived in the sea. When the silica is dissolved and reformed in the limestone as irregular nodules or streaks of *chert* or *flint,* the rock is called *cherty limestone.*

Limestone is sometimes formed from limy mud and from sand-sized grains of limestone eroded from older limestones, then carried downstream and deposited in a nearby sea. Under certain favorable conditions, limestone can form as a chemical precipitate from sea water without any organic agency. The "milky" seas of the Bahamas may represent this kind of deposition.

Limestones can easily be distinguished from other hard rocks which they superficially resemble by the ease with which they may be scratched and by the fact that they effervesce when treated with an acid. Every geologist who finds it necessary to identify rocks in the field carries with him a small bottle of dilute hydrochloric acid. A drop of this will cause limestone to "fizz," forming small bubbles of carbon dioxide.

Dolomite.—When considerable magnesium is present in addition to calcium, the rock is known as a dolomite. Composed of calcium-magnesium carbonate $(CaMg)CO_3$ and named in honor of Dolomieu, an early French geologist, dolomite is firmer and more resistant than pure limestone. The European mountains known as the Dolomites derive their name from this rock, of which they are largely composed. Unlike pure limestone, dolomite does not effervesce with cold acid. There are various intergrades between limestone and dolomite and the term *dolomitic limestone* is frequently used.

Chalk.—This rock is a calcareous powder which, under the microscope, is found to consist largely of minute shells of foraminifera and other protozoa as well as of microscopic plants.

Glacial Deposits.—The material transported by glaciers is a special kind of sedimentary rock. Such a deposit may include accumulations of sand, gravel, clay, and boulders, all mingled together to form a *till*. This material was scoured from the soil and bedrocks of the land over which the glaciers advanced. Till from older glaciations, that has been completely consolidated—for example, those of the Pre-Cambrian and Permian—is known as a *tillite*.

Igneous Rocks

Igneous rocks have been formed by the solidification of molten masses or magmas which have upwelled from within the earth. Igneous rocks may be classified into two groups, according to their method of origin:

INTRUSIVE	EXTRUSIVE
dikes	lava flows
sills	tuffs
laccoliths	breccias
necks	
stocks	
batholiths	

An *intrusive* igneous rock is a magma that rose from the depths of the earth but cooled and solidified before reaching the surface. Although intrusive magmas were originally surrounded by other kinds of rocks, they are frequently exposed by the subsequent erosion of the softer overlying rocks. An *extrusive* igneous rock is a magma that has reached the surface and there solidified into a rock mass. These types of igneous rocks are frequently called volcanic rocks. Several of the more common igneous structures are shown diagrammatically in Figure 2.

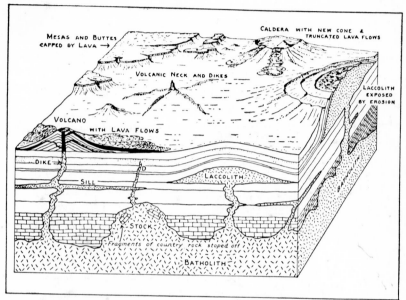

Fig. 2. Diagram showing a stock, batholith, dike, lacolith, volcano, and other igneous rocks. (By permission, from *Fundamentals of Earth Science,* by Henry D. Thompson, Copyright 1947 by Appleton-Century-Crofts, Inc.)

INTRUSIVE IGNEOUS ROCKS

Dike.—This is the simplest form of igneous rock. In this case a molten magma from deep within the earth flowed into a fissure or crevice in an existing rock. The fissure may have crossed rocks of either igneous, sedimentary, or metamorphic type; in the case of sedimentary rocks, the fissure filled by the magma always crossed the sedimentary plane at an angle. (If it flowed parallel to the plane, the cooled magma is considered to be a sill.) Dikes vary in length from a few yards to many miles, and in thickness from less than an inch to a thousand or more feet.

Sill.—When igneous rock occurs between and parallel to the layers of stratified rock, it is known as an *intrusive sheet* or *sill.* Sills are frequently found when the stratified rocks are distinctly bedded, as is the case with shales and sandstones, so the magma was able to penetrate between and separate the layers. When the sediments contain-

Fig. 3. Stone Mountain, Georgia. The eroded remnant of an even larger mass of granite that is thought to have been intruded during Paleozoic time.

ing the sills have been upturned by subsequent folding or faulting, it is not uncommon for the softer sedimentary rocks to be weathered away, leaving the intrusive sheet to form a conspicuous sedimentary feature. This was the origin of the Palisades along the Hudson River and the Watchung Mountains of New Jersey.

Laccolith.—In its typical form, a laccolith is a dome-shaped igneous rock with a flat base, intruded into sedimentary rocks between the bedding planes. The overlying beds are frequently raised in the form of a dome. Laccoliths are numerous in parts of western North America, for example in the Henry Mountains of Utah, but have not been recognized in eastern North America.

Necks.—Very often an extinct volcano will retain large masses of hardened magma in the conduit that leads from the crater to unknown depths. When erosion has removed the volcanic cone as well as the surrounding softer rocks, this hardened igneous mass of the conduit may persist in the form of a *volcanic neck,* marking the site of the original volcano. The structure is usually more or less circular in section and may vary from a few hundred yards to more than a mile in diameter. Volcanic necks of this kind form a conspicuous feature of the landscape of southern Arizona and New Mexico. Ship Rock in New Mexico is a well-known example of a volcanic neck.

Stocks.—Masses of igneous rock that have intruded into the upper layers of the earth and have solidified in a more or less cylindrical form are called *stocks.* Some of the granite hills of New England, as well as some of the mountains of the Piedmont Plateau, such as Stone Mountain, Georgia (Figure 3), are generally regarded as stocks.

Batholiths.—Very large stocks are called *batholiths.* These include the major granite mountain masses of New England and eastern Canada, as well as some of those of the Piedmont Plateau on the eastern edge of the Appalachians, from New York southward. A batholith differs from a laccolith in that the former is not known to have a definite floor.

EXTRUSIVE IGNEOUS ROCKS

Lava.—Magmas which reach the surface and flow over the surface rocks are called *lava.* When hardened, they are usually called *lava flows* or *extrusive sheets.* Although lava flows are usually associated with volcanoes, flows can occur independent of any actual volcanoes. These are known as fissure eruptions. They exist today in Iceland, and are known to have been frequent in the Columbian Plateau (Idaho, Washington, and Oregon) in the recent geologic past. There are two main kinds of lava, both of which are generally known by their Hawaiian names. *Aa* is jagged, fairly hard, and slow moving as a lava stream, while *pahoehoe* has a smooth, ropy, or wrinkled surface that results from the cooling of a fluid, fairly rapidly flowing lava stream. Figure 4 shows some extruded lava, now hardened, near Golden, Colorado.

Fig. 4. Butte at Table Rock near Golden, Colorado. Extruded lava flows from the resistant layer on top of the less resistant sandstone of the Denver formation. The lava was extruded during Paleozoic time, about 55,000,000 years ago.

Ash and Tuff.—In addition to molten lava, usually poured from the crater or side vent of a volcano, great quantities of ash and dust are often thrown into the air through the crater of the cone. When hardened, this ash is known as *tuff*. It not infrequently contains the imprints of fossil leaves if the ash fell on land, or it may contain the remains of fish or shells if the ash fell in the sea. The birth of the new volcano, Parícutin, in Mexico, has given scientists an opportunity to study the burial and fossilization of plants in volcanic ash and tuff.

Breccia.—In addition to the fine ash or dust ejected by an active volcano, considerable coarser material is also thrown into the air.

This material is classed as *lapilli* if less than 3 inches in diameter, and as volcanic bombs if larger. Bombs up to several feet in diameter are known. When hardened, this type of volcanic material is known as *volcanic breccia*. In some ways a breccia resembles a conglomerate, although in the former the pebbles are angular, while in the latter they are well rounded.

Physicochemical Classification of Igneous Rocks

So far, we have discussed igneous rocks according to their mode of origin. It is also possible to classify them according to their physical-chemical composition. However, since this classification is based upon a more or less detailed knowledge of mineralogy as well as chemistry and physics, it will be mentioned only very briefly here.

In general, igneous rocks are classed as *acidic* or *basic*, depending upon the amount of silica (SiO_2) present. Rocks of high silica content are usually light in color and of relatively low specific gravity. Basic rocks, on the other hand, contain a considerable amount of lime, magnesia, and iron. They are usually dark in color because of their iron content. It is difficult to set the boundary line between acidic and basic rocks, and many rocks are classed as *intermediate*.

A working knowledge of mineralogy is required to identify most igneous rocks; consequently, even superficial descriptions necessitate the use of numerous technical terms, especially the names of various minerals. Among the more common igneous rocks are the following:

Granite.—An acidic igneous rock which may be white, gray, pink, red, or green. It is a coarse-grained rock made up of an aggregate of visible crystals of quartz and feldspar, with a minor amount of other minerals such as hornblende and mica. Granite is the most abundant rock in the continental crust of the earth and forms the main constituent of batholiths.

Rhyolite.—An acidic igneous rock, usually light in color. Most or all of its crystals are of microscopic size.

Syenite.—An acidic rock with less silica than granite. Most syenites are composed of orthoclase feldspar and hornblende, with plagioclase feldspar, apatite, and magnatite as accessory minerals.

Diorite.—A coarse-grained basic (or intermediate) rock composed of feldspar and some ferromagnesian minerals. It contains little or no quartz.

Gabbro.—A coarse-grained rock very similar to diorite, but with dark minerals predominating.

Basalt.—The fine-grained equivalent of gabbro. It is impossible to distinguish the individual grains with a hand lens.

Diabase.—Similar to gabbro or basalt, but with the feldspar crystals arranged in a texture of long and interlaced narrow rods. The individual grains can be distinguished with a hand lens. The term *trap-rock* is frequently used for various basic igneous rocks including diorite, gabbro, basalt, and diabase.

Metamorphic Rocks

Metamorphic rocks are igneous or sedimentary rocks that have been altered by heat, pressure, chemical action, or by all three metamorphic agents. This process is known as *metamorphism*. When sedimentary rocks are metamorphosed they become harder and more crystalline and lose their original laminations, while the fossils usually become distorted or are entirely destroyed. When igneous rocks are metamorphosed they frequently become banded, and will cleave or split into definite layers. Some metamorphic rocks have been so completely altered that it is almost impossible to determine their original nature, or even whether they were sedimentary or igneous. This is true of some of the schists and gneisses in the Philadelphia area.

Quartzite.—Sandstone that has been altered, probably under great pressure, becomes quartzite. Silica has been deposited on the individual sand grains, causing the interspaces to be completely filled and the rock to be much harder. When a sandstone is broken, it breaks *around* the grains, while quartzite, when broken, breaks *across* the grains.[1]

Slate.—Metamorphosed shale becomes slate. The original bedding appears only as color bands, while a secondary cleavage is formed which is usually oblique to the original bedding. This characteristic secondary cleavage is known as *slaty cleavage*. It was caused by the compression to which the rock has been subjected, so that slate from different localities, or even from various parts of the same quarry, may have very different angles between the cleavage bedding and that of the original shale. The color of slate varies between black,

---

[1] In some cases, when the sand grains are completely bound together by the cementing action of silica, the resulting quartzite may be classed as a sedimentary rock.

FIG. 5. Wissahickon gneiss showing quartz vein, folding, and joint cracks. West Manayunk, Pennsylvania.

gray, green, and red, depending mainly upon the color of the original shale. Finally, slate is always much harder than shale.

Marble.—When limestones or dolomites are altered by heat or pressure, or both, they become marble. The individual crystals have increased in size with the result that marble is harder and more compact than limestone. Most marbles take a good polish. If the original rock was dolomitic limestone or dolomite, the metamorphosed product is known as *dolomite marble,* while pure carbonate of lime produces *lime marble.*

Gneiss.—This is a banded, coarsely textured metamorphic rock with a rough foliation. Feldspar is an important constituent. It is possible for either sedimentary or igneous rocks to become metamorphosed to a gneiss, and it is frequently impossible to determine the character of the original rock. Probably a great deal of gneiss was formed by the compression and flow of granite, and this is probably the origin of part of the Wissahickon and Baltimore gneiss of Pennsylvania and Maryland (Figure 5). Gneisses are frequently called *granite gneiss, diorite gneiss,* or *syenite gneiss,* depending upon their composition.

Schist.—This is a crystalline rock with finer texture than gneiss and usually darker in color. It may contain mica (*mica schist*), hornblende (*hornblende schist*), or talc (*talc schist*). The common variety in New England and the eastern Appalachians is mica schist, as in the Wissahickon formation. Most schist is thought to have been formed, by metamorphism, from impure limestone or, less frequently, from conglomerates and shales. On the other hand, some igneous rocks may also have been metamorphosed to schist, and it is frequently very difficult or impossible to determine the origin of a schist. It is related to a gneiss on the one hand and to a shale on the other. A schist splits easily into bent or crumpled layers, the so-called *schistose cleavage.* The layers are not as uniform as in *slaty cleavage,* nor as coarse as in *gneissic cleavage.*

Metamorphic rocks are characterized by folds and faults (see Chapter 3). In all cases, these rocks were given their present character during periods of active movement of the earth's crust. In a sense, metamorphic rocks have two different geologic ages, that of the rocks from which they were derived, and the age during which metamorphism actually took place. In general, however, the original age of the rock is used.

The following table shows the relationship of the principal kinds of rocks:

	SEDIMENTARY ROCKS		METAMORPHIC ROCKS
	Unconsolidated	Consolidated	
	silt and clay	→ shale	→ slate; schist
	sand	→ sandstone	→ quartzite; quartzitic schist
	gravel	→ conglomerate	→ conglomerite; gneiss
	limy ooze	→ limestone	→ marble
	shells	→ coquina	→ marble

IGNEOUS ROCKS

granite; syenite	→ gneiss
felsite; tuff	→ slate; schist
diorite; gabbro; diabase	→ schist; serpentine

FURTHER READING

The references for Chapters 1–4 will be found at the end of Chapter 4.

CHAPTER 2

THE GEOLOGIC TIMETABLE

Just as the historian divides the history of the world or that of a country into periods such as the Renaissance and the Victorian era, so does the geologist find it convenient and necessary to separate geologic time into various divisions and subdivisions. The historian is dealing with more recent and accurate records and is usually able to date his events in actual years. Such accurate dating is not possible for the geologist, who has to be content with correlating events within eras and periods and can determine only an approximate date in terms of years.

Eras.—The events of the earth's geological history seem to group themselves naturally into five major time units which are called *eras*. From the *oldest to the youngest*, these are:

5. Cenozoic
4. Mesozoic
3. Paleozoic
2. Proterozoic
1. Archeozoic

Much less is known about the two earlier eras than about the later ones, largely because their fossil record is almost completely blank. Life did exist during these eras, but we know very little about it. Archeozoic life was probably limited to small unicellular organisms that have not been preserved in the rocks. While some physiologic advances had been made by Proterozoic time, life was still relatively simple and unfamiliar, and the forms were not very well adapted for preservation as fossils. The rocks that were laid down during these first two eras are so ancient, probably more than 500,000,000 years old, and have been subjected to so much metamorphism, that any fossils which may have been present have been in great part destroyed or are so altered as to be unrecognizable.

The chronological history of the three later eras has been deciphered much more completely with the aid of the fossil record. Consequently, these eras have been divided into *periods* and the periods in turn into smaller subdivisions such as *epochs* and *ages*. The table on page 2 shows the generally accepted classification of the eras and periods.

23

These are arranged in chronological sequence, with the oldest at the bottom.

Dividing Lines.—There are, of course, no sharp dividing lines between the periods, or even between the eras. However, the earth seems to have undergone certain episodes of intense activity such as mountain building, vulcanism, and the like. Many of these episodes were almost world-wide in effect while others were purely local. The world-wide episodes of mountain building, together with the accompanying uplift and erosion, form very convenient boundary lines for the major periods of geologic time. Furthermore, these changes were usually accompanied by important changes in plant and animal life. During the times when the ancient seas retreated from the land the marine animals living in their waters continued to evolve. When the seas returned, they brought with them new forms of marine life. An unconformity caused by a long erosion period accompanying, or following mountain building, may account for a significant break in the faunal record, and thus be an indication of a dividing line.

It must also be emphasized that these divisions are largely arbitrary and that the dividing lines are not necessarily the same in different parts of the world. In some places, periods or eras seem to merge into one another without any perceptible break. However, the classification given in the table on page 2 is the one usually used by American geologists and is a convenient tool for the discussion and study of fossil life.

Systems.—All the stratified rocks of any period make up a *system*. That is, we speak of rocks of the Cambrian or Cretaceous system.

Groups, Series, and Formations.—The rocks of a system are still further subdivided into *groups, series,* and *formations*. For example, the rocks of Late Cretaceous time make up the Gulf System, while various smaller units of the Gulf System include the Matawan group and the Merchantville formation. Actually, the formation is the fundamental unit, and we should perhaps say that formations are combined into series, and series into groups. A formation is defined as the smallest mappable stratigraphic unit. Occasionally, formations are still further subdivided into *zones* and *facies,* generally based on faunal changes or on purely local conditions that are not mappable over a wide area.

Thousands of formations have been described from different parts of the world. The tables preceding Chapters 9 to 26 list the main formations of that period, as described from New York, New Jersey, and nearby states. Any attempt to list and correlate all the formations described from eastern North America would require a very large sheet of paper and would be much too complicated for this book. A series of correlation charts of surface formations of North America is being prepared under the auspices of the National Research Council and the Geological Society of America, and the first few have already been published in the *Bulletin* of the Society. The American Association of Petroleum Geologists is now planning a somewhat similar series of charts emphasizing the subsurface formations.

A formation is named for the place where it is first described, that locality becoming its *type locality*. A formation described in one area may, upon further study, prove to be equivalent to another formation previously described from another place. In that case, according to the rule of priority, the earlier name takes precedence. As an example, the Cape Fear formation was described by L. W. Stephenson for some Cretaceous deposits in North Carolina. Later work has shown that this formation is apparently continuous with the Tuscaloosa formation described in 1887 from Alabama. Therefore the name "Cape Fear formation" has been dropped, and that of the Tuscaloosa extended into North Carolina.[1]

Sometimes it is not wise to extend formation names over a wide area. For example, the Raritan formation described from New Jersey is probably contemporaneous with the Tuscaloosa farther south. However, since this cannot be proved definitely, and since the distances are so great, geologists prefer to retain the two different names. Correlation tables, such as those given in abbreviated form at the beginning of various chapters in this book, and more extensively in the publications of the Geological Society of America, the American Association of Petroleum Geologists, and the United States Geological Survey, aid us in understanding the nomenclature of the formations in different places.

While geologists are usually careful to select good outcrops or exposures for their type sections, some of the earlier workers did not always designate an exact locality. For instance, the Cape May formation of southern New Jersey (Pleistocene) has no precise type locality, having been described from the "Cape May Peninsula."

It was formerly considered poor practice to name a formation known only from a well; consequently, subsurface formation names were not considered valid. However, with the recent advances in a subsurface geology largely brought about by the oil industry, it now seems desirable to recognize such formational names. When a subsurface for-

[1] According to the customary usage of the United States Geological Survey, an abandoned or obsolete formation name, when used at all, is placed within quotation marks.

mation is subsequently shown to be equivalent to a named surface formation, the former name is usually dropped. In a few cases, confusion has resulted because of the uncertainty of the exact correlation between the surface and the subsurface formations.

Sometimes a formation name is given that has been used previously for another formation in a different place. In this case, the duplicate name is invalid, and must be dropped. For example, the term "Murfreesboro zone" was used for a phase of the Miocene in North Carolina. The zone was named for the town of Murfreesboro, North Carolina, and was regarded as part of the Yorktown formation. It was later found that the name Murfreesboro had previously been used for an Ordovician formation in Tennessee, named for a town of the same name. Therefore the name for the Miocene zone was dropped. A new name could have been found, but it is now generally regarded merely as zone No. 1 of the Yorktown formation.

Fortunately for the geologist attempting to name a new formation, an excellent book by Grace Wilmarth of the United States Geological Survey [2] lists and defines every stratigraphic name, formation, group, and series used in the United States up to 1936. It is now relatively simple to avoid duplication of stratigraphic names. Duplication of a formation name from North America with one from another part of the world is permissible.

Often a formation will be described and later work will show it to be made up of several major units, each worthy of formational rank. In that case, the original name is advanced to the rank of a group, with the smaller units becoming formations. Consequently, there are often differences of opinion as to whether a certain unit constitutes a group or a formation. In the tables in this book, many units are given as formations whereas some geologists would prefer to regard them as groups. However, here the smaller names are omitted except when deemed essential for an understanding of the geological history.

Fourfold Division of Geologic Time.—At one time geologists divided geologic time into three major divisions which they called Primary, Secondary, and Tertiary. Later a fourth, or Quaternary, division was added. In general, these terms meant (1) the core of the mountains, mainly of crystalline rocks; (2) the flanks of the mountains, mainly of sandstones, shales, and limestones, and frequently fossiliferous; (3) the foothills, mostly of unconsolidated gravels, sands, and marls; and (4) alluvial, glacial, and other surface deposits. This classification has been largely abandoned because it was later shown

[2] Grace Wilmarth, *Lexicon of Geologic Names of the United States,* U.S. Geol. Surv. Bull. 896 (1938).

that the various divisions had little time significance. Accordingly, the first two names were dropped from general use, while the final two, Tertiary and Quaternary, have been retained as subdivisions of the Cenozoic Era. Some European geologists also retain the terms Primary and Secondary.

Most geologists today regard the Tertiary as a period of the same order of duration as the Cambrian, Ordovician, or other periods of the Paleozoic. The subdivisions of the Tertiary, such as Eocene, Miocene, etc., are epochs, each of relatively short duration.

In a recent book, Dr. Richard F. Flint, of Yale University, has suggested that the terms Tertiary and Quaternary be dropped altogether, and that all the epochs, Paleocene to Recent, inclusive, be regarded as a single period of the Cenozoic Era. While the arguments for this change are undoubtedly very sound, it is difficult to drop terms that have been in usage for so many years. Therefore, the terms Tertiary and Quaternary will be used occasionally in this book, although an effort will be made to employ the smaller unit terms such as Eocene and Miocene, or the larger unit, Cenozoic, whenever practical.

The reader must not think, because so much space is devoted to the epochs of the Cenozoic, that they were of as long duration as the various periods of the Paleozoic. The fact is that more attention is given to these later and shorter episodes of geologic time for the simple reason that we know more about them. The rocks of these later epochs have been less altered by metamorphism, and less obscured by subsequent geologic events; it is therefore easier to decipher their history.

Time.—Throughout the book, frequent use of the term *time* will be found. Not only will we speak of Devonian time and Miocene time, but also of smaller units such as Yorktown time and Jackson time, named for individual formations or groups. This is a convenient terminology in discussing the geological history of a region. Recently there has been a general agreement among geologists to use the words "Lower," "Middle," and "Upper" for rock units and "Early," "Medial," and "Late" for time. Thus, the Lower Cambrian rocks were deposited during Early Cambrian time.

Measuring Geologic Time.—No one is able to measure geologic time accurately, in terms of years. In the case of a few Pleistocene deposits such as the varved clays laid down in layers in glacial lakes, a more or less accurate time estimate in years has been reached. In general, geologists are satisfied with the *relative* geologic age of a formation. Stratigraphic studies determine the chronological order of the formations, groups, and system, and some clue as to the relative age can frequently be obtained from criteria such as the thickness of the deposit or the kind of sediment, or by other means.

In recent years more scientific methods, primarily based on studies of the elements helium, lead, radium, actinium, and thorium in rocks, have been used to determine the age of certain formations. The figures given in the table on page 2 are based upon such studies, especially those of the National Research Council.

Various radioactive elements are used in determining the age of certain rocks. For example, some igneous rocks contain the mineral pitchblende, which in turn contains the element uranium. This element is known to disintegrate at a rate that is remarkably uniform under varying conditions. Atoms of helium are emitted, and the final products of the disintegration process are helium and lead. The rate of disintegration can be determined by counting the lead atoms given off within a specified time from a definite amount of uranium.

Experiments of this kind have shown that 1 gram of uranium produces 1/7,600,000,000 gram of lead per year. From this the following formula has been devised:

$$t = \frac{\text{Pb}}{\text{U}} \times 7{,}600{,}000{,}000$$

which means that age of the rock t is equal to the lead Pb–uranium U ratio, times 7,600,000,000. This method is useful only in the case of unweathered igneous rocks containing uranium.

The oldest rocks so far dated by the lead–uranium ratio method are some Archeozoic pegmatites on Winnipeg River, Manitoba, where the age determination is 2,300,000,000 years. The use of other radioactive elements in determining the age of igneous rocks gives comparable figures. The lead method is particularly adapted for age measurements of pegmatites, while the helium method is better suited for magnetites. Because of the gaseous nature of helium, and the fact that it may escape from rocks, this method is not as accurate for the age determination of the most ancient Pre-Cambrian rocks. A method has recently been devised to measure the age of certain rocks, especially pegmatites, by a study of the element strontium. This is especially adaptable to rocks of very early Pre-Cambrian age.

Dr. W. F. Libby and his staff at the Institute for Nuclear Research at the University of Chicago have developed a method of determining the age of wood and peaty material by means of a study of radioactive carbon, C^{14}. This isotope of carbon is present in the atmosphere and in all living organisms, in fixed proportion to ordinary carbon. When the organism dies, the radioactive carbon (C^{14}) disintegrates at a steadily decreasing rate; therefore, the ratio between radiocarbon and ordinary carbon diminishes over a period of time.   In about 5,568 years it is half gone, and in about 20,000 or 25,000 years it is entirely gone.   The age of certain woods and carbonaceous material can therefore be determined with very little error by means of a study of this radioactive material.   Unfortunately, the method works only for specimens younger than 25,000 years.   It is, however, very useful for dating archaeological material as well as specimens of late Pleistocene age.

FURTHER READING

The references for Chapters 1–4 will be found at the end of Chapter 4.

CHAPTER 3

HOW GEOLOGISTS READ ROCKS

We have discussed the various types of rocks and learned something about the methods by which they were formed. We have also briefly examined the geological timetable and learned that the earth has been in existence for a very long period of time, probably something over two billion years. Next, it will be necessary for us to examine the methods by which the geologist attempts to read and interpret the rocks.

We have seen that the consecutive layers or beds of the same kind of material, laid down during a continuous time interval, make up a *formation* which is usually named from the place where it was first described. Various structures within a formation frequently give clues to the method of origin of the formation, and therefore help us decipher the geological history of the region. Structures are present in sedimentary, igneous, and metamorphic rocks, but are probably most significant and less difficult to study in the first of these three groups.

Sedimentary Rock Structures

Strike and Dip.—Sedimentary rocks are usually approximately horizontal when laid down, but in many cases crustal movements cause them to become tilted or folded. The angle at which a bed slants downward beneath the surface is called the *dip*. The *strike* is the direction of the horizontal edge of the inclined bed, and is always at right angles to the dip. The dip is measured in direction and degrees, while the strike is given in direction. Strike and dip are shown diagrammatically in Figure 6.

Syncline and Anticline.—When the dips are uniform over a wide area (that is, with the same angle), the beds are said to form a *monocline*. However, it is often found that the angle will vary, indicating a fold in the strata. When these strata are folded in the form of an arch, they are said to form an *anticline*. On the other hand, when they dip to form a trough, they form a *syncline*. Large series of synclines are frequently termed *synclinoria*, and large series of anticlines are called *anticlinoria*.

30

It should be remembered that the existence of a syncline or anticline in the rocks does not always find expression in the present topography of the region. A syncline may actually occur on a hill while an anticline may occupy a valley. A monocline, syncline, and anticline are shown diagrammatically in Figure 6, while Figure 7 shows an actual anticline.

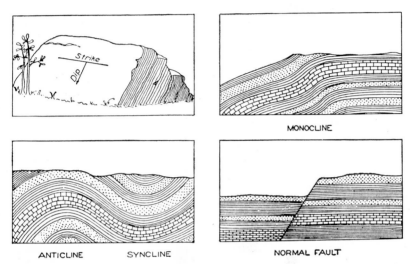

FIG. 6. Sketches illustrating strike, dip, monocline, anticline, syncline, and a normal fault. (Pennsylvania Geol. & Topog. Surv.)

Geosyncline and Geanticline.—It was formerly the practice for geologists to speak of synclines and anticlines of great width—100 miles or more—as geosynclines and geanticlines. However, in recent geological literature the term geanticline has been dropped and a geosyncline is generally thought of as a sagging area of deposition which contains considerable quantities of sediment. Thus a geosyncline, when folded, may consist of numerous synclines and anticlines. The term geosyncline is used rather frequently in this book because, throughout the course of geologic history, a great many sediments have been deposited in the major geosynclines of the world. In the region emphasized in this book the most important geosyncline is that of the Appalachian region. A comparable trough is that of the Cordilleran region, while other and less important geosynclines occur elsewhere, an example being the Ouachita trough in Arkansas.

Many geologists think that a major geosyncline is now forming along the Gulf of Mexico, from Louisiana to Texas. The great quantities of silt carried down the Mississippi River have, since the beginning of the Tertiary Period, produced sediments some 30,000 feet

Fig. 7. Anticline in Devonian rocks along the Juniata River near Amity Hall, Pennsylvania.

in thickness. This is comparable to the thickness of the sediments washed into the Appalachian Trough during the Paleozoic Era. Perhaps some mountains analogous to the Appalachian Range will rise there at some future geologic time. The location of this future range is a matter for speculation. Perhaps it will be parallel to the Gulf Coast and extend through northern Louisiana and Arkansas, or perhaps it will be south of the Gulf Coast, in the present Gulf of Mexico or the West Indies.

Faulting.—All rocks at or near the surface of the earth are cut by transverse cracks called *joints,* usually occurring at right angles to the bedding. Joints are frequently very useful in connection with the mining of coal, the building of tunnels, the excavation of quarries and other construction work. Joints are also useful in carrying ground water; at other times they present serious problems to engineers.

When there has been movement between two blocks of the earth along these joint planes, or along other large fractures in the earth's crust, we speak of the crack or fracture as a *fault.* Movement along a fault may amount to only a few inches, or it may be of a magnitude

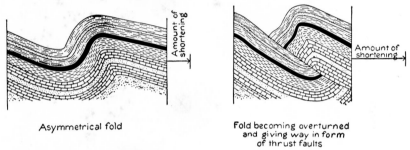

Asymmetrical fold

Fold becoming overturned
and giving way in form
of thrust faults

Fig. 8. Sketches illustrating thrust faulting. (Pennsylvania Geol. & Topog. Surv.)

of several thousand feet. If the accompanying movement is merely up or down, we have what is called a *normal fault.* On the other hand, when fault planes are inclined at a low angle, the strata on opposite sides may be shoved past each other. If the movement has been such as to cause the beds on the upper side of the inclined fault plane to override the beds of the lower side, we have a *thrust fault* or *reverse fault.* Reverse faults indicate compression of the strata where they are formed, while normal faults show tension. In the case of thrust faulting, or overthrusts, rocks of a much younger age may overlie older rocks. An example is the Lewis Overthrust of Glacier National Park, where ancient Pre-Cambrian rocks were thrust on top of much younger Cretaceous sediments. Figure 6 shows a diagrammatic representation of a normal fault, while Figure 8 shows a thrust fault.

Folding.—We have seen that rocks laid down in a horizontal plane become folded to form synclines and anticlines, and frequently, under greater stress, become broken to form normal or thrust faults. This folding process is beautifully demonstrated in the Appalachian Mountains of Pennsylvania, Maryland, and West Virginia. Apparently a tremendous force has folded, crumpled, and broken the Paleozoic rocks that were originally laid down horizontally on the bottom of an inland sea which once covered this region. This folding and faulting involved a considerable amount of crustal shortening. According to an estimate by the late Dr. George H. Ashley, formerly State Geologist of Pennsylvania, the shortening between Altoona and Philadelphia may have been as much as 100 miles. "If the western part of the state stood still when the folding took place, then the eastern end may have been where is now the Atlantic Ocean." This period of folding and faulting took place in connection with the so-called "Appalachian Revolution" (period of mountain building) during the Permian Period, which will be further discussed in Chapter 16.

Folding usually takes place in a region where there has previously been a great amount of sedimentation and crustal sagging. For instance, prior to the uplift and folding of the Appalachian Mountains, some 30,000 feet of sediments had been deposited in the trough or geosyncline that occupied the present position of the Appalachian Mountains.

Folding accompanying mountain building is a very complex process. It is frequently associated with a general uplift such as that which contributed to the formation of the Appalachians, the Rockies, and other important mountain ranges. Furthermore, the action ordinarily continued for a very long period of time, usually one or more major geologic periods. The first indications of an uplift of the Appalachians took place in the Ordovician period and is called the Taconic Revolution. The uplift produced mountains in New York State and New England. Uplift, and perhaps folding, also took place in Pennsylvania long after the major Appalachian Revolution of Permian time. The sinking of the Appalachian Trough, which may have brought about the later formation of the mountains, was intermittent rather than continuous, and was interspaced with long periods of stability and temporary uplift.

No completely satisfactory explanation has ever been given for the cause of such folding. Horizontal compressive forces within the earth's crust undoubtedly played an important role. It also seems probable that when sinking had proceeded to considerable depths, the rocks reached a zone of higher temperatures. They were expanded by the heat and thus rendered soft and more susceptible to crushing and folding.

Unconformities.—We have found that a formation represents the continuous deposition of uniform kinds of sediment. Usually, after the deposition of sediment on the bottom of the sea for a considerable length of time, some earth movement causes the land to be uplifted, with the result that the former sea bottom becomes dry land and erosion takes the place of deposition. When the region is again submerged by the sea, new deposits are laid down on the irregular and eroded surface of the former formation. Such a relationship is called a *disconformity* if the new beds are essentially parallel to the older beds, and an *unconformity* if the older beds had been tilted or folded before the deposition of the new beds. In practice, however, many geologists use the term unconformity for both kinds of breaks.

If the second formation is laid down on the first without any intervening period of erosion, the two formations are said to be *conformable*. In many cases it is difficult to recognize the dividing line between two conformable formations. Frequently there will be a change in lithology, as from sandstone to shale, although the transition is often so gradual that it is difficult to pick the exact boundary.

Since geologic history is interpreted from sediments and from the fossils in the sediments, unconformities and disconformities represent important breaks in the record. Fortunately, however, a break that may occur in one region may be equivalent to a continuous stratigraphic section elsewhere; in this way it is possible to supply the locally missing pages of geologic history. For example, if we had only the rocks of New Jersey to work with we would have no record of events taking place during the Carboniferous or Jurassic periods, for no deposits of those ages are presented in that state. However, by a comparison with the section in other parts of the country, we are able to infer a few of the events that took place during these periods. Such breaks are especially important in the study of fossils. In an ideal section we might have representatives of all the evolutionary ancestors of a given animal. However, no section is complete and there are many unconformities or gaps. It is only by comparing sections from different parts of the world that we can obtain even a partially satisfactory record of the development of the various fossil groups. The study of the various layers of rocks, their unconformities, their origin, and their relative age as told by their fossils is called stratigraphy and is one of the most important subdivisions of geologic science.

Other Structures of Sedimentary Rocks.—Various other structures are present in some sedimentary rocks and help to interpret the conditions under which they were laid down. For example, deposits made in shallow water with strong shifting currents are frequently laid down in layers inclined at various angles. Because these layers do not conform to the main surface of sedimentation, the structure is called *cross-bedding*. Such deposits are frequently characteristic of deltas, while a very similar kind of cross-bedding by wind action can be seen in sand dunes.

Fig. 9. Ripple marks in Cambrian limestone at Raubsville, Pennsylvania. The limestone was originally deposited on the floor of the sea. The folding accompanying the Appalachian Revolution caused it to assume its present vertical position.

Other characteristic structures found in some sedimentary rocks are ripple marks (Figure 9), mud cracks, nodules, and concretions. The first two were formed in the same way as similar structures are being formed today. Concretions may form around fossils or other extraneous material in the sediment, while nodules may be formed by chemical action, as in the case of flint and chert. Amateur collectors frequently make the mistake of considering concretions and nodules as fossils.

Igneous Rock Structures

Structure is less conspicuous in igneous rocks than in those which are sedimentary in origin. The bedded structure of some igneous rocks is frequently caused by successive flows of lava. Lava sheets often assume a columnar structure in cooling because of contraction, the columns being six-sided prisms which stand at right angles to the cooling surface. Many examples of this structure can be seen in the traprock quarries of the Triassic igneous rocks of Pennsylvania and New Jersey.

Metamorphic Rock Structures

Some metamorphic rocks possess the structural features of the sedimentary or igneous rocks from which they were derived. In many cases, however, this structure has been obscured or lost during the process of metamorphism. For example, such metamorphic rocks as the Baltimore gneiss and the Wissahickon schist do not preserve the structure of the original rock; in fact we cannot even be sure what the original rock was. Instead, they have definite and characteristic structures of their own, such as foliation, contortion, and joints. Other structures such as cleavage in slate, gneiss, and schist are also the direct results of metamorphism.

FURTHER READING

The references for Chapters 1–4 will be found at the end of Chapter 4.

CHAPTER 4

MOVEMENTS OF LAND AND SEA

Changes in the relative position of sea and land have been taking place for countless millions of years and are taking place every day. It is not always possible to measure these changes or, in fact, even to know for certain that some changes are actually taking place. Let us first examine some changes that take place in the ocean every day, changes which can readily be observed and measured.

Movements of Ocean Water

Tides.—Anyone who has spent any time along the seashore knows that the boundary between sea and land is not always a sharp line. To begin with, along the shores of most oceans we find daily changes in tide that may cause the strand line to shift anywhere from a few inches to several miles. The fundamental cause of the tide is the differential attraction of the moon, and to a lesser extent of the sun, on the earth. Variations in the rise of the tide are dependent largely upon the nearness of the moon and upon the configuration of the shore line.

Along the east coast of the United States, south of Cape Cod, the tidal rise as a rule varies between three and six feet on a moderately sloping shore. Along most of these ocean beaches the intertidal zone varies from 10 to 50 feet in width. However, along some bays and inlets where the shoreland is very flat—for example, along Delaware Bay—this same tidal range of only five feet produces an intertidal zone more than a mile in width.

Farther to the northeast, owing to the constriction in the shore line along the Gulf of Maine, the tides rise some 25 feet. However, because of the relatively steep slope of the shoreland, the intertidal or littoral zone has not increased greatly in width. Still farther to the north, in the narrow waters of the Bay of Fundy, we encounter tremendous tides, ranging up to 40 feet, and at the time of the abnormal spring tides, to as much as 70 feet in height. Here, even with the relatively steep shores of New Brunswick and Nova Scotia, there is often a decidedly noticeable shift in the strand line with the change from high to low tide. For example, the Gaspereau River

FIG. 10. Low and high tide at Wolfville, Nova Scotia.

Fig. 11. Low and high tide on Gaspereau River near Wolfville, Nova Scotia.

near Wolfville, Nova Scotia, is navigable for fairly large ships at high tide, while at low tide there is barely enough water to float a canoe (Figures 10 and 11). Another example of the tremendous change in the tide is found at the Reversing Falls at St. John, New Brunswick. Here, twice a day, with the change from low to high tide, there is a change in the direction of the falls or rapids.

Other remarkable tidal effects are to be noted along the shores of James Bay, the southern extension of Hudson Bay that projects

FIG. 12. Three-mile-wide intertidal zone, Charlton Island, James Bay, Canada.

southward into Ontario and Quebec. In the southern part of this Bay, near the estuary of the Moose River, there is a tidal rise of some 15 feet. Because of the extreme flatness of the shoreland, the intertidal zone may be as much as three to five miles in width (Figure 12). This phenomenon makes travel rather difficult in this region. One may be camping on the tidal flats, presumably far from the strand line, only to find the camp site covered by the sea a few hours later. Picture also the discomfort of the canoeist who, at the fall of the tide, finds himself stranded on a low sand hill, out of sight of water.

On the other hand, many seas of the world have no tide at all, or one that is measured only in inches. The Mediterranean is practically tideless, as is the Sea of Japan, parts of the Arctic Ocean, and various other bodies of water.

Tidal Bores.—Occasionally the incoming tide advances up a river or estuary as a solid wall or wave of water, known as a bore. This phenomenon can be seen on the Petitcodiac River at Moncton, New Brunswick, where a five-foot wave advances up the river from the Bay of Fundy (Figure 13). Similar tidal bores occur in rivers of other parts of the world, notably the Ganges, the Amazon, and the Seine. In former years a conspicuous tidal bore was known in the delta of the Colorado River in northern Mexico. Accounts of early explorers tell of the dangers of navigation at the head of the Gulf of California and mouth of the river. However, the diversion of so much

FIG. 13. Tidal bore, Petticodiac River, Moncton, New Brunswick, Canada.

water from the Colorado River for irrigation, power, and water supply has so changed the equilibrium in the delta that the tidal bore has ceased to exist.

Waves and Currents.—In addition to the tides, there are two other factors that cause a movement of sea water, namely, waves and currents. Normal waves are caused by wind blowing over the surface of the water. A wave breaks when it reaches shallow water and the upper part of the wave pushes forward and collapses. Other waves, known as *tidal waves* or *tsunamis,* are caused by earthquakes. These may be 40 or more feet in height and may travel hundreds or even thousands of miles. For example, the waves caused by submarine earthquakes near the Aleutian Islands in 1946 were felt in the Hawaiian Islands, some two thousand miles distant.

Currents may be either local or of great extent. Of the local currents we should mention *shore currents*, which are determined by the prevailing winds and the configuration of the coast line, and *rip currents*, which occur along the shore and frequently move through the breakers; a rip current is often called an "undertow." The broad drifting movements of the ocean are called *ocean currents* and include the Gulf Stream, the Labrador Current, the Humboldt Current, and various others of similar nature. They are largely determined by the earth's wind systems and by the rotation of the earth.

Diastrophism

In addition to the more or less predictable changes in strand line caused by waves, tides, and currents, many other types of changes are taking place. Some involve movement of the land, while others involve changes in sea level. All movements of the earth's crust that result in vertical or horizontal changes or displacement of rocks are called *diastrophism* (from the Greek "turning through").

Recent Uplift and Sinking of the Land.—A few years ago it was rather generally accepted that the coast of New Jersey was sinking at the rate of a quarter-inch a year, or two feet a century. While it is now agreed that many of the changes along this coast are explainable by other factors, such as a rise in sea level and the erosive action of the waves and currents, the fact remains that a sinking has occurred at many places along our eastern and southern coasts, although the average sinking is by no means as great as was once supposed. The remains of Indian shell heaps and camp sites in south Louisiana, some 28 feet below sea level, are excellent proof that the land in the vicinity of the Mississippi Delta has been sinking within the past few hundred years. A still more convincing proof is the fact that the ruins of the old town of Balize, which was abandoned about 1870, are now below several feet of mud near the mouth of the Mississippi River. The weight of the huge quantities of mud and silt brought down by the Mississippi River has caused a gradual sinking of the land. Further evidence of the sinking of the land can be found in many other parts of the world. For a discussion of the present movements of land along the east coast, see Chapter 26.

Just as we can find evidence for the sinking of the land in many parts of the world, so can we find good evidence that the land has risen in other places. Along the coast of New England and eastern Canada one can find "raised beaches" with sea shells and other fossils that are mute evidences that the land has risen, and is perhaps still rising (in that region). Many abandoned beaches can be seen along lakes such as Lake Champlain and Lake Superior; in some cases the position of these beaches clearly shows a pronounced uplift.

Many of these uplifts are undoubtedly due to the melting of the Pleistocene glaciers of northern North America. It is generally believed that much of northern North America was pushed down by the tremendous weight of the Pleistocene ice and that, after the retreat of the ice, the land has been gradually rising. The abandoned shore lines of New England and Canada are one proof of this rise. There is some evidence that the land has not yet fully recovered from the effect of the removal of this ice load, and is still slowly or intermittently rising. There are certain low islands in the estuary of the Moose River and James Bay that are not on the old maps; according to the old inhabitants, the islands have risen out of the sea. Various Arctic travelers tell of finding old Eskimo camp sites with attachments for boats too far above present sea level for any present practical use.

In many places the rise of the land is due to the process of mountain formation. In eastern Cuba, for instance, as well as along the coast of California and western Mexico, there is evidence of an uplift of the land in recent time, both historically and geologically. This uplift, obviously, has no connection with any glacial ice.

Uplift and Sinking of the Land in the Geologic Past.—The changes in the level of the land discussed thus far are occurring today, or have occurred in the relatively recent geologic past (Pleistocene). As we attempt to trace the geologic history from the Pre-Cambrian to the Recent we find many evidences of both a rising and a sinking of the land. In fact, the unstable nature of the earth's crust has been largely responsible for its complicated history, which we will record in subsequent chapters.

Changes in Sea Level

Until a few years ago it was thought that most, if not all, changes in the relative position of the sea and land were caused by movements of the earth's crust (diastrophism). Our ideas have had to be revised to consider the possibility that many of these changes were brought about, not by movements of the land, but by changes in sea level.

Studies of the glacial geology of the Pleistocene, particularly those by the Swedish geologists De Geer and Antevs, have demonstrated that at the climax of the last glacial advance, enough water was removed from the sea to lower its level by as much as 300 feet. Conversely, during the interglacial stages of the Pleistocene, the climate was milder than at present and less ice was on the land. The borrowed water was returned to the oceans, with the result that the interglacial sea level was higher than at present. Estimates vary for this probable rise of sea level, but the amount is probably somewhere between 30 and 300 feet.

Fossils from Pleistocene formations from New Jersey southward, once thought to have been deposited when the land was depressed, are now generally believed to have lived during an interglacial stage when the sea level was at least 30 feet higher than at present. This dating is further substantiated by the fact that many of the species are those that are now living in slightly warmer latitudes, thus suggesting that a warmer climate existed during the interglacial stage. (See Chapter 25.)

Delaware and Chesapeake Bays represent "drowned" valleys of the Delaware and Susquehanna Rivers. This drowning was caused by a rise in sea level that has taken place since the retreat of the last glaciation, or within about 12,000 years. The occurrence of the deep canyon of the Hudson River in the "Continental Shelf" off New York Harbor can be partly explained by changes in sea level, although in this case, a sinking of the land probably also took place.

If some of the changes in the relative position of sea and land of the Pleistocene can best be explained by movements in sea level rather than of the land, is it not possible that some of the similar changes of earlier periods are also partly to be explained by changes in sea level? The geological history of many of the earlier periods is now being restudied in view of this possibility. The geologic history of earlier periods is, of course, obscured by subsequent events, and it may not be possible to determine the cause of the various changes, or indeed ever to obtain a complete history of the events that took place.

Earthquakes

Earthquakes are generally, but not always, associated with volcanoes. The regions of the earth most susceptible to earthquakes are those which are most active geologically. Earthquakes may occur in those regions where there are numerous active volcanoes, or where the land is undergoing a definite movement. The frequent earthquakes in Mexico are probably associated with the active or dormant volcanoes of that country. In fact, the sudden eruption of Parícutin in the State of Michoacán was preceded by violent earthquakes which were felt in various parts of Mexico. The numerous earthquakes of

California are associated with the present slow rise of the Coast Range. Earthquakes are frequently associated with recent active faults. For example, the San Andreas Fault of California extends from San Francisco Bay to the Imperial Valley.

Fig. 14. Damage from earthquake at Charleston, South Carolina, in 1886. (U.S. Geol. Surv.)

Eastern North America is relatively free from violent earthquakes, a fact that might be expected since there is very little earth movement taking place in the East at the present time. The mild earthquakes that are felt from time to time in the Middle Atlantic states and adjacent regions may possibly be accounted as local movements along the lines of some old Triassic faults, or as the slight upward readjustments of land which had been depressed by the weight of the Pleistocene ice.

Only two areas in eastern North America have experienced quakes of major intensity. One of these, near the junction of the Ohio and Mississippi Rivers, was the scene of the tremendous earth disturbances

Fig. 15. Craterlet formed by Charleston earthquake. (U.S. Geol. Surv.)

of 1811–12, culminating in the earthquake of New Madrid, Missouri. This was one of the most violent quakes on record, but fortunately the region was very sparsely inhabited at that time. The disturbance changed the course of the Mississippi River overnight and created several new lakes. The New Madrid earthquakes are thought to have been caused by movements along a fault in the Paleozoic rocks underlying the alluvial rocks of the region.

The most disastrous earthquake of eastern North America in recent years took place in Charleston, South Carolina, on August 31, 1886. One possible explanation for this quake is a movement along a Triassic fault in the Summerville-Charleston area. Figures 14 and 15 were taken shortly after the quake and show some of the effects.

A few earthquakes of moderate intensity have occurred in New England, but these have caused relatively little damage. The most serious one on record occurred in the Boston area in 1755.

While few violent earthquakes are to be expected in eastern North America in the foreseeable future, it is undoubtedly true that many violent quakes took place here during the geologic past, particularly in connection with the volcanic activity of the Pre-Cambrian, the Ordovician, and the Triassic, and during the mountain building at the close of the Paleozoic.

Volcanoes

While there are no volcanoes in eastern North America at the present time, there has been intense volcanic activity at various times during its geologic history. There was probably considerable volcanic activity during the earliest recorded stage—the Pre-Cambrian—but the action is so ancient that it is impossible to obtain a clear picture of what happened. Another period of volcanic activity occurred during the Ordovician, demonstrated by the presence of volcanic ash, or bentonite, in various places in Pennsylvania and adjacent states. It is possible that during this stage mountain-building forces accompanying the volcanic activity altered or metamorphosed older sedimentary or igneous rocks forming the Wissahickon schist, the Baltimore gneiss, and other conspicuous formations of the Piedmont region of Pennsylvania, Maryland, etc. On the other hand, some geologists believe that this metamorphism took place earlier, in the Pre-Cambrian Era.

Another period of vulcanism occurred during the Triassic Period about 175,000,000 years ago. The Palisades of the Hudson River were formed as a result of this activity, as were the "trap" dikes of Connecticut, New Jersey, and Pennsylvania.

As we proceed with the geological story of America, it will be noted that volcanoes played an active part at various times in different parts of the country. At the present time, Mt. Lassen in

FIG. 16. Mexico's new volcano, Parícutin.

northern California is the only active volcano in the continental United States, although it is known that some have been active in Arizona and New Mexico within the past thousand years. There was considerable vulcanism during the late Tertiary and Pleistocene in western North America, as is demonstrated by the relatively unweathered lava deposits such as those of the "Craters of the Moon" in Idaho. The geysers of Yellowstone Park and Crater Lake in Oregon are further evidences of recent vulcanism.

That vulcanism is still in evidence in North America is clearly demonstrated in Mexico by the new volcano, Parícutin. Born on February 20, 1943, Parícutin has continued to grow until it is (in 1952) about 1,300 feet in height (Figure 16). Although still quite active, it is probable that Parícutin, like other "cinder cones" of its kind,

FIG. 17. Lava from Parícutin.

will gradually become dormant. It is of particular interest because geologists have had an opportunity to observe its behavior almost from the moment of its birth. It is also remarkable because it is one of the few cases of the birth of a volcano within historic

Fig. 18. Lava advancing from Parícutin. Note the volcanic ash in the foreground.

time. While there are many other "cinder cones" not far from Parícutin, one of which, Jurullo, was active as late as 1759, there has been no active volcano in the immediate vicinity within historical times. Several villages were destroyed by the advancing lava from Parícutin, while ash fell as far distant as Mexico City, 200 miles away. Figure 17 shows a piece of lava from Parícutin, while Figure 18 shows the lava advancing along a road. The activity of Parícutin, as well as the presence of dormant and extinct volcanoes in western

Mexico, is thought to be correlated with a rise of the land along the west coast of Mexico and Central America. Volcanic activity increases toward the south, along the Pacific coast of Guatemala, El Salvador, Nicaragua, and Costa Rica.

FURTHER READING FOR CHAPTERS 1–4

CARSON, RACHAEL L. *The Sea Around Us.* New York: Oxford University Press, 1951.

DALY, R. A. *Our Mobile Earth.* New York: Charles Scribner's Sons, 1926.

EMMONS, W. H., THIEL, G. A., STAUFFER, C. R., and ALLISON, I. S. *Geology, Principles and Processes.* New York: McGraw-Hill Book Co., Inc., 1949.

FENNEMAN, N. W. *Physiography of Eastern United States.* New York: McGraw-Hill Book Co., Inc., 1938.

FENTON, C. L. *Our Amazing Earth.* New York: Doubleday & Co., Inc., 1938.

HOLMES, ARTHUR. *Principles of Physical Geology.* New York: The Ronald Press Co., 1945.

LONGWELL, C. R., KNOPF, ADOLPH, and FLINT, R. F. *Physical Geology.* New York: John Wiley & Sons, Inc., 1939.

PETTIJOHN, F. J. *Sedimentary Rocks.* New York: Harper & Bros., 1949.

RUSSELL, I. C. *Volcanoes of North America.* New York: The Macmillan Co., 1924.

SHAND, R. F. *Eruptive Rocks.* New York: John Wiley & Sons, Inc., 1947.

SHROCK, R. R. *Sequence in Layered Rocks.* New York: McGraw-Hill Book Co., Inc., 1948.

CHAPTER 5

WHAT IS A FOSSIL?

Definition.—Fossils may be defined as the remains or traces of animals or plants that lived in a period earlier than the present. Many people think that a specimen must be petrified or altered to be regarded as a fossil. This is not true. As will be shown, many fossils are completely unaltered and could not be distinguished from modern specimens if they were placed side by side. The word "fossil" comes from the Latin *fossum*, meaning "dug up"; in a literal sense, a fossil is something that is dug from the earth. However, this does not give the real meaning of the word because it is not true that all fossils are dug from the earth, nor is it true that every specimen that is dug from the earth is a fossil.

Another popular misconception is that all species known as fossils are extinct. The truth of the matter is that many species have persisted unchanged for millions of years and their fossils, found in Tertiary deposits, are identical with modern representatives of the species.

How old must a specimen be to become a fossil? According to our definition, a fossil is the remains or trace of an animal or plant that lived in a period earlier than the present. When did the *present* begin? What is the difference between an "old shell" and a "young fossil"? In general, any specimen which lived before the end of the last glacial stage (about 12,000 years ago) is regarded as a fossil. However, this figure is admittedly very arbitrary, especially since the ice retreated from different places at different times. However, it is convenient to use the end of the last glacial stage as a dividing line between a fossil and a recent specimen.

Unaltered Fossils

According to the definition given above, fossils may be altered or unaltered. The former more closely fit the popular conception of a fossil in that they have been petrified or "changed to stone." The latter most closely resemble living animals and plants and often cannot be distinguished from them. There is no chemical alteration of the organic material, although decay of the soft parts usually takes place.

52

Preservation of Flesh.—In a few instances, the flesh of animals is preserved. The best-known examples of this kind of fossil are the frozen mammoths of northern Siberia. These animals were abundant in this region during the Late Pleistocene, perhaps 15,000 years ago. It is probable that many of these creatures fell into vast crevasses of the ice or were trapped in bogs. In either case they perished very quickly and, because of the low temperatures, bacterial action was so slow that they have been preserved in a remarkably fresh condition (Figure 19). In a few cases, pieces of undigested food were found in the stomachs of these ancient elephant-like creatures.

It is sometimes said that these animals were so perfectly preserved that, when they were first uncovered a few years ago, they were fresh enough to be used as food. While there is good evidence that this "frozen meat" was fed to dogs with no disastrous results, it is questionable whether it has been eaten by humans to any great extent. One former traveler through northeastern Siberia told the writer that, in the few cases he knew, the men who tried to eat the meat became very sick. He believed that this was due to the fact that the meat was partly decayed before it had been frozen and was therefore unfit for human consumption. As further evidence that this fossil meat is not normally edible, this traveler pointed out that in certain regions of Siberia, where these frozen mammoths are especially common, the natives are, or were at that time, in a state of near starvation, and yet did not touch the frozen meat.

Occasionally pieces of flesh are attached to the bones of animals preserved in tar- or oil-soaked grounds. So far, no flesh has been found on the bones from the well-known La Brea tar pits in Los Angeles, although the bones are exceptionally well preserved. However, across the Atlantic, the skeletons of two rhinoceroses, with skin and hair attached, have been recovered from the oil- and brine-soaked sands of Galicia in eastern Poland (now a part of Russia). See Figures 20 and 21.

Mummies.—In very dry climates it is not unusual to find that the flesh of animals has been mummified. A few such fossils have been found in dry caves, but these are generally of relatively recent age, probably Pleistocene or even younger. In 1948 the mummified remains of a baby mammoth with trunk and forelimb were obtained from gold-bearing gravels near Fairbanks, Alaska (Figure 26).

Preservation in Amber.—Amber, or fossil resin from plants, frequently contains the remains of insects. Many of these are so perfectly preserved that microscopic details of wings and scales can be

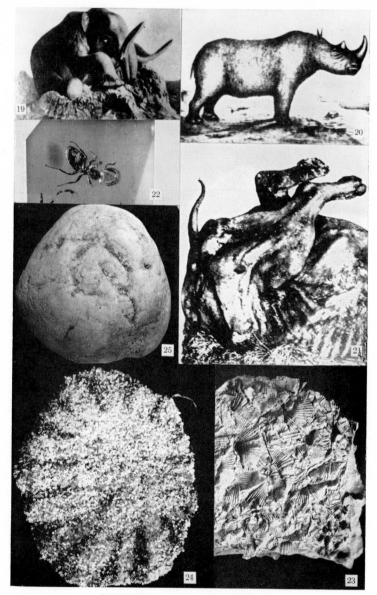

PRESERVATION OF FOSSILS

FIG. 19. Bereskova mammoth from frozen tundra in Siberia.

FIG. 20. Restoration of wooly rhinoceros. (Museum, Krakow, Poland.)

(Continued on opposite page.→)

observed (Figure 22). In addition to insects, small crustaceans, spiders, mammal hairs, and bird feathers have been found preserved in this way. The best-known deposits of amber come from the Baltic Coast of Germany and from Zanzibar on the east coast of Africa. Many pieces of amber containing fossil insects are made into jewelry and are sold for good prices.

Unaltered Shells and Bones.—Shells deposited in sand and clay often remain unaltered for millions of years. While it is true that the majority of unaltered fossil shells date from the Pleistocene or late Tertiary, excellent examples of perfectly preserved shells are known of Cretaceous or even earlier age. The rich Cretaceous fauna from Coon Creek, Tennessee, contains many wholly unaltered shells and is a classic example of this kind of fossil. Some practically unaltered brachiopod shells have been found in the loose sandstones of the Trempeleau group in Wisconsin. These fossils date from the late Cambrian, perhaps 450,000,000 years ago.

In some cases a fossil shell can be distinguished from a recent one only because the former is extinct. However, it is not always possible to make this distinction because the particular species in question may have persisted from the Miocene to the present time.

Shallow excavations along the New Jersey coast frequently uncover large numbers of marine fossils. When the excavations are at a considerable distance from the present shore line, it is apparent that the shells found are fossils which probably lived during the latter part of the Pleistocene epoch, perhaps some 100,000 years ago. On the other hand, when the excavations or dredgings are near the shore line, they encounter a mixture of recent and modern specimens. In very few instances can the fossils be recognized because they are the remains of totally extinct species; in other cases, the species now extinct in New Jersey waters can be found living in the warmer waters of the Carolinas or Florida. These fossils indicate a former warm climate in New Jersey, probably during an interglacial stage.

FIG. 21. The hind part of a wooly rhinoceros as preserved in the oil sands of Galicia. (Museum, Krakow.)

FIG. 22. Ant preserved in amber. (Amer. Mus. Nat. Hist.)

FIG. 23. Altered fossils. Some brachiopods (*Spirifer*) from Devonian shale in West Virginia.

FIG. 24. A fossil in the making. A partially mummified jellyfish (*Dactylometra quinquecirrha*) from the shores of the Gulf of Mexico at Biloxi, Mississippi.

FIG. 25. A "petrified potato"—a good example of a pseudofossil. Closely resembling a potato in size, color, but not weight, this pseudofossil is actually a quartz pebble.

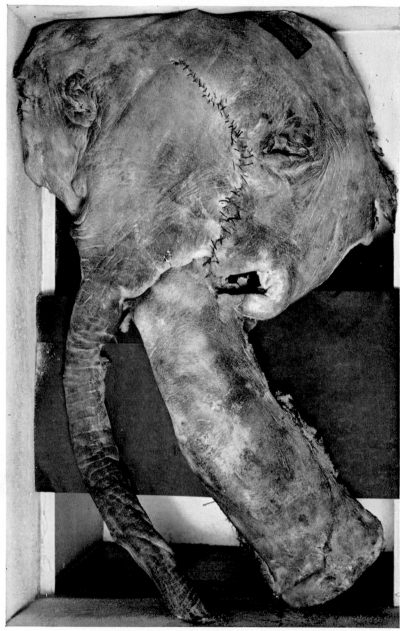

Fig. 26. Mummified baby mammoth obtained by hydraulic gold operations at Fairbanks, Alaska. (Amer. Mus. Nat. Hist.)

In the case of those species which are known from both the Pleistocene deposits and the recent seas of New Jersey, it is usually impossible to tell whether they are fossil or recent.

Likewise, it is difficult to tell whether shells washed onto a beach are all modern. If a beach is near a fossil deposit, shells washed from the fossil locality are mixed with the modern shells of the present sea. For example, the beaches along the western shore of Chesapeake Bay contain a mixture of modern shells and those washed from the Miocene deposits which crop out along this bay for many miles. Often the Miocene species are extinct, but in other cases the descendants of the Miocene forms are still living in these waters and cannot be distinguished from their ancestors of 20,000,000 years ago. Even the color markings are occasionally, although not usually, preserved on the fossils.

In the case of an unaltered shell, there are two ways to determine whether it is a fossil or not. First, if the animal species is extinct, it is most probably a fossil; secondly, if it was found in a place not close to the present sea, or to an historically recent sea, and has clearly not been artificially buried, it is evidently a fossil.

The same difficulty is involved in the differentiation of fossil and recent unaltered bones. The matter of extinction is not so clearly defined in this instance because numerous vertebrate animals have become extinct within historic times. For example, a skeleton of a passenger pigeon, which was so abundant in eastern North America a hundred years ago, would not be considered a fossil.

Unaltered Wood.—Unaltered pieces of wood are occasionally found in Pleistocene and Tertiary formations. Peat is the best preservative for wood and whole trunks of trees are often found buried in Pleistocene peat bogs. In Cape May County, New Jersey, "fossil" cedar logs were once "mined" for use as shingles for roofs of houses. These logs, which were probably several thousand years old, were found to be in perfect condition when they were brought to the surface.

A large trunk of a cypress tree was discovered a few years ago in Philadelphia, during the excavations for a subway. Since this is slightly beyond the present geographic limit of this tree, it is believed that this fossil trunk dates from the last interglacial stage, 100,000 years ago.

Slightly altered wood is often found in lignite deposits, some of which is at least as old as the Cretaceous. When first unearthed, some of this wood appears to be unaltered, but after drying in the air for a short time it usually begins to crack and disintegrate.

Altered Fossils

Petrifactions.—Most fossils, especially those from the older formations, have been "petrified" or "altered." "Petrified" literally means "turned to stone," while the more accurate term *altered* indicates that some physical or chemical change or alteration has taken place. Decomposition usually destroys the soft parts of buried animals, causing the remaining hard parts to be very porous. At the same time, ground water fills these pores or crevices with minute particles of lime, calcite, or silica. The original shell or bone may not necessarily be altered chemically, but is greatly increased in weight because of the added deposit of mineral material. Thus the chance of preservation is increased. This process is sometimes called *permineralization.*

Replacement.—Sometimes ground water completely dissolves the original bone or shell and replaces it with another substance (Figure 23). This replacement is accomplished so slowly and completely, molecule by molecule, that very often even the detailed microscopic structure is still visible in the replaced fossil. This is especially true when the replacing material is lime or calcite. Shells or other fossils replaced by silica or pyrite usually display less of the original structure. On the other hand, petrified wood, in which the wood cells have been replaced by silica, has exceptionally good microscopic structure.

Carbonization.—Plants or animals which decay under water frequently leave a thin film of carbon that may retain the original form and structure to a remarkable degree. The delicate fern and other plant leaves in the rocks of Pennsylvanian age from the Coal Regions are excellent examples of fossils produced by carbonization. The famous Cambrian fossil localities near Field, British Columbia, contain jellyfish, worms, trilobites, and other remains preserved in great detail by this process of carbonization. Near Holzmaden, Württemberg, Germany, the remains of marine reptiles and many other animals have been found with a thin film of carbon remaining as a residue of the soft parts of the body.

Casts and Molds.—It frequently happens that an animal or plant buried in a fine-grained rock will disintegrate or be removed by solution, but will leave behind it a complete impression. This impression is called a *mold*. A cast of the original organism can be obtained by filling this mold with some plastic substance such as plasticene, wax, or latex. Many minute details of external structure such as spines, nodes, or ribs can be seen on casts made by this method.

A *natural cast* occurs if the mold is filled in by nature with a mineral substitute. When the replacing substance is a mineral such as calcite, pyrite, or chalcedony, the replacement is called a *pseudomorph* because the original form is not preserved perfectly. Occasionally, the outer layers of a shell are worn away, leaving a mold which shows the internal structures. This kind of preservation is characteristic of the Lower Miocene deposits of the Trent formation near Belgrade, North Carolina. (See Figure 263, page 329.)

Fossil Medusae.—Jellyfish or medusae, because of their delicate structure and high water content, are rarely preserved as fossils. A few fossil jellyfish have been preserved under ideal conditions, and

Fig. 27. Fossils in the making. Partly mummified jellyfish on the hot sands of the Gulf of California at El Golfo, Sonora, Mexico. Note footprint and sun glasses for scale.

their remains occur in rocks of various ages in such widely separated places as New York state, Alabama, Texas, Arizona, and Bavaria. Figure 24 shows a mummy of a recent jellyfish (*Dactylometra quinquecirrha* Desor) picked up on the beach of the Gulf of Mexico at Biloxi, Mississippi. It had apparently been stranded on the beach and partly covered by sand. Sand grains had been pressed against the jelly umbrellas of the animal, causing the original shape and design to be kept as the animal dried out in the sun. The adherence of these hot sand grains, held in position by the sticky organic material of the animal's body, resulted in the mummification of the specimen.

If a mummy similar to this had been permanently buried in sand or clay, under conditions favorable for its further preservation, it might have become a fossil. Of course, the radiating design might have been lost, but enough of the structures could have remained to give a clue to its identity. Figure 27 shows a group of somewhat similar dried and hardened jellyfish picked up from the hot beach of the Gulf of California, at El Golfo, Sonora, Mexico. Possibly such fossils do exist in the rocks, but, because of the lack of detailed structures, have not been recognized as medusae. These two figures may be regarded as fossils in the making.

Traces

It will be recalled that our definition of a fossil included the expression "remains or traces" of animals of the past. So far, we have dealt with the actual remains, either altered or unaltered, of the fossilized animal or plant. In the case of some casts or molds, the question might be raised as to whether we were dealing with the actual remains of the animal or merely a trace. On the other hand, fossil footprints, burrows, trails, and the like can clearly be classified as traces of former life rather than as the remains themselves.

Footprints.—When animals walk or crawl over mud or soft sand, they usually leave records of their presence in the form of footprints or trails. When these muds and sands harden to sandstone and shale, these traces are frequently retained in the rock. Footprints of dinosaurs are fairly common in the Triassic shales of the Connecticut Valley. Such a fossil cannot be said to be the remains of a dinosaur, for the actual fossil remains may occur many miles away from where the animal became buried in a bog or swamp. It is, however, a trace of the dinosaur, and as such can be regarded as a fossil. Very important information can sometimes be deduced from fossil footprints. For example, one can determine whether the animal walked on two or four feet, while the distance between the footprints may give some clue to the animal's height and weight. (See Figure 175, page 244.)

Obviously, only a very small percentage of footprints made by animals are ever preserved as fossils. Conditions must be ideal for their preservation. An interesting example of how fossil footprints may be preserved recently came to the attention of the writer. At several places along the Atlantic Coast, especially in New Jersey and Delaware, there are deposits of peat containing the remains of grass, bushes, and occasionally trees. This peat is often exposed close to the low tide line and is believed to represent former land that extended out to sea, perhaps a hundred years ago. (See Chapter 26, Figure 293.) Normally, this peat is covered with a thin layer of beach sand. However, this sand is sometimes washed away after storms, leaving the peat exposed to the air. After a heavy storm in April, 1929, this peat was well exposed between the tides near the lighthouse at Cape May Point, New Jersey. In the peat, or old meadow sod, could be seen the remains of a former log or corduroy road that led from the present beach in the direction of Prissy Wick Shoal, now submerged in 10 feet of water, but where, according to tradition, the original Cape May Lighthouse was located. In the sod near the road footprints of horses could be seen. It is impossible to say how old these traces are, but it was obvious that they had been there for many years because the sod had not been uncovered for a long time. The fact that these tracks have persisted in the sod, under a thin layer of superimposed sand, and covered by the tides twice a day, is highly interesting and suggestive of how fossil prints are made and preserved.

Trails.—Worms, amphibians, and other crawling animals leave trails in the same way that walking animals leave footprints. They are generally less distinct and there is often a difference of opinion as to the kind of animal that produced certain trails. Trails common in some Paleozoic rocks are regarded as having been made by worms, limuloids (king crabs), and various other animals, or as impressions of seaweed (algae).

Burrows.—Some animals, such as worms, burrow through the ground. Sometimes these burrows are preserved as fossils, although it is usually very difficult to determine the kind of animal that made a particular burrow.

Coprolites.—These are the excrement or castings that have passed through the alimentary canal of any prehistoric animal. Coprolites of certain kinds of fish, amphibia, and reptiles are most common. They are usually hardened but after careful examination it is frequently possible to recognize parts of the animals and plants that were used as food. Coprolites are fairly numerous in the Triassic rocks of Pennsylvania, New Jersey, and Connecticut.

Gastroliths.—These are smoothed pebbles swallowed by dinosaurs as well as other reptiles and birds to help grind the food that they could not chew. These specimens, sometimes called "gizzard stones," often occur in clusters and possibly represent all that remains of the stomach of a dinosaur or other animal. They are particularly numerous in the Cretaceous formations of Kansas, South Dakota, and Wyoming.

Gastroliths may be recognized by their high polish, which illumines the small concavities as well as the projecting surfaces, thus differing from stream-induced polish. Very frequently, the pebbles swallowed by the dinosaurs were fossiliferous, thereby rendering the resulting specimen doubly a fossil!

Impressions.—These are somewhat similar to molds, but are extremely shallow. Under this heading may be considered the impressions of jellyfish and dragonflies from the lithographic stone at Solnhofen, Bavaria.

Pseudofossils

Most museum curators are constantly receiving specimens of fossils for identification. While the majority of these are actually fossils, there are always a few that, while they resemble fossils, are not of organic origin. Some of these are mentioned below.

Dendrites.—These are mineral growths, usually of manganese oxide, which develop in underground water. They frequently resemble a fossil fern.

Concretions and Nodules.—As we have seen in Chapter 3, concretions are of mineral origin and are formed around fossils or other extraneous material. Although concretions may form *around* fossils, they are not fossils themselves. Nodules, sometimes confused with concretions, are formed directly by chemical action, as is the case with nodules of flint and chert. Concretions and nodules often closely resemble actual fossils in shape and markings, and are thus erroneously regarded as such.

Certain rounded or oval concretions found in the Devonian rocks of Pennsylvania have been submitted as "dinosaur eggs." (The fact that dinosaurs did not live during the Devonian time was not appreciated by the collector.) Other concretions from the Triassic of Pennsylvania with peculiar markings caused by weathering have been "identified" as fossil footprints.

Pebbles.—Pebbles of quartz, chert, and the like frequently resemble fossils and are identified as such by the uninitiated. Pebbles have recently come to the writer's desk that have been identified as a "fossil turtle's head," a "bird's beak," and a "fossil potato" (Figure 25, page 54).

FURTHER READING

The references for Chapters 5–7 will be found at the end of Chapter **7.**

CHAPTER 6

A CLASSIFICATION OF ANIMALS

There is no perfect classification of animals because the system used by one worker will not be accepted by another. A scientist who has specialized in a certain group of animals, such as the corals, for example, will recognize many subdivisions of that group which would not be apparent or important to a worker in another field.

According to common practice the members of the animal and plant kingdoms have been arranged into certain major groups or *phyla* (from the Greek word for race). These phyla are occasionally divided into sub-phyla, which in turn are broken down into classes, orders, and families. A family is composed of certain genera, which, in turn, are made up of separate species.[1] There is no agreement as to the number of phyla, or upon the arrangement of the classes and orders within the phyla. What one worker may call a phylum may be divided into two or more phyla by another worker; conversely, some scientists prefer to combine the phyla into a smaller number of major units.[2]

The classification employed in this chapter is admittedly arbitrary and is presented here in order to give a background for the discussion of fossils in later chapters of the book. A few less conspicuous or less important groups of animals have been omitted, while other groups have been combined or separated as seemed desirable for the present study.[3]

The reader will observe that not all groups of animals and plants are represented in the fossil state. While this book does not attempt to discuss those animals which exist only in the present day, recognition of the more important groups has been made in the table. When a group (phylum, class, or order) is not known as a fossil it is indicated in the table by the symbol *.

[1] Just as a formation is the fundamental stratigraphic unit, and related formations are combined into groups and series, so is the species the fundamental taxonomic unit. It would probably be more accurate to say that related species are grouped together into genera and families.

[2] Preston Cloud, in a footnote to a recent article, states that the minimum number of phyla recognized by any worker is nine, and the maximum thirty-five. "Some Problems and Patterns of Evolution Exemplified by Fossil Invertebrates," *Evolution*, II, 322 (1948).

[3] As an example of classification, the common hard-shelled clam or quohog would be classified as follows: PHYLUM Mollusca, CLASS Pelecypoda, ORDER Telodesmacea, FAMILY Veneridae, GENUS *Venus*, SPECIES *mercenaria*.

PHYLUM I. PROTOZOA

(One-celled animals)

CLASS MASTIGOPHORA (Flagellated protozoa)

Cell wall fixed, shape permanent; equipped with one or more flagellae; usually without skeleton. Includes free-living forms such as *Euglena, Volvox, Synura,* and parasitic forms such as *Trypanosoma* and *Giardia.* One order, Dinoflagellata, possesses skeletons of cellulose and has been reported questionably from the Cretaceous of Europe. Modern dinoflagellates include *Noctulica* and *Peridinium.*

The members of the family, Silicoflagellidae, of the Order Chrysomonadida, have siliceous skeletons and have been found in Cretaceous rocks of California and elsewhere. Dr. G. D. Hanna has shown these to be valuable horizon markers.

CLASS SARCODINA (Amoeboid protozoa)

Changeable body form with pseudopodia. Various orders of free-living, colonial, and parasitic forms, including the modern *Amoeba,* the fungus-like Mycetozoa, the spherical Heliozoa, and others.

Two orders are known in the fossil state:

1. FORAMINIFERA

Shelled protozoa, mostly of microscopic size (Figure 28), although a few, especially of Eocene age, reach 100 mm. in diameter. Foraminifera are mostly bottom-dwelling forms, although some, such as *Globigerina,* live on the surface of the sea. The so-called globigerina ooze of the deep ocean bottoms is made up of great masses of these tiny shells. Many rocks, such as those from which the pyramids of Egypt were built, are composed of millions of shells of foraminifera. Range: Cambrian(?), Ordovician to Recent.

2. RADIOLARIA

Marine protozoa with a chitinous membrane and usually an outer skeleton of silica; usually more delicate than the foraminifera, and consequently not as well preserved as fossils. These shells make up the radiolarian ooze of the very deep sea bottom. Especially well preserved fossils in the Devonian Caballos chert of Texas and the Miocene of Barbados. A few are known from the Calvert formation (Miocene) of Maryland and the Deepkill chert (Ordovician) of eastern New York. Range: Pre-Cambrian to Recent.

CLASS INFUSORIA (Ciliated protozoa)

Fixed body wall; locomotion by cilia; usually no skeleton; includes *Paramecium* and many other living forms. A few minute forms, fam-

Fig. 28. Models of foraminifera: (A) *Uvigerina*, (B) *Cibicides*, (C) *Textularia*, (D) *Nonion*. (Chicago Nat. Hist. Mus.)

ily Tintinidae, have skeletons of chitin(?) and are known from the Jurassic and Lower Cretaceous of the Balaeric Islands and elsewhere.

*CLASS SPOROZOA

Parasitic forms, incapable of movement. No fossil record.

PHYLUM II. PORIFERA

(The sponges)

CLASS CALCISPONGIA

Skeleton of calcareous spicules. Fossil forms include *Barroisia*, while living sponges of this class include *Grantia* and *Leucosolenia*. Range: Devonian to Recent (possibly earlier).

CLASS SILICISPONGIA

Skeleton of siliceous spicules. Includes the greater number of fossil sponges (*Hydnoceras, Microspongia, Protospongia, Hindia*, etc.); all living fresh-water sponges and most marine sponges (*Euplectella*, Venus Flower Basket), *Spongilla* (fresh-water sponge), *Microciona, Cliona, Chalina*, etc. Range: Cambrian to Recent.

CLASS CERATOSPONGIA

Skeleton primarily of horny fibers. Rare as fossils; a few from the Carboniferous, Jurassic, and Cretaceous. Includes the modern bath sponge (*Euspongia*).

*CLASS MYXOSPONGIA

Sponges with no skeleton; no fossil record.

CLASS PLEOSPONGIA (Archaeocyathidae)

Conical to cylindrical, with double calcareous wall inclosing central axis cavity; walls perforate with space between septae; attached by base (Figure 29). Sometimes classed with the corals. Restricted to the Cambrian.

Fig. 29. Archaeocyathid (Pleospongia), from Australia.

PHYLUM III. COELENTERATA
(Jellyfish, corals, etc.)

CLASS HYDROZOA

Hydroids, hydroid medusae, siphonophores (pelagic hydroids), and hydrocorals.

The Order Hydrocorallinae consists of colonial coral-like animals with two kinds of apertures in the calcareous external skeleton: gastropores for the feeding polyps and dactylopores for the food-producing members of the colony. Includes the modern *Millepora* and a few fossil forms (e.g., *Milleaster*). Range: Triassic to Recent.

A few other fossils have been referred to the class Hydrozoa.

CLASS STROMATOPORIDEA

Colonial coral-like, calcareous reef-building organisms. They are composed of numerous concentric laminae, separated by interspaces and supported by radial pillars. The polyp apertures are on the upper surface of the laminae. Classified on the basis of internal structure, and it is therefore necessary to obtain polished surfaces or thin sections for determination of species. Of uncertain relationship and sometimes included in the Hydrozoa. Range: Ordovician to Devonian.

CLASS SCYPHOZOA (Jellyfish)

Medusae with hydroid stage reduced or absent. Includes modern jellyfish such as *Cyanea, Dactylometra*, etc., and a few fossil forms. Range: Pre-Cambrian to Recent.

CLASS CONULARIDA

Forms of uncertain relationship, now believed to be closely related to the scyphozoa. They possessed a thin shell and transverse septae. Formerly classed as mollusks. Range: Ordovician to Jurassic.

CLASS GRAPTOZOA (Graptolites)

Formerly classed with the coelenterates, but now placed in the phylum Chordata with the protochordates. (See page 78.)

CLASS ANTHOZOA (Corals, Sea Anemones)

Sub-class Tetracoralla

Simple or compound corals with bilateral symmetry, with vertical septae developing in groups of four. Includes the cup corals (*Zaphrentis, Streptelasma, Heliophyllum*, etc.). Range: Ordovician to Permian.

Sub-class Hexacoralla

Corals with radial symmetry; vertical septae developing in groups of six. Includes modern reef corals as well as smaller colonial forms such as *Astrangia*. This sub-class also includes the Actinaria (sea anemones) which have no hard parts. Range: Triassic to Recent.

Sub-class Tabulata

Colonial corals with calcareous skeletons composed of long tubular corallites with many tabulae or horizontal partitions; septae poorly developed. Honeycomb coral (*Favosites*), chain coral (*Halysites*), organ-pipe coral (*Syringopora*), etc. Range: Ordovician to Permian.

Sub-class Alcyonaria (Octocoralla)

Composite corals; skeleton usually calcareous or horny; usually eight tentacles or mesenteries. Includes the modern sea fans and sea pens. One family (Heliolitidae) restricted to the Paleozoic; others Mesozoic to Recent; usually rare as fossils.

*PHYLUM IV. CTENOPHORA

(Ctenophores; comb jellies)

PHYLUM V. ECHINODERMATA

Sub-phylum Pelmatozoa

(Stemmed or attached)

Fig. 30. Crinoid stalks, showing ringlike plates.

CLASS CYSTOIDEA (Cystoids)

Stemmed or stemless; body plates arranged in irregular (asymmetrical) manner, e.g., *Pleurocystites* (Figure 31). Range: Cambrian to Permian.

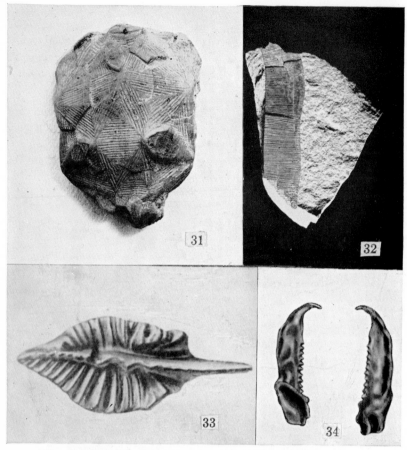

FIG. 31.   Cystoid (*Pleurocystites*).   (Chicago Nat. Hist. Mus.)
FIG. 32.   Silurian worm, *Lecathayus*.
FIG. 33.   Conodont.   (W. Youngquist.)
FIG. 34.   Scolecodont or worm jaw.   (E. R. Eller.)

CLASS EDRIOASTEROIDEA

Flexible body (calyx); irregular plates; discoidal in shape; attached but without stem; five curved unbranched grooves. E.g., *Edrioaster*. Rare. Range: Cambrian to Carboniferous.

CLASS BLASTOIDEA (Blastoids, sea buds)

Globular-shaped forms encased in a shell made up of regular plates (Figures 41, 42, and 43). Range: Ordovician to Permian (especially Mississippian).

TYPICAL ANIMAL FOSSILS

FIGS. 35, 36. Coiled trilobites, *Caly-mene*.

FIG. 37. Ordovician brachiopod, *Platy-strophia ponderosa*, Kentucky.

FIG. 38. Crinoid.

FIGS. 39, 40. Stalks of crinoid.

FIGS. 41, 42, 43. Pennsylvanian blastoids (*Pentremites* sp.).

FIG. 44. Eocene eel from Italy.

FIG. 45. Corkscrew bryozoan, *Archimedes compoctus*—Mississippian of Illinois.

CLASS CRINOIDEA (Crinoids, sea lilies)

Stalked, plant-like animals made up of a stem, body, and a series of arms. The stem is marked by conspicuous joints while the body is covered with a series of limy plates (Figures 30, 38, 39, and 40). Range: Ordovician to Recent.

Sub-phylum Eleutherozoa

CLASS ASTEROIDEA (Starfish)

Because of their loosely arranged plates, starfish are rarely found as fossils. Range: Ordovician to Recent.

CLASS OPHIUROIDEA (Brittle stars; serpent stars)

Similar to Asteroidea, but with a well-defined central disc and wormlike arms (Figure 46). Rare as fossils. Range: Devonian to Recent.

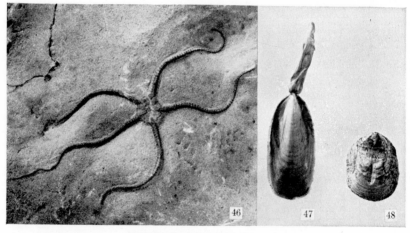

TYPICAL ANIMAL FOSSILS

FIG. 46. Jurassic brittle star or Ophuroidea.

FIG. 47. Modern brachiopod (*Lingula unguis*).

FIG. 48. Ordovician brachiopod (*Lingula cincinnatiensis*).

CLASS ECHINOIDEA (Sea urchins, sand dollars)

Globular animals with spines. The five-pointed star impressed on the top is usually conspicuous. Spines and plates of the test or shell are abundant at many localities and perfect specimens are not uncommon. Range: Ordovician to Recent.

CLASS HOLOTHUROIDEA (Sea cucumbers)

Elongate animals, usually with a rather soft skeleton made up of minute calcareous plates which are occasionally preserved as fossils. Completely preserved animals are rare. Range: Cambrian to Recent.

PHYLUM VI. PLATYHELMINTHES [4]

(Flatworms)

A few fossil flatworms are known as parasites in Carboniferous or Tertiary insects, and are found as marine forms in the Jurassic Solnhofen limestone.

PHYLUM VII. NEMATHELMINTHES

(Roundworms, threadworms)

Very rare as fossils. Range: Cambrian to Recent.

*PHYLUM VIII. TROCHELMINTHES

(Rotifers, Microscopic "wheel animalcules")

PHYLUM IX. ANNELIDA

(Segmented worms)

CLASS CHAETOPODA

Segmented worms covered with hairs (setae). Some of these worms were equipped with chitinous jaws known as scolecodonts (Figure 34), which are frequently preserved in rocks; in fact, numerous species have been described on the basis of the jaws alone. Other Chaetopoda, which lacked jaws, lived in tubes that they built. Perfect worm fossils are rare (Figure 32), although tubes, castings and impressions are common in some formations. Range: Pre-Cambrian to Recent.

CLASS SIPUNCULOIDEA

A small group of worms including the modern *Sipunculus*. Burrows of *Skolithos* and other similar forms, as well as certain Cambrian worms whose entire bodies have been preserved as fossils, are tentatively placed in this class. Range: Cambrian to Recent.

*CLASS HIRUNIDEA (Leaches)

[4] The Platyhelminthes, Nemathelminthes, Trochelminthes, and Annelida are frequently combined into a super-phylum, Vermes (Worms).

PHYLUM X. BRYOZOA

(Corallines, moss animals)

*CLASS ENTOPROCTA

CLASS ECTOPROCTA

Small colonial forms whose calcareous skeletons form large masses or "reefs." Superficially, the individual members of the colony, called zoaria, resemble corals, but anatomically are more closely related to the brachiopods (Figure 45). Range: Cambrian to Recent.

PHYLUM XI. BRACHIOPODA

(Brachiopods, lamp shells)

Superficially, because of their two valves, the brachiopods resemble bivalved mollusks. However, they are more primitive anatomically and the arrangement of the shell is quite different. While the shells of the bivalved mollusk are generally equal and lateral, the valves of the brachiopod are unequal and dorsal-ventral in position, while each valve is equilateral. In other words, the two shells of a bivalve are mirror images of each other, while the two halves of each shell of a brachiopod are the same. Brachiopods are divided into two classes based on embryonic development, composition of shell, and the presence of articulating processes. (See Figures 37, 47, and 48.)

CLASS INARTICULATA

No hinges, or hinges poorly developed. Range: Pre-Cambrian to Recent.

CLASS ARTICULATA

Hinges well developed. Range: Cambrian to Recent.

PHYLUM XII. MOLLUSCA

CLASS AMPHINEURA (Chitons)

Limpet-like mollusks with a shell composed of eight plates. Because of the fragile nature of the shell, they are rarely found as fossils. Fragments of fossil chiton shells are occasionally found in Miocene and Pleistocene deposits of the Atlantic Coastal Plain. Range: Ordovician to Recent.

CLASS PELECYPODA (Clams)

These are compressed, usually symmetrical mollusks with a shell of two valves. They are distinguished from the brachiopods by their equal, but unequilateral valves, each one being roughly the counterpart of the other. The class is sometimes called Lamellibranchiata. Range: Cambrian(?), Ordovician to Recent.

CLASS GASTROPODA (Snails)

Univalved mollusks. The shell may be conical or saucer-shaped, but is usually coiled into a spiral. Range: Cambrian to Recent.

CLASS PTEROPODA

Swimming mollusks with a foot which is adapted into winglike fins. Forms "pteropod ooze" at the bottom of the ocean. Sometimes classed with the Gastropoda. Examples are *Hyolithes* and *Tentaculites* from the Paleozoic and *Clio,* Tertiary to Recent.

CLASS SCAPHOPODA (Tooth shells)

Elongate, tubular shells, usually curved and tapering and open at both ends. The Dentalium of modern seas belongs in this class. Range: Ordovician to Recent.

CLASS CEPHALOPODA

ORDER NAUTILOIDEA

The animal lives in a straight or coiled shell from which the head and tentacles project. The soft parts or body of the animal are contained in the outermost compartment or chamber of the shell. Internally, the shell is divided by septae into a series of chambers filled with gas and connected by the siphuncle. The lines forming the union of the septa with the shell are known as the suture lines. The design of these suture lines is frequently of importance in the classification of nautiloids. The class includes the straight type (*Orthoceras*), slightly curved (*Cyrtoceras*), loosely coiled (*Ryticeras*) to closely coiled types (*Nautilus*). The only modern representative is the genus *Nautilus* (pearly or chambered nautilus). Range: Cambrian(?), Ordovician to Recent.

ORDER AMMONOIDEA

The ammonites include a wide variety of forms including straight types such as *Bactrites,* loosely coiled (*Mimoceras*), erratically coiled (*Hamites*), spirally coiled (*Turrilites*) and closely coiled forms (*Agoniatites*). The suture lines separating the compartments are more complex than in the nautiloids and frequently are ornamented with well-developed lobes and saddles. Here again, the design of the suture lines is of importance in the classification of the group. Range: Late Silurian to Cretaceous.

Order Coleoidea (Belemnites, Squid)

Skeleton internal. The order includes the cigar-shaped Belemnites of the Mesozoic as well as the modern octopus, squid, and cuttlefish. Range: Triassic to Recent.

PHYLUM XIII. ARTHROPODA

CLASS CRUSTACEA

Order Trilobita (Trilobites)

Extinct arthropods. The animal is composed of three regions, the head (cephalon) with compound eyes, the thorax, and the tail (pygidium). Jointed appendages were present, but are seldom preserved. Many trilobites had the ability to coil up in the manner of the modern "pill bug." These animals reached their climax during the Early Paleozoic and then declined rapidly, until they were totally extinct at the end of the Paleozoic era (Figures 35 and 36). Range: Cambrian to Permian.

Order Branchiopoda (Phyllopods)

Small crustacea, either with no carapace or with a bivalved shell, the latter group being the only one represented in the fossil record. "*Estheria*," a small but common form in Devonian and Triassic rocks and *Schizodiscus*, a Devonian genus, are the best-known fossils of this order. Range: Cambrian to Recent.

Order Ostracoda (Ostracodes)

Small bivalved crustaceans. Many are difficult to identify because of their small size and lack of shell ornamentation (e.g., *Leperditia*). Others have highly ornamented shells (Figures 49, 50, and 51). It is

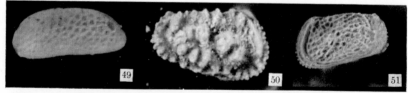

Figs. 49, 50, 51. Cretaceous ostracodes. (F. Swain.)

of interest that these tiny fossils are one of the few groups in which males can be distinguished from females. Range: Ordovician to Recent.

Order Cirripedia (Barnacles)

Degenerate crustacea; the young are free swimming but the adults are attached to some object. Fossils are generally composed of shells or plates, and are fairly common in some Tertiary and Pleistocene formations. Range: Ordovician to Recent.

* ORDER COPEPODA (Copepods)

Minute crustaceans with no carapace. The copepods form a large part of the plankton of present-day oceans.

ORDER MALACOSTRACA

This is the most conspicuous group of Crustacea living at the present time. It includes the crabs, shrimps, lobsters, crayfish, woodlice, pill bugs, and various other forms. Range: Cambrian to Recent.

CLASS MYRIOPODA

Air-breathing arthropods including the millipedes and centipedes. Possibly among the first air-breathing animals to invade the land from the sea. Range: Devonian to Recent.

CLASS INSECTA

This class includes all true insects and is sometimes called the Hexopoda. Range: Devonian to Recent.

CLASS ARACHNIDA

ORDER EMBOLOBRANCHIATA

This group includes the spiders, scorpions, mites, and ticks, and comprises the terrestrial members of the class Arachnida. Not common as fossils. Range: Silurian to Recent.

ORDER MEROSTOMATA

This is the water-breathing division of the class Arachnida. It consists of two main divisions, one containing the Xiphosura, or horseshoe crabs. The genus *Limulus* (the modern horseshoe crab or king crab) or its ancestor *Protolimulus* has remained almost unchanged from the Middle Paleozoic (Devonian) to the present day. Primitive merostomes—the Synxiphosura—lived from the Cambrian to the Silurian and were undoubtedly the ancestors of the true Xiphosura. The other group contains the Eurypterids or sea scorpions. These forms probably originated in salt water but migrated to brackish or fresh water during the existence of the group. Some Eurypterids, such as *Pterygotus buffaloensis*, attained a length of nine feet or more. They are not common, although a fair number of species have been found in the Silurian rocks of New York state. The Eurypterids lived from Late Cambrian to Pennsylvanian time.

PHYLUM XIV. CHORDATA

Sub-phylum Protochordata

Primitive or degenerate animals, mostly worm-like, which possess a notochord during an early stage of their life history. The group includes the modern *Molgula* (tunicate or sea squirt), as well as the slender *Amphioxus, Balanoglossus,* and *Cephalodisca.*

CLASS GRAPTOZOA (Graptolites)

Colonial organisms, the individuals living in small cups (thecae) attached to a chitinous stalk. Superficially, they resemble hydroids and until recently have been classed with the Coelenterata. In 1946, while studying the developmental stages of graptolites found in Ordovician rocks of Poland, Professor Kozlowski showed that these animals are related to the modern *Cephalodisca* and should be placed in the sub-phylum Protochordata. Range: Late Cambrian to Mississippian.

Sub-phylum Vertebrata [5]

(Animals with a vertebral column)

CLASS 1. PISCES (Fish and their relatives)

Sub-class Agnatha (Jawless vertebrates)

Includes the order Cyclostomata (lamprey eels) of modern seas as well as several groups of fossil forms. The most significant fossil Agnatha are the ostracoderms, which in turn are divided into several orders. These were primitive fish-like animals which were covered with an external armor of plates or scales. No trace of backbone has been found in any ostracoderm fossil, and they may have possessed only a notochord or a very primitive backbone. Range: Cambrian(?), Ordovician to Devonian (ostracoderms).

Sub-class Placodermi

Primitive-jawed types made up of several orders, the most important being:

ACANTHODII

Small and the least specialized of the placoderms, sometimes called spiny sharks although they are not related to the true sharks. Examples are *Acanthoides* and *Bothriolepis.* Range: Devonian to Permian.

---

[5] No attempt will be made to give a complete classification of the vertebrates. Only those groups which are most conspicuous in this book will be mentioned, and they are not necessarily arranged in systematic order.

ARTHRODIRA (Armored fish)

Fish with bony plates over their head and body. An example is *Dinicthys*. Range: Devonian.

Sub-class Chondrichyes

The cartilaginous fishes, divided into two main groups:

ELASMOBRANCHII

Sharks, rays, and skates. Range: Devonian to Recent.

HOLOCEPHALI

Chimaeras (Mesozoic-Recent) and their Paleozoic ancestors, the brachydonts.

Sub-class Osteichthyes (Bony fishes)

Divided into two parts, the Actinopterygii and the Choanichthyes. The following are the principal orders:

ACTINOPTERYGII

Chondrostei. Primitive Paleozoic and Triassic bony types, and a few degenerate survivors. Frequently called ganoids, although that term is rather general and is also applied to other groups.

Holostei. The ray-fins of middle Mesozoic time and a few modern descendants.

Teleostei. The teleosts or modern bony fish that appeared suddenly at the beginning of the Cretaceous (Figure 44). Range: Cretaceous to Recent.

CHOANICHTHYES

Crossopterygii. Fish with lobed fins. The part of the fin belonging to the internal skeleton is large and scaly, forming a lobe to which the fin rays are attached. This group was thought to have existed only from the Devonian to the end of the Mesozoic, until a living example of this group was obtained off the coast of South Africa in 1939. The crossopterygians are equipped with both gills and lungs, and are frequently regarded as the ancestors of the land-living vertebrates. The Mesozoic representatives of this group are called Coelacanths. Range Devonian to Recent.

Dipnoi. Lung fish that obtain oxygen from the air through lungs as well as from the water by gills. Probably an aberrant offshoot of the early crossopterygians. Range: Devonian to Recent.

CONODONTA

Organisms of uncertain affinities, ranging in size from a fraction of a millimeter to two millimeters or more. Conodonts have been assigned by paleontologists to Crustacea, Cephalopods, Gastropoda, Annelida, and Vertebrata. The majority of recent workers believe that the Conodonta represent the jar armor of an extinct order of primitive fish. In spite of their uncertain position in the animal kingdom, conodonts make excellent horizon markers. In some ways they resemble scolecodonts (worm jaws) but are distinguished by their characteristic shapes and the fact that they are made of calcium phosphate of higher specific gravity than that of the scolecodonts (Figure 33). Range: Ordovician to Permian.

CLASS 2. AMPHIBIA

Sub-class Apsidospondyli

Labyrinthodonta. Frequently called Stegocephalia. An extinct group of amphibia characterized by heavy bodies and broad flat skulls. Range: Devonian(?), Mississippian to Triassic.

Salientia. Frogs and toads (Anura). Range: Triassic to Recent; and range of their ancestors (Eoanura and Proanura): Pennsylvanian to Triassic.

Sub-class Lepospondyli

Includes the newts, salamanders, and their direct ancestors (Urodela), Eocene to Recent, as well as several extinct groups of salamander-like animals.

CLASS 3. REPTILIA

Cotylosauria (Cotylosaurs). Primitive reptiles which are the ancestors of many other groups of reptiles. Range: Pennsylvanian to Triassic.

Pelycosauria (Pelycosaurs). Early land reptiles such as the fin back or *Dimetrodon.* Range: Pennsylvanian to Permian.

Therapsida. Includes the theriodonts and other mammal-like reptiles, which are the ancestors of the mammals. Range: Permian to Triassic.

Chelonia (Turtles). Range: Permian to Recent.

Ichthyosauria (Ichthyosaurs). Fish-like reptiles, some of great size. Range: Jurassic to Cretaceous.

Protorosauria. Small primitive reptiles, possibly the ancestors of the plesiosaurs. Range: Permian to Jurassic.

Sauropterygia. Includes the nothosaurs (ancestors of the plesiosaurs), Triassic; the plesiosaurs, Triassic to Cretaceous; and the placodonts (specialized sauropterygians), Triassic.

Thecodontia. Reptiles of which some were probably the ancestors of the dinosaurs. Some were armored. One important group comprises the *Phytosauria* (phytosaurs), crocodile-like thecodonts, but not the ancestors of the crocodiles. Range: Triassic.

Dinosauria (Dinosaurs). Usually divided into two groups:

Saurischia, those whose hip bones resemble those of a typical reptile. Range: Triassic to Cretaceous.

Ornithischia, those with hip bones resembling the hip bones of a bird. Range: Jurassic to Cretaceous.

Pterosauria. Pterodactyls and other flying reptiles. Range: Jurassic to Cretaceous.

Crocodilia. Crocodiles. Range: Triassic to Recent.

Squamata. Lizards and snakes as well as the Cretaceous mosasaurs. Range: Cretaceous to Recent.

CLASS 4. AVES

Birds. Range: Jurassic to Recent.

CLASS 5. MAMMALIA

Mammals. Range: Triassic to Recent (especially Cenozoic).

FURTHER READING

The references for Chapters 5–7 will be found at the end of Chapter 7.

CHAPTER 7

A CLASSIFICATION OF PLANTS

The following classification of plants, like the classification of animals given in the previous chapter, is somewhat arbitrary. Indeed, several different systems of plant classification are in general use, but the one given here is considered to be most convenient for the present purpose. It may be noted that the first three phyla are frequently grouped into a single phylum called the Thallophyta.

PHYLUM I. SCHIZOPHYTA

(Bacteria)

Microscopic one-celled organisms which have been reported in a few rocks. Range: Pre-Cambrian to Recent.

PHYLUM II. ALGAE

One-celled and in some groups many-celled plants of both fresh and salt water. Some fossil forms resemble modern seaweeds, while others were more massive and secreted layers of calcium carbonate. Members of genera such as *Cryptozoon* deposited thick layers of lime in their tissue and grew into large cabbage-like heads (see Figures 71 and 72). Modern descendants of the cryptozoa include *Lithothamnion* and *Corallina,* the incrusting algae of modern tropical seas.

There is some question whether the cryptozoa represent individual species or aggregations made up of various species. Therefore, the use of genus and species names for certain of these colonies is perhaps misleading. Range: Pre-Cambrian to Recent.

One specialized group of algae is that comprising the diatoms. These are microscopic one-celled plants enclosed in a silica shell consisting of two valves. They inhabit fresh and salt water, and their siliceous valves are frequently valuable as index fossils of certain geological horizons (Figure 52). Range: Jurassic to Recent.

PHYLUM III. FUNGI

Fossil fungi are exceedingly rare. Perforations apparently made by fungi have been noted in some Silurian shells and a few fungal threads have been found under the bark of some Pennsylvanian trees. Also,

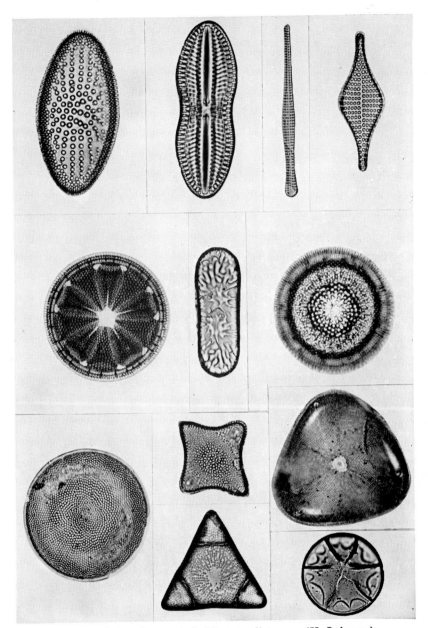

Fig. 52. Some characteristic Miocene diatoms. (K. Lohman.)

some fungal growths have been observed in petrified wood from the Tertiary of Idaho.

PHYLUM IV. BRYOPHYTA

(Mosses and liverworts)

Fossil representatives of this group are very rare. Examples of the liverwort *Conocephalum* have been reported from a few Tertiary formations, and a few leafy liverworts were found in the Carboniferous

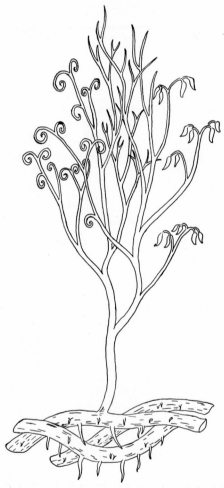

Fig. 53. Psilophyton from Gaspé. (Redrawn from *The Geological History of Plants,* by Dawson, Copyright 1888 by D. Appleton-Century Co., Inc.)

deposits of England. Mosses are practically unknown in the fossil state prior to the Pleistocene, although a moss-like plant (*Naiadota*) has been described from the Mesozoic of England.

PHYLUM V. PSILOPSIDA

A curious group of plants known only from a few genera of primitive Devonian forms and two modern species. The best-known representatives of the group are the Devonian *Psilophyton* (from the Gaspé region of Canada) and *Rhynia* (from Rhynie, Scotland). These plants had a woody stem about half an inch in diameter, and leafless branches rising about 2 feet in height. These were among the most primitive of land plants, and were probably the ancestors of the ferns (Figure 53). The modern species belong to the genus *Psilotum*.

PHYLUM VI. ARTHROPHYTA (SPHENOPSIDA)

(Fern allies, horsetails, calamites)

This phylum was once included with the Pteridophyta (ferns), but is now regarded as a separate phylum. It includes the Paleozoic rushes, the best-known genus being *Calamites*. During Pennsylvanian time some of these rushes attained the size of forest trees. They are characterized by their jointed stalks, with a cluster of leaves (annularia) at the nodes. Spores were present in small cones. The modern representative of the group are the horsetails and scouring rushes, placed in the genus *Equisetum*. In contrast to the large trees of the Paleozoic, the modern horsetails rarely are more than 2 or 3 feet in height. Range: Devonian to Recent.

PHYLUM VII. LEPIDOPHYTA (LYCOPSIDA)

(Scale trees, club mosses)

The fossil members of this phylum include such large-scale trees as *Lepidodendron* and *Sigillaria* which flourished in the swamps of the Coal Age. Some of these plants reached six feet in diameter and 200 feet in height. A conspicuous scar marked the place where the leaves were attached to the branches. Modern descendants of the scale trees are the club mosses or lycopods, including the genera *Lycopodium* and *Selaginella*. Like the survivors of the giant Arthrophytes of the Paleozoic, the living representatives of the Lepidophyta are small in size.

PHYLUM VIII. PTERIDOPHYTA (PTEROPSIDA)

(Ferns)

This group made their appearance during the Devonian and was particularly abundant during the Carboniferous. Some of the Tree Ferns of the Age of Coal reached 50 feet in height. Spores are present on the underside of the leaves (Figures 54 and 55). Range: Devonian to Recent.

Fig. 54. Fossil fern from coal regions of Pennsylvania.

PHYLUM IX. PTERIDOSPERMATOPHYTA

(Seed ferns)

Similar to the ordinary ferns except that they reproduced by seeds instead of spores. Some of the seed ferns of the coal swamps were 60 to 70 feet in height. Range: Devonian to Permian.

FIG. 55. Leaf of fern from coal measures at Mazon Creek, Illinois.

PHYLUM X. CYCADOPHYTA

(Cycads)

This group includes the living cycads (such as the genus *Cycas*) or Sago palms, as well as several extinct groups of cycad-like plants. Cycads probably appeared during the Devonian and were present, although not abundant, during the Carboniferous. By the Mesozoic, however, they had become the dominant feature of the plant life of the land. In fact, the Jurassic period is sometimes called the Age of Cycads. Range: Devonian to Recent.

PHYLUM XI. CONIFEROPHYTA

(Conifers, etc.)

This group includes the conifers (cone-bearing trees such as pine, spruce, etc.) as well as several less important groups. One group is known as Cordaites, named in honor of the early botanist Corda, and includes some Paleozoic trees which were tall and slender with branches only at the crown. Some reached a height of 100 feet. The most important genus is *Cordaites*.

Another group of the Coniferophyta comprises the ginkgos, represented by the modern Maidenhair tree or *Ginkgo*. The genus appeared as far back as the Permian and is fairly abundant in some deposits of the Triassic, Jurassic, and Cretaceous ages. Only a single species is known to be living today. The term Coniferophyta is practically equivalent to the older term Gymnospermae.

PHYLUM XII. ANGIOSPERMOPHYTA

(Flowering plants)

Flowering plants first appeared in the lower Cretaceous and have been the dominant plants since the Eocene. Not only are the plants themselves frequently preserved in the rocks, but also their pollen grains are occasionally found, especially in the younger formations. In fact, many of the details of the climatic history of the Pleistocene have been worked out by a study of the pollen and spores of angio-

FIG. 56. Miocene palm leaf from Mississippi.

sperms and conifers obtained from ancient peat beds. The fossil palm shown on Figure 56 is an example of an angiosperm.

FURTHER READING FOR CHAPTERS 5–7

ANDREWS, H. N. *Ancient Plants and the World They Live In.* Ithaca: N. Y. Comstock Publishing Co., Inc., 1947.

AUGUSTA, JOSEF. *Divy Prasveta.* (*Wonders of the Primeval World.*) Prague: Touzimski a Moravec, 1942. (In Czech; excellent color restorations of ancient life by Zdenek Burian.)

BERRY, E. W. *Tree Ancestors; a Glimpse into the Past.* Baltimore: The Williams & Wilkins Co., 1923.

BUCHSBAUM, RALPH. *Animals Without Backbones.* Chicago: University of Chicago Press, 1938.

COLBERT, E. H. *The Dinosaur Book.* New York: McGraw-Hill Book Co., Inc., 1951.

CUSHMAN, J. A. *Foraminifera, Their Classification and Economic Use.* Cambridge: Harvard University Press, 1940.

FENTON, C. L. *Life Long Ago.* New York: John Day Co., Inc., 1937.

GOLDRING, WINIFRED. *Handbook of Paleontology for Beginners and Amateurs; Part 1, The Fossils.* New York State Museum Handbook 9 (1950).

GREGORY, WILLIAM K. *Evolution Emerging.* New York: The Macmillan Co., 1951.

JONGMANS, W. J. "Het Wissland Aspect van het Bos in de Oudere Geologische Formaties," in *Hout in alle tijden* by W. B. Beekman. Heerlen, Netherlands: 1949. (Excellent illustrations of restorations of ancient plants.)

KOZLOWSKI, ROMAN. "Les Affinités des Graptolites," *Biological Reviews*, XXII (1947), pp. 93–108.

ROMER, ALFRED. *Vertebrate Paleontology.* Chicago: University of Chicago Press, 1945.

SEWARD, A. C. *Plant Life Through the Ages.* New York: The Macmillan Co., 1931.

SHIMER, H. W. *An Introduction to the Study of Fossils.* New York: The Macmillan Co., 1933.

SHIMER, W. W., and SHROCK, R. R. *Index Fossils of North America.* New York: John Wiley & Sons, Inc., 1944.

TWENHOFEL, W. H., and SHROCK, R. R. *Invertebrate Paleontology.* New York: McGraw-Hill Book Co., Inc., 1935.

ZITTEL, KARL. *Text Book of Paleontology* (edited by C. R. Eastman). New York: The Macmillan Co., 1913.

CHAPTER 8

THE ORIGIN OF THE EARTH

To serve as a background for the discussion of the geological history of the earth, three of the best-known theories of the origin of the earth are briefly outlined at this time. All of the theories which have been suggested, thus far, contain assumptions which fail to fit all the known facts about the history of the earth. The problem is still being attacked by geologists and astronomers and it is hoped that a combination of their efforts will eventually result in a better understanding of this complicated problem.

Nebular Hypothesis

This was originally proposed by the philosopher Kant in 1755 and was later elaborated by the French astronomer Laplace in 1796. According to this hypothesis, the sun and its planets were formed from a single large rotating disc-shaped gaseous cloud, or nebula, which reached far beyond our most distant planet. It was assumed that in the beginning the nebula was hot and was spinning slowly. As the gas cooled, the nebula shrank in size and at the same time increased its speed. Finally, the outer portions of the gaseous mass became detached because the centrifugal force was greater than the gravitational force. According to this hypothesis, the various rings that broke off from the original nebula became the planets, and the sun became the final remnant of the original nebula. The origin of the earth according to the Nebular Hypothesis is shown diagrammatically in Figures 57 and 58.

Objections.—Present-day astronomers believe that no such condensation of hot gas at the rim of a spinning nebula would take place. Furthermore, according to this hypothesis, the sun should possess almost all of the energy of the solar system, since the sun's mass is equal to about 99 times that of all the planets combined. Actually, the planets possess about 98 per cent of the energy (angular momentum) of the solar system. In addition, if rings had been given off by the sun, and if more were to be given off, there should be an equatorial bulge on the sun, but this is not in evidence. There are

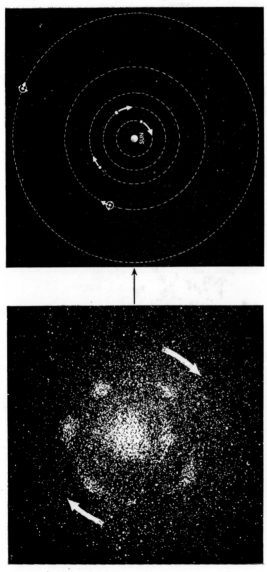

FIG. 57. Origin of the earth according to Kant (1755). Left, clotting mass of gas and dust in rotation. Right, clots grow by accretion to form planets and satellites. Remainder of nebula contracts to form the sun. (Thornton Page, Yerkes Observatory.)

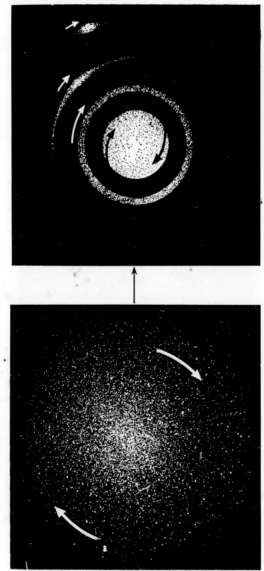

Fig. 58. Origin of the earth according to Laplace (1795). Left, rotating nebula. Right, cooling nebula shrinks, spins faster, and is expected to leave rings of gas to condense into planets. Remainder forms the sun. (Thornton Page.)

numerous other astronomical objections to this hypothesis which, in its original form, is not accepted by scientists today.

Planetesimal Hypothesis

This hypothesis was proposed by the astronomer F. R. Moulton and the geologist T. C. Chamberlin in 1895. According to these scientists, a star passed close to the sun, causing tidal bulges to appear on the sun. The sun was therefore disrupted while great masses of material were torn away from it in a series of "bolts." These were eventually formed into solid "planetesimals" which gathered together to form the planets. Secondary nuclei formed the satellites which revolve around the planets. Meteors are regarded as planetesimals that are still being attracted to the earth. The origin of the earth according to the planetesimal theory is shown diagrammatically in Figure 59.

Objections.—It is now doubted that the planetesimals could collect together to form the planets. Rather, it has been suggested that they would likely break up into very small bodies, or else would be dissipated as gas. Furthermore, there is considerable evidence to suggest that the earth passed through a molten stage in its history, while the Planetesimal Hypothesis assumes that the earth was originally solid. It is believed that the earth has a metallic core, mainly composed of nickel and iron, surrounded by concentric layers of less and less dense material, the uppermost later being of granite exposed at the surface, or beneath a thin veneer of sedimentary rocks. This does not favor the Planetesimal Hypothesis, which assumes that the earth was solid because it was formed by a combination of the planetesimals.

The Gaseous Hypothesis

This hypothesis was proposed by the astronomer Sir James Jeans and the geophysicist Harold Jeffries in 1917. While retaining some of the features of the Planetesimal Hypothesis, it attempts to answer some of the objections to this view. According to these two British scientists, the sun was disrupted by the gravitational pull of another star at a time when they were in close proximity to each other. Some material was drawn out from the sun, increasing in quantity as the star neared the sun, and then decreasing as the star moved away. (In a later expansion of this hypothesis, Jeffries suggested that the star and sun actually collided.) A spindle-shaped filament of incandescent gas formed and stretched out to the limits of our solar system.

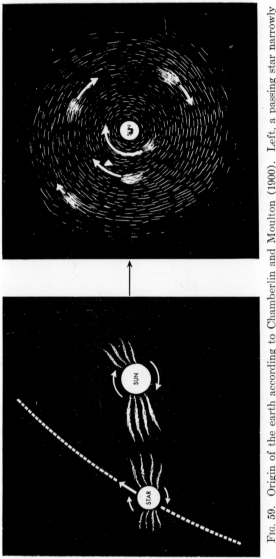

FIG. 59. Origin of the earth according to Chamberlin and Moulton (1900). Left, a passing star narrowly misses the sun. High eruptions are expected to occur on both as they pass. Right, the sun is left with a vast number of planetesimals which condense from the erupted gases and slowly coagulate to form planets. The intruding star should also have planets forming. (Thornton Page.)

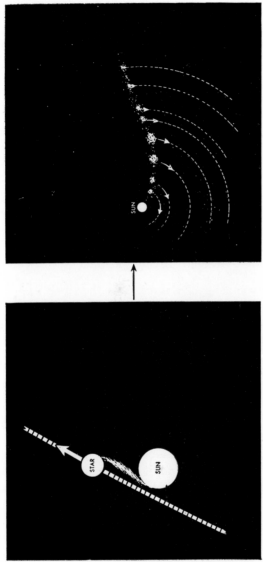

Fig. 60. Origin of the earth according to Jeans and Jeffries (1917). Left, a passing star sideswipes the sun, tearing out a long filament of gaseous material. Right, the gas is expected to cool and condense into planets, the largest one in the middle and smaller ones at either end. (Thornton Page.)

These filaments became unstable and broke up into a number of units, which became spherical and cooled to form the planets.

As the newly formed planets approached the sun in their first revolution around that parent body, small tidal strains occurred on the planets, similar to those induced on the sun by the passing of a star. The gaseous material broken loose from the planets by the tidal pull of the sun became the satellites or moons of the planets (Figure 60).

Objections.—The same objection applies to this explanation as applies to the Nebular Hypothesis, namely, that the energy is not evenly distributed among the sun and its planets, as would be assumed from the Gaseous Hypothesis. In an attempt to overcome this objection, Dr. Henry Norris Russell assumed that the sun was a double star, and that, after its collision with a third star, the smaller unit of the double star broke up to form the planets, asteroids, and satellites, while the larger unit remained as the sun. According to this view, the energy of the planets may have been inherited from the disrupted part of the "twin suns." However, there are still other complicated astronomical objections to this interpretation.

Recent Investigations

Various new hypotheses of the origin of the earth have been proposed, but they can generally be regarded as variations of one or more of the three discussed above. In 1936, Lyttleton, one of Russell's students, showed mathematically that, if the sun had a close companion spinning around it, a third star might have side-swiped the companion and carried it away, leaving a filament of its gas revolving around the sun. This filament, which would have retained considerable energy (angular momentum), might have produced the planets. (See Figure 61.)

In 1939, Spitzer, another of Russell's students, calculated that the material pulled out of the sun could not possibly condense into planetesimals or planets. Instead, it would expand to form a gaseous nebula. The English astronomer Hoyle in 1944 suggested that a nova explosion might have taken place. In other words, a star passing near the sun might have blown up, throwing off large shells of material. Parts of the nova shell might have been caught by the gravitational pull of the sun to form the planets, while the nova (new star) moved away. (See Figure 62.)

Other scientists (among them Berlage, Alfven, and Weizsäcker), utilizing their knowledge of modern mathematics and physics, have advanced new theories which can be regarded as adaptations and

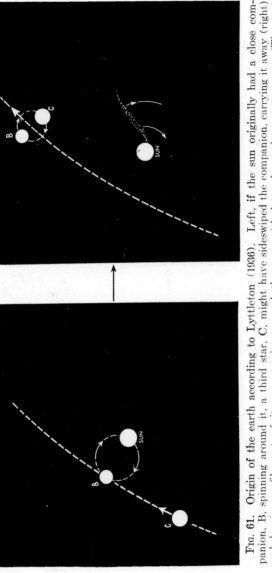

FIG. 61. Origin of the earth according to Lyttleton (1936). Left, if the sun originally had a close companion, B, spinning around it, a third star, C, might have sideswiped the companion, carrying it away (right) and leaving a filament of its gas moving around the sun, with lots of angular momentum. (Thornton Page.)

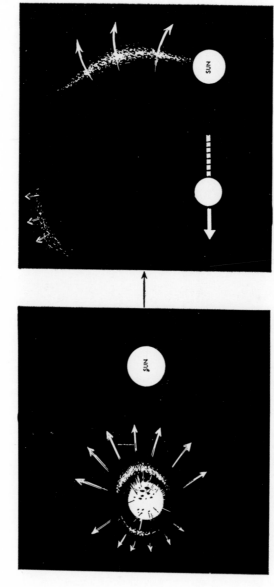

FIG. 62. Origin of the earth according to Hoyle (1944). Left, a star near the sun might have blown up, throwing off a large shell of material, possibly more in one direction than the other. Right, part of the nova shell could have been caught by the sun's gravitation, while the nova itself recoiled away from the one-sided explosion. (Thornton Page.)

extensions of the original Nebular Hypothesis of Laplace. So, perhaps the pendulum is swinging back to the ideas of the eighteenth and early nineteenth centuries, although of course modifying them with the interpretations of the present day. Dr. Carl Dunbar points out that the most plausible conclusions regarding the origin of the earth are:

1. That the (solar) system is not eternal, but came into being more than two billion years ago through reorganization of pre-existing matter.
2. That Earth and the other members of the solar system were genetically related in their origin.
3. That Earth and Moon passed through a molten stage, and
4. That Earth was essentially full grown before geological processes of erosion and sedimentation began on it.[1]

FURTHER READING FOR CHAPTER 8

DUNBAR, CARL O. *Historical Geology.* New York: John Wiley & Sons, 1949, pp. 68–90.

DUNCAN, JOHN C. *Astronomy.* New York: Harper & Bros., 1946.

GAMOW, GEORGE. *Biography of the Earth.* New York: The Viking Press, 1941.

PAGE, THORNTON. "The Origin of the Earth," *Physics Today,* I, No. 6 (1948); reprinted in Ann. Report of the Smithsonian Inst. for 1949, pp. 161–74.

RUSSELL, HENRY N. *The Solar System and Its Origin.* New York: The Macmillan Co., 1935.

SMART, W. M. *The Origin of the Earth.* London: Cambridge University Press, 1951.

WEIZSÄCKER, C. F. VON. "Evolution of Galaxies and Stars," *Astrophysical Jour.,* CXIV, No. 2 (1951), pp. 165 ff.

WHIPPLE, FRED L. *Earth, Moon and Planets.* Philadelphia: The Blakiston Co., 1941.

[1] Carl Dunbar, *Historical Geology* (New York: John Wiley & Sons, Inc., 1948), p. 89. Quoted by permission.

CHAPTER 9

THE PRE-CAMBRIAN

The Beginning of the Record

The beginning of the geological history of eastern North America is shrouded in mystery, as is the case of other parts of the world. The very long period of time prior to the beginning of more or less definite fossil records of the Cambrian period is usually spoken of as the Pre-Cambrian. People frequently get the impression that this was a relatively unimportant period in the earth's history. This is far from the case. True, fewer details are known about the Pre-Cambrian than about any of the later periods, but this does not necessarily signify that it was an unimportant era. Probably the most significant events of the entire earth's history were taking place during this era, but they are so ancient, and are so obscured by later events, that we may never have a clear understanding of their chronology.

	Pennsylvania	New Jersey	New York
PRE-CAMBRIAN (may be Ordovician)	Wissahickon	Wissahickon	Manhattan
PRE-CAMBRIAN	Baltimore	Franklin Pochuck	Grenville Fordham

Pre-Cambrian time was very long—longer than all the rest of geologic time. The Cambrian is thought to have begun about 520,-000,000 years ago, while Pre-Cambrian time goes back at least two billion years. Students of the Pre-Cambrian have divided it into two major parts, the Archeozoic and the Proterozoic, and these in turn have been subdivided into various phases. However, for our purpose it will be sufficient to treat the Pre-Cambrian as a whole, and not devote much attention to the various divisions. In the first place, the scarcity or absence of fossils makes it extremely difficult to correlate the various Pre-Cambrian deposits of even nearby localities. Furthermore, the tremendous amount of folding of the earth's crust, the volcanic action, and the other geological activity that has taken place during and since this remote period in our earth's history have so greatly altered or metamorphosed these Pre-Cambrian rocks that they are now among the most complex on the entire earth's surface.

It is generally believed that during an early formative stage in the earth's history there was tremendous volcanic activity, accompanied by intrusions of molten rocks. Eventually this material cooled and formed the granites and other constituents of the upper part of the earth's crust. Igneous activity continued intermittently throughout Pre-Cambrian time, and these igneous rocks of undetermined thickness now occur, either altered or unaltered, in all regions of the earth. Many of those that were once deeply buried are now exposed by erosion. Many of the rocks have been metamorphosed, and in most cases are overlain by more recent sedimentary deposits. Because of their position beneath other beds and because of their intricate nature, these Pre-Cambrian rocks are frequently spoken of as the "basement complex," which is thought to occur at depths varying from the surface to more than 30,000 feet throughout the world.

It is impossible to draw a line between the granites and other rocks of the upper part of the earth's crust, and those igneous and metamorphic rocks formed during the various stages of the Pre-Cambrian era. It is also frequently difficult to draw a sharp line between the Pre-Cambrian and the early Paleozoic formations. For this reason, the term "basement complex" is often applied to all basal igneous or metamorphic rocks, whether of Pre-Cambrian or Paleozoic age. For instance, the age of the granite underlying the Atlantic Coastal Plain is in doubt, some geologists calling it Pre-Cambrian, others calling it Paleozoic.

These ancient Pre-Cambrian rocks slowly cooled and began to be eroded. The weathered material from them was carried down, by a succession of streams and rivers, into the primordial sea. However, this sea was unlike our oceans of today. Life, if present at all, was limited to minute unicellular organisms. Furthermore, the water of the seas was probably fresh, for it must have taken many millions of years for the Pre-Cambrian rivers to carry down enough salts to make the sea water saline.[1]

The erosion of the igneous rocks, probably largely by wind and running water, caused the formation of the first sedimentary strata in this primordial sea. These were probably first composed of sandstones and mudstones (shales) followed, later, by limestones. But these sediments were not left alone. Volcanic activity continued and most of

[1] According to another interpretation, the sea was originally more salty than today, having acquired the salts from the gases in the primordial atmosphere.

the sedimentary rocks were folded and crushed and intruded by lava and other igneous material, causing the original sedimentary masses to be metamorphosed to schists, gneisses, and other complex rocks.

The Franklin limestone of Pennsylvania and New Jersey is one of the oldest sedimentary rocks of the eastern United States. These limestones have been intruded by igneous materials from the interior of the earth. The intruded limestones are often replaced by pegmatites which brought with them from the core of the earth considerable iron, zinc, and other minerals. Other Pre-Cambrian sedimentary limestones, which may or may not be of the same age as the Franklin, occur in eastern Pennsylvania, New Jersey, and nearby states. Muds of the ancient Pre-Cambrian seas have been altered to slates and schists in many parts of the world.

The complexity of these very ancient rocks makes it difficult to tell their age. It is apparent that a great deal of igneous action and metamorphism took place during the Pre-Cambrian periods, and definitely continued well into the Paleozoic. It is therefore extremely difficult to tell whether certain gneisses or schists are of Pre-Cambrian age or of a later period. The Wissahickon schists of the Philadelphia area may have been formed during the Pre-Cambrian, or perhaps much later, during Cambrian or Ordovician time. The same thing is true of the Manhattan schist and certain similar rocks of New York City. On the other hand, the Baltimore gneiss and the Fordham gneiss are definitely Pre-Cambrian. Many of the rocks of the Adirondacks are clearly of Pre-Cambrian age, and are among the oldest in the world. These were also intruded by volcanics, causing immense deposits of iron and other minerals to occur in the region. Extensive Pre-Cambrian areas occur in New England, in a belt along the eastern edge of the Appalachians from New York to Alabama, and over a very large part of eastern Canada, the so-called "Canadian Shield" (Figures 63 and 64). The Adirondacks are probably an outlier of the Pre-Cambrian rocks of the Canadian Shield, while the areas in New England and from New York City southward are localized areas, the exact relationship to the Canadian Shield being uncertain.

At least three times during the Pre-Cambrian there was extensive mountain building. Many of the sedimentary and metamorphic rocks were pushed upward to high elevations and folded to form immense mountains and mountain ranges. One period of mountain building, accompanied by the intrusion of granitic magmas, formed high mountains in the Laurentian Uplands of eastern Canada. These were later leveled down, or "peneplaned" to their present condition. At other times there was extensive glacial action, as revealed by the presence of tillite in the Huronian rocks in the Lake Huron area. This tillite

FIG. 63.   Eroded Pre-Cambrian granite of the Canadian shield exposed along the shores of Hudson Bay at Churchill, Manitoba.

FIG. 64. Folded gneiss of Pre-Cambrian age along the shores of Hudson Bay at Chesterfield Inlet, Northwest Territories.

is composed of the now-consolidated masses of boulders transported by these ancient ice sheets.

Pre-Cambrian History of North America

As we remarked above, the Pre-Cambrian history of North America can only be deciphered imperfectly from the rocks now in evidence. Most of the knowledge which we have has been derived from a study of Pre-Cambrian rocks outside the region treated in this book. The following table summarizes the Pre-Cambrian history of North America, as revealed in the studies of a wide area of rock outcrops, especially the Pre-Cambrian in Canada, adjacent Michigan, Minnesota, and Wisconsin, in the thick section exposed in the Grand Canyon of the Colorado River, and in the Glacier National Park region.

ARCHEOZOIC ERA (OR ARCHEAN TIME)

1. Cosmic history; formation of the earth; volcanic activity.
2. "Unrecoverable history."
3. Keewatin Time. Deposition of sedimentary rocks interbedded with igneous intrusions. These are especially conspicuous in the Lake Superior region. Keewatin Time was characterized by periods of intense metamorphism. Sedimentary rocks such as the Franklin limestone (New Jersey), Glenarm series (Pennsylvania and Maryland), and the Grenville series (New York and Quebec) probably date from this stage.
4. Laurentian Revolution. Mountain building in eastern Canada.
5. Period of erosion.

6. Temiskaming Time. Deposition of marine and alluvial material.
7. Algoman Revolution. Mountain building in Ontario.
8. Long period of erosion.

PROTEROZOIC ERA (OR ALGONKIAN TIME)

9. Huronian Time. Deposition of marine sedimentary rocks; extensive glaciation. Best developed in the region around Lake Huron and Lake Superior. Several relative minor periods of erosion. Formation of rich iron deposits.
10. Keweenawan Time. Extensive deposition of lava flows formed from fissure eruptions, interspersed with red sandstones and shales which are probably of continental origin. Best developed in northwestern Minnesota and adjacent, Wisconsin. Native copper abundant in lavas and conglomerate.
11. Period of erosion.
12. Penokean Revolution in northern Michigan. Other major revolutions of this stage include the Killarney (in Ontario), the Belcher (in Hudson Bay), and the Labrador (in Ungava Peninsula).
13. Erosion interval between Proterozoic and Paleozoic.

Pre-Cambrian Life

Very few fossils have ever been observed in Pre-Cambrian rocks, and none from the area emphasized in this book. It does not necessarily follow, however, that little life existed at that time. On the contrary, there must have been a great many different varieties of living creatures in existence. The fauna of the Lower Cambrian includes representatives of numerous groups of animals, including sponges, corals, brachiopods, mollusks, and trilobites. Even though they are relatively primitive, they must have had ancestors that were even more primitive than they, and these ancestors must have lived in the Pre-Cambrian seas.

The few fossils that have been found in Pre-Cambrian rocks are very poorly preserved, and it has been almost impossible to determine their position in the animal or plant kingdoms. No positively identified fossils have been found in Archeozoic rocks. Some peculiar markings found in the Archeozoic Grenville limestone of Canada were thought for a long time to have been deposited by a very primitive animal, and the name *Eozoön canadense* (Canada's Dawn Animal) was given to it. Later, the markings were believed to have been formed by very primitive kinds of calcareous algae (seaweed). However, most modern paleontologists are of the opinion that these markings are entirely of inorganic origin, being merely variations in the rock structure. One of these specimens is shown in Figure 65.

Indirect evidence of Archeozoic life is found in the presence of graphite deposits in many rocks of this era. The graphite is thought to have been formed from carbon derived from some lowly form of plant life. Certain limestone formations are possibly partly of organic origin, although it is generally believed that the majority of the

Fig. 65. *Eozoon canadense,* once thought to be the world's most primitive fossil. (Redpath Museum.)

Pre-Cambrian limestones could have been formed in water without the presence of animal or plant life.

Much more distinct fossils have been found in Proterozoic rocks. Reefs of undoubted algal origin occur in Proterozoic rocks of the Grand Canyon in Arizona, the Belt Series of Montana, near Caborca in Sonora, Mexico, and at various places in Michigan and Minnesota (Figure 66). The secretions or limestone reefs built by these calcareous algae superficially resemble coral reefs. So far, no fossil algae have been discovered in the Proterozoic rocks of the Piedmont Plateau. Probably these rocks have been too greatly altered by igneous action or by pressure, with the result that the fossils, if originally in the deposits, are now completely unrecognizable.

Other kinds of Proterozoic fossils include primitive sponges, usually represented merely by minute spicules, jellyfish, worm borings and trails, and some microscopic structures questionably identified as Radiolaria. These latter were found many years ago by Professor L. Cayeaux in the Pre-Cambrian rocks of Brittany, France, and were described in detail, although they were hardly more than 0.01 mm. in diameter. Later work has cast some doubt on these identifications.

One of the most amazing discoveries in the field of Pre-Cambrian life was that of Dr. C. L. Walcott. In 1915, he reported the presence

FIG. 66. Reef of *Cryptozoon* sp. of Pre-Cambrian age, one mile east of Iron Mountain, Michigan. (Chicago Nat. Hist. Mus.)

of bacteria, less than 0.001 mm. in diameter, associated with calcareous algae in the Pre-Cambrian rocks of Glacier National Park. More recently, C. L. and M. A. Fenton reported the finding of very primitive (inarticulate) brachiopods or lantern shells in the Pre-Cambrian rocks of Montana. The identification of these specimens, likewise, has been questioned by some workers, although there is every reason to believe that such animals did exist in Pre-Cambrian time.   The type specimen to this brachiopod, known as *Lingulella montana* is shown in Figure 67.

After making an analysis of the Early Cambrian life, Professor Percy E. Raymond concluded that "Pre-Cambrian fauna consisted of naked Protozoa, siliceous sponges, primitive coelenterates (perhaps jellyfish), segmented worms, inarticulate brachiopods, the latter accompanied by creatures resembling their ancestors." Various theories

Fig. 67.   The Pre-Cambrian brachiopod *Lingulella montana*, from the Belt Series west of White Sulphur Springs, Montana.

have been expounded to explain the lack of Pre-Cambrian fossils.   A few are listed here:

1. Destruction by metamorphism.
2. The lack of calcium in the sea prevented the formation of skeletons which could be preserved as fossils (R. A. Daly).
3. There were no skeletons because the waters were too acid (A. C. Lane).
4. All Pre-Cambrian rocks now accessible were deposited on land or in fresh water (C. L. Walcott).
5. Life originated on land and did not reach the sea until Cambrian time (R. C. Chamberlain).
6. Pre-Cambrian organisms lacked hard parts because they lived in the surface waters of the ocean, where skeletons would have been a drawback because of their weight (C. E. P. Brooks).
7. Pre-Cambrian animals were motile and did not need skeletons; skeletons developed later (in the Cambrian) as a result of the adoption of a sessile or sluggish mode of life (P. E. Raymond).

Probably the truth lies in a combination of these various theories, perhaps with emphasis on the last two.

Economic Resources of the Pre-Cambrian

Pre-Cambrian rocks are noted for their mineral contents. In fact, the term "Pre-Cambrian" is in general usage among miners and prospectors and is associated with the actual and potential wealth of the rocks of the Pre-Cambrian Canadian Shield. Only a few of the more significant minerals of this age will be itemized here.

Iron.—The very extensive iron deposits of the Lake Superior region in Michigan, Wisconsin, and Minnesota are of Huronian (Pre-Cambrian) age. A recent estimate indicated that this area produces about 85 per cent of all the iron that is mined in the United States. A large open-pit mine in the Mesabi Range of Minnesota is shown in Figure

FIG. 68. Iron ore mine in the Mesabi Range, Minnesota. (U.S. Steel Corp.)

68. Pre-Cambrian rocks in other parts of the world also contain immense quantities of iron ore. A few years ago a very extensive deposit of iron ore was discovered near the headwaters of the George, Whale, and Swampy Rivers, some 300 to 400 miles north of the Gulf of St. Lawrence, on the Quebec-Labrador boundary. Great hope is held for the future development of this area, and it is thought by some that it may in time supplant the iron mines in the Lake Superior region, when they are exhausted.

The Pre-Cambrian rocks of Pennsylvania and New Jersey contain iron ore (magnetite), and mining has been undertaken at a number of places. For many years, important mines were located at Ringwood, Passaic County, New Jersey. At present, they are not in operation, although mining is carried on at several places in Warren and Morris Counties. The magnetite deposits in the vicinity of South Mountain, Pennsylvania, are at least of potential economic value. Recently the magnetite deposits of the Adirondacks have assumed importance as a source of iron, and extensive mining operations are under way.

Copper.—Copper has been mined in Michigan since the days of the Indians and at present forms one of the state's principal mineral resources. The most important mines are in the Pre-Cambrian rocks of the Keweenaw Peninsula. Copper is also mined from the Pre-Cambrian rocks of Sudbury, Ontario; Rouyn, Quebec, and elsewhere in the Pre-Cambrian Shield of Canada. Important deposits of copper are also mined at Ducktown, Tennessee.

Silver.—This mineral is known from numerous localities in the Pre-Cambrian rocks of eastern Canada, the chief producing area now being in the vicinity of Cobalt, Ontario. It is also found associated with copper in Michigan, Montana, etc.

Gold.--Numerous gold mines exist in the Pre-Cambrian of eastern Canada. Among the more important mines are those of the Porcupine district in Ontario and those in the vicinity of Rouyn in Quebec.

Radium and Uranium.—In 1930, extensive deposits of the mineral pitchblende were discovered in the vicinity of Great Bear Lake in northern Canada. These rocks have assumed a tremendous importance in recent years because of the use of uranium in the development of atomic energy. The ores occur in both Pre-Cambrian sedimentary and igneous rocks.

Zinc.—Large deposits of zinc occur in the Franklin limestone of Pre-Cambrian age at Franklin Furnace and Ogdensburg, in Sussex

County, New Jersey. The New Jersey Zinc Company operates one of the largest zinc mines in the country in this vicinity.

Other minerals frequently associated with Pre-Cambrian rocks include asbestos, cobalt, nickel, vanadium, and titanium.

Water.—Rocks of all ages that are sufficiently porous and permeable are potential sources of ground water, and thus are of considerable economic importance.

FURTHER READING FOR CHAPTER 9

COLEMAN, A. P. *Ice Ages, Recent and Ancient.* New York: The Macmillan Co., 1929, pp. 220–41.

DUNBAR, CARL O. *Historical Geology.* New York: John Wiley & Sons, Inc., 1949, pp. 91–127.

LEWIS, H. V., and KUMMEL, H. B. *The Geology of New Jersey.* Geol. Surv. of New Jersey Bull. 50 (1940), pp. 56–61.

MOORE, RAYMOND C. *Historical Geology.* New York: McGraw-Hill Book Co., Inc., 1949, pp. 67–88.

RAYMOND, PERCY. "Pre-Cambrian Life," *Bull. Geol. Soc. Amer.,* XLVI (1935), pp. 375–92.

REEDS, CHESTER A. *The Geology of New York City and Vicinity.* Amer. Mus. Nat. Hist. Guide Leaflet 56 (1930).

CHAPTER 10

THE CAMBRIAN

The Cambrian period of geologic time derives its name from Cambria, the Roman name for Wales, where the rocks were first studied by Professor Adam Sedgwick of Cambridge University in 1833. The term was originally intended to include part of the rocks of the next younger period of time, the Ordovician, but the term is now applied only to the oldest period of the Paleozoic era.

	Pennsylvania	New Jersey	New York
UPPER CAMBRIAN	Allentown	Middle Kittatinny	Little Falls Theresa Potsdam
MIDDLE CAMBRIAN	Elbrook	—	—
LOWER CAMBRIAN	Tomstown Chickies	Lower Kittatinny Hardyston	Stissing(?) Poughquog quartzite

Lower Cambrian

Pre-Cambrian time was followed by a very long period of erosion. Along the Atlantic coast the land was high and the sea probably retreated far beyond its present limits. Since there was no deposition on the present land, and since no sediment was laid down to become rocks, we are unable to tell very much about the interval between Pre-Cambrian and Cambrian time. This erosion interval was probably much shorter than the erosion interval at the end of the Archeozoic era.

When the curtain next goes up on our geological drama we find that hundreds and perhaps thousands of feet of sediment laid down during Pre-Cambrian time, along with countless cubic miles of igneous and metamorphic rocks, have been removed by erosion and carried by streams and rivers to some distant sea. The erosion interval was brought to an end by a slow sinking of the land along the present line of the Appalachian Mountain range. This sinking was probably

112

caused by the great weight of sediments carried down from the highlands on the two sides of the geosyncline.

The waters of the ocean slowly advanced along this depression, first moving northeastward from the ancient Gulf of Mexico across what is now Alabama, through Pennsylvania, New Jersey, and New York. As Figure 69 shows, they extended as far as Labrador, where they again joined the open ocean.

Appalachia.—Meanwhile, the land southeast of this advancing sea was high and mountainous. This ancient rugged land mass, or group of islands, has been called Appalachia by geologists and must not be confused with the present Appalachian Mountains. Most of the rocks of this ancient Appalachia have long since eroded and are deeply buried in southern New Jersey and adjacent coastal states as far south as Florida. How far east this continent (or these islands) extended is not known but Appalachia may, at times, have extended as much as 100 miles east of our present shore line. To the north of Appalachia was another extensive high region called Acadia, probably separated from Appalachia by a narrow strait which connected the inland sea with the ancient Atlantic Ocean, perhaps near the site of New York City.

Recent students of geology have expressed the belief that Appalachia may not have been the extensive continent pictured by earlier workers and as shown in most paleogeographic maps. Certainly the land was there, but it may have consisted of a series of chains of islands not unlike the Japanese or Indonesian Archipelagoes of today. While most of the sediment washed westward into the Appalachian geosyncline probably came from Appalachia, it is possible that at certain times considerable material was derived from the lowlands west of the Appalachian Trough.

As the waters of this Early Cambrian inland sea advanced over the depressed area, they spread out the rock material derived from the east and the west and deposited it on the sea bottom. These sands and gravels thus came to rest at the bottom of the sea on the eroded surface of the Pre-Cambrian formations. The break between these two is frequently, but not always, well marked, and, as stated previously, is called an unconformity.

Hardyston-Chickies Quartzite.—The sands and gravels of this Early Cambrian sea hardened to sandstone and conglomerate and in some cases were altered or metamorphosed to quartzite. In New Jersey, this formation is called the Hardyston quartzite, and is well exposed near the town of Hardyston in Sussex County, as well as near Hamburg and Great Meadows. The same deposit in southeastern and eastern Pennsylvania is called the Chickies quartzite, and is exposed west of the Delaware Valley, near Philadelphia.

Similar sandstones and quartzites extend south along the Appalachian Mountains and are especially well developed near Harpers Ferry, West Virginia. The coarse character of these sediments indicates that Appalachia, as well as the land to the west of the trough, was very high and that the rivers bringing the material down to the sea had steep gradients and considerable transporting power. The exceptionally hard character of the Chickies and Hardyston sediments has caused them to resist erosion better than many neighboring formations of shale and limestone. Hills such as Mount Joy and Mount Misery at Valley Forge and Mount Penn at Reading, being partly composed of these quartzites, are conspicuous features of the landscape in this part of Pennsylvania.

Tomstown or Lower Kittatinny Limestone.—By the time the Hardyston and Chickies formations had been deposited, Appalachia had been considerably eroded, so the rivers flowing westward from this continent to the inland sea were bringing finer and finer material. As a result, the course sediments of Early Cambrian age were followed by the deposition of shales and then limestones, which were later altered to dolomites. These constitute the second phase of the Lower Cambrian in this area.

In New Jersey these may form the lower part of the Kittatinny limestone which is well exposed near Phillipsburg in Warren County and

---

A NOTE ON PALEOGEOGRAPHIC MAPS

Paleogeographic maps are at best only generalizations. Even if we were able to decipher the complete geological history of the earth, the only way to represent it adequately would be by an animated moving picture showing the constant changes in the relative position of sea and land. The conventional method of presenting paleogeographic maps is to show one map for each period or epoch. It must, of course, be borne in mind that such maps represent only a few frames of the complete moving picture film. For example, no single map can represent the paleogeography of Early Cambrian time. An attempt has been made, however, to show the maximum advance of the sea during the various periods and epochs. Many features, such as the eastern shore line of Appalachia, will probably never be determined, and are shown on the maps as wavy lines. The series of maps used in this book is intended to give the reader a general idea of the geography of North America during its geological history and should not be interpreted as showing the detailed position of the ancient shore lines. (Base maps courtesy McKinley Publishing Company of Philadelphia.)

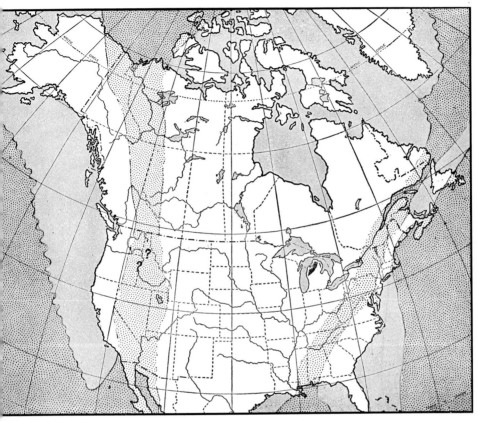

FIG. 69. Early Cambrian. The Appalachian geosyncline was filled with an inland sea that extended from Alabama to Newfoundland. Its western counterpart, the Cordilleran geosyncline, probably extended from Lower California to the Arctic Ocean. The "Atlantic" phase of the Cambrian sea, east of Acadia-Appalachia, is shown in eastern Newfoundland, Nova Scotia, and extreme eastern Massachusetts.

at Peapack in Morris County. In Pennsylvania and Maryland these deposits are called the Tomstown group. Shales and limestone of this age contain marine fossils in the York and Lancaster Valley.

Deposits of similar character and age show that this Early Cambrian sea extended throughout most of the Appalachian trough from Alabama to the Gulf of St. Lawrence. The sediments are thicker both north and south of Pennsylvania, a fact that suggests that there was deeper water near the two entrances of the inland sea.

East of Appalachia.—The Early Cambrian seas also existed east of Appalachia and Acadia, that is, in the present Atlantic basin. But we know much less about this phase of the sea because most of the rocks and sediments deposited at that time now lie far beneath the ocean floor, many miles out at sea. In a few places the Lower Cambrian sea advanced westward over the present land, and here we can read the records from the rocks that are still exposed. For instance, remnants of the oceanic or Atlantic phase of the Lower Cambrian can be seen near Boston, Massachusetts; in New Brunswick, on Cape Breton Island; and in Newfoundland.

Some of the faunas of the Atlantic phase of the Cambrian are more closely related to those of Europe than to those of the Appalachian geosyncline. It therefore seems probable that there was a shallow water ridge extending from northern North America to Europe, probably via Greenland, thus permitting the migration of shore forms between the two continents. These European shore forms apparently reached the eastern shore of Appalachia, but few of them appear to have entered the Appalachian geosyncline.

Middle Cambrian

In Middle Cambrian time, the inland sea withdrew to the southwest from a large part of the trough, so few marine sediments of this age are to be found along the present Appalachian chain. The sea may not have withdrawn completely, and it is possible that there were a few shallow bays in the Appalachian Trough. However, the almost complete lack of Middle Cambrian fossils in this region leads to the conclusion that the trough must have been largely drained at that time.

Middle Cambrian seas, however, did exist east of Appalachia, and fossil reminders of this sea, in the form of trilobites and other marine fossils, are known from Middle Cambrian rocks in New Brunswick, Newfoundland, and eastern Massachusetts. Another arm of the Middle Cambrian sea probably extended along the present St. Lawrence Valley, and down into what is now the state of Vermont.

Upper Cambrian

Appalachian Trough.—In Late Cambrian time the sea again flooded the Appalachian trough or geosyncline (Figure 70). Appalachia had been eroded to a relatively low continent or archipelago and the streams flowing from it were sluggish, carrying only fine material which formed the limestone and dolomites of the Late Cambrian. In New Jersey and eastern Pennsylvania the limestones of the Allentown formation (Middle Kittatinny) represent this phase of the Cambrian. Wave marks and cross-bedding suggest that the water was relatively shallow and frequently disturbed by currents and waves. Fossils are not abundant, but a few poorly preserved trilobites occur in the rocks near Peapack and Newton, New Jersey, and near New Hope and Portland, Pennsylvania. Fossil algae (Cryptozoa) are also present near Carpentersville, New Jersey; Bethlehem, Pennsylvania; Antietam, and Sharpsburg, Maryland; and Saratoga, New York. Several of these fossils are shown in Figures 71 and 72.

In southeastern Pennsylvania, Late Cambrian deposits are also represented by the Conococheague limestones, which occur in the northern extension of the Shenandoah Valley. Some of the caves of Virginia (e.g., Grand Caverns) are in limestone of the Conococheague formation. The Late Cambrian sea not only covered parts of what is now the Shenandoah Valley of Maryland and Virginia but also covered the western part of North Carolina and parts of Georgia and Alabama. It extended northward and submerged much of what is now New York State. The Adirondack Mountains, however, being composed of uplifted Pre-Cambrian rocks, stood above this Cambrian sea, either as an island or a series of islands. The Late Cambrian deposits of New York State have been divided into various formations, the most important being the Potsdam sandstone, the Theresa limestone, and the Little Falls dolomite. The Potsdam sandstone represents the coarser material washed from the Adirondack Mountains.

Western North America.—The Late Cambrian seas were much more extensive than those of either the Early or Middle Cambrian. Throughout the entire Cambrian there had been a "Cordilleran Geosyncline," the western counterpart of the "Appalachian Geosyncline." It extended northward from Lower California and Sonora, in Mexico, through Arizona, Nevada, Idaho, and Montana to Alberta and eastern British Columbia in Canada, and north to the Arctic Ocean. To the

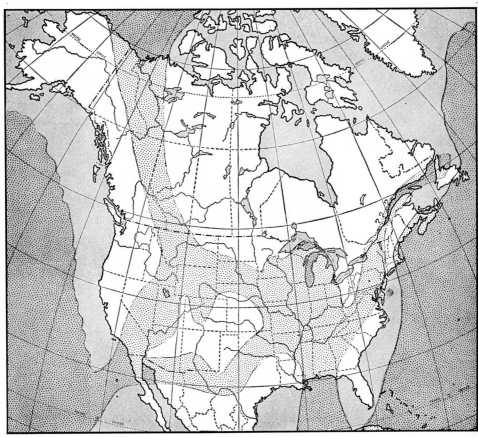

FIG. 70. Late Cambrian. The seas had spread eastward and westward from the two major geosynclines, submerging most of the present area of the United States. The "Atlantic" phase of the sea is still shown east of Acadia-Appalachia. The Ouachita geosyncline is shown connecting the southern parts of the Appalachian and Cordilleran geosynclines.

FIG. 71. Reef of Cambrian cryptozoa in Allentown limestone near Freemansburg, Pennsylvania.

FIG. 72. Individual heads of calcareous algae (*Cryptozoon* sp.) in Cambrian limestone at Carpentersville, New Jersey.

west of this sea was the land Cascadia, which extended westward into the present Pacific Ocean. The detailed history of this geosyncline is as complex as that of its eastern analog; although of considerable interest, it does not concern us here.

By Late Cambrian time, the waters of the Cordilleran Trough had extended eastward across the United States as an epeiric or inland sea, first into the present Mississippi Valley, and finally to join the marine waters of the Appalachian Trough. By Late Cambrian time, almost all the United States from eastern California (Cascadia) to the shores of Appalachia was submerged by a shallow sea. There must have been numerous islands, and the sea probably did not cover this vast region continually. It may have advanced and retreated several times, forming temporary bays and estuaries.

The End of the Cambrian Period.—Cambrian time came to an end with a widespread elevation of the land. The inland sea retreated entirely from the Appalachian Trough and the rocks it had laid down in the trough were subjected to extensive erosion. At the same time, mountains were being formed in various places, notably the Green Mountains of Vermont, but these were probably not of great height.

Cambrian Life

As we saw in the discussion of Pre-Cambrian life, there must have been a considerable number of marine animals and plants living in the world before Cambrian time, but that the records of most of these are lost in obscurity. When the curtain went up at the beginning of the Cambrian, there were already on the earth representatives of many of the major phyla of animals, as well as numerous varieties of primitive sea plants (calcareous algae).

Plants.—Plant life of the Cambrian probably existed only in the oceans. Algal reefs (Cryptozoon, etc.) similar to those which were formed during the Proterozoic era, continued to thrive during Cambrian time. Such fossil reefs are well exposed near Saratoga, New York; Finesville and Carpentersville, New Jersey; and Freemansburg, Pennsylvania. (See Figures 71 and 72.)

Protozoa.—While marine protozoa must have been in evidence during Cambrian time, we have only the vague records of a few questionable forms of foraminifera which have been observed in the Upper Cambrian limestones of Pennsylvania. Possibly the majority of the foraminifera of this period had not yet developed shells sufficiently hard or suitable for preservation in the rocks.

Porifera (Sponges).—The sponges of the Cambrian are few and rather small. Most belong to the class Silicispongia. About twenty-five genera are known.

An interesting group of animals known as the Archaeocyathidae was abundant in some of the Cambrian seas. These are reef-building forms whose position in the animal kingdom is uncertain, but most

Fig. 73. The Cambrian Period. Left foreground, the trilobite *Paradoxides harlani;* right, sponges and jellyfish. (J. P. Cowan, Hughes Tool Co.)

paleontologists think that they were a specialized type of calcareous sponge. Consequently, they have been renamed Pleospongia, and placed in the phylum Porifera. However, other paleontologists prefer to place them in the phylum Coelenterata, with the corals. Possibly the advent of the true corals in the later periods of the Paleozoic had something to do with the extinction of the Archaeocyathidae. At any rate, they formed immense reefs in the Early Cambrian seas and their fossils can be found today in Labrador and Nevada, and in many other parts of the world.

Coelenterata.—As far as we can judge from the record of the rocks, there were no corals in the Cambrian seas. Some well-preserved medusae or jellyfish have been found in Middle Cambrian rocks (Burgess shale) near Field, British Columbia. This locality, discovered by Walcott in 1910, is a dark slate-colored shale containing some 130 species of animals in a remarkable state of preservation, with a record of many of their soft parts clearly visible in the rock. A few

CAMBRIAN FOSSILS

FIG. 74. A questionable Cambrian jellyfish, *Dactyloidites asteroides,* from Washington County, New York. (Chicago Nat. Hist. Mus.)

FIG. 75. Cambrian trilobite, *Olenellus,* from Vermont. (B. F. Howell.)

FIG. 76. Primitive trilobite (*Agnostus*), from Sweden. (A. H. Westergard.)

FIG. 77. Worm tubes of *Skolithos,* from Reading, Pennsylvania. (B. F. Howell.)

specimens of questionable fossil medusae, *Dactyloidites asteroides* (Figure 74) have been found in Lower Cambrian rocks of Washington County, New York.

Graptolites, small plant-like animals of doubtful affinity, but possibly related to the modern pterobranchs, existed in the Late Cambrian seas. They did not form a conspicuous part of the ocean life until the beginning of the Ordovician.

Echinodermata.—This phylum was represented in Cambrian seas only by some small primitive cystoids (relatives of the sea urchin). Several possible Holothurians or sea cucumbers were described by

Walcott from the Burgess shale of British Columbia, but their exact relationship is uncertain.

Worms.—While many beautifully preserved annelid worms are present in the Burgess shale, the most usual Cambrian fossil worm is *Skolithos*. Its burrows are often present in Cambrian sandstones,

Fig. 78. Borings of the worm *Skolithos* in Chickies quartzite at top of Mount Penn, near Reading, Pennsylvania.

sometimes giving them the name "Pipe Rock." A number of species of *Skolithos* occur in the Hardyston sandstone of Pennsylvania, for example, near Valley Forge and Reading (Figures 77 and 78).

Brachiopods.—The brachiopods or lantern shells formed about 30 per cent of the life of the Cambrian seas, to judge from the abundance of their fossils. During the Early and Middle Cambrian epochs these were almost all small forms of a primitive group (Atremata), with phosphatic shells that are not articulated with each other. They must have been very numerous in some places, especially New York State, for their fossils are exceedingly abundant. Some of the Early Cambrian genera in this region are *Micromitra, Obolella, and Kutorgina*. During the Late Cambrian epoch more advanced types of brachiopods with calcareous shells began to appear. Three genera known from the Late Cambrian of New York, New Jersey, and Pennsylvania are *Lingulella, Westonia,* and *Orusia.*

Mollusks.—Gastropods formed only a very minor element of the life of Cambrian times. A few small primitive cone-like shells (*Scenella*) are present in some Early Cambrian rocks, but it was not until the end of the Cambrian that any variety of shelled snails existed. Cephalopods (squid, etc.) are represented only by some doubtful forms. The genus *Hyolithes,* of uncertain relationship, was abundant in some of the Cambrian oceans.

Trilobites.—These crustaceans were the dominant animals of the Cambrian seas. As stated in Chapter 6, these arthropods are now totally extinct, but were distantly related to the present-day king crab (*Limulus*). The trilobites constituted about 50 per cent of Cambrian fossils and are frequently used as index fossils to date and correlate the various Cambrian formations in different parts of the world.

Certain genera are characteristic of different phases of the Cambrian and therefore help in the dating of formations. The trilobites of the Lower Cambrian are usually small with short tails to their bodies. The genus *Olenellus* and related genera are characteristic of the Lower Cambrian of North America. Three genera of Cambrian trilobites are shown in Figures 73, 75, and 76. While most of the trilobites are relatively small (between one and four inches in length), a few reached a much greater length. The Middle Cambrian *Paradoxides harlani* from Braintree, Massachusetts, reached a length of 18 inches and was truly a giant of its time. By the Late Cambrian there was a great variety of trilobites in the seas, and many had developed considerable ornamentation. The two genera *Dikelocephalus* and *Olenus* are characteristic of the Late Cambrian.

Other Cambrian Arthropoda included the Onychopora (*Aysheaia*) from the Burgess shale, some Merostomes (ancestors of the king crabs) and a few Eurypterids or sea scorpions. This latter group was to become much more prominent in the Ordovician and Silurian.

Bryozoa.—Until very recently, the presence of Bryozoa in the Cambrian was suggested only by some very doubtful specimens. In 1947, however, Dr. Madeleine Fritz of the Royal Ontario Museum in Toronto described two primitive species of Bryozoa from Upper Cambrian rocks of Alberta, which she referred to a new genus *Archaeotrypa.*

Chordata.—This group has also, until fairly recently, been regarded as absent from Cambrian rocks. However, in 1925 Professors Charles Schuchert and B. F. Howell collected a specimen from the Middle

Cambrian of St. Albans, Vermont, that was tentatively identified as a skin plate of a primitive chordate, possibly an ancestor of the Ostracoderms, a group of fish-like animals that were to be slightly more conspicuous in the Ordovician. This plate was described by W. L. Bryant as *Eoichthys howelli*.

The two groups of animals most conspicuous by their absence from the Cambrian rocks are the corals and the pelecypods (clams). Perhaps the fossil remains of these two groups also will be found in some yet undiscovered Cambrian fossil locality. Indeed, a few fossils that may be the remains of small clams have been found in Cambrian strata.

Economic Resources of the Cambrian

Except for their more or less obvious uses for building stone, road metal, and lime, the rocks of Cambrian age, at least in eastern North America, have relatively little economic importance. Limestones and dolomites from Pennsylvania and New Jersey are quarried for various purposes, and certain of the Cambrian limestones contain at least potential iron resources.

Iron.—Iron deposits caused by contact metamorphism between Triassic igneous intrusions and Cambro-Ordovician limestones occur at various places in Pennsylvania, notably at Cornwall in Lebanon County and at French Creek near St. Peters, Chester County. For further discussion, see Chapter 17.

Oil.—Although traces of oil have been reported from Cambrian rocks in various parts of the world, none of them proved to be of commercial value until 1948. In that year oil was produced from Cambrian rocks in the Lost Soldier Field in Sweetwater County, Wyoming, at a depth of 6,288 feet. It is, however, highly probable that the oil is not indigenous to the Cambrian formation, but has migrated laterally from younger oil-bearing formations.

FURTHER READING

The references for Chapters 10–16 will be found at the end of Chapter 16.

CHAPTER 11

THE ORDOVICIAN

The term "Ordovician" was first used by Professor Charles Lapworth of Birmingham University in 1879 and was derived from the Ordovicii, an ancient tribe that lived in Wales at the time of Julius Caesar. It replaced the term "Lower Silurian" proposed by Murchison in 1835. As we have already seen in Chapter 10, the term "Cambrian" was originally intended by Sedgewick to include rocks of Ordovician age.

	Pennsylvania	New Jersey	New York	
UPPER ORDOVICIAN	Juniata Bald Eagle Martinsburg	— — Martinsburg	Oswego	CINCINNATIAN
			{Trenton—	
MIDDLE ORDOVICIAN	Mercersburg Shippensburg Chazy "Stones River"	Jacksonburg	Chazy	CHAMPLAINIAN
LOWER ORDOVICIAN	Beekman- town	Upper Kittatinny = Beekmantown	Beekman- town	CANADIAN
ORDOVICIAN(?)	Wissahickon	Wissahickon	Manhattan	

Lower Ordovician or Canadian

After the Cambrian seas withdrew from North America, the continent was low and flat. Erosion at that time was feeble, so the gap between the Cambrian and Ordovician is not as pronounced as the gaps between many of the other periods. Consequently, it is often so difficult to draw the line between the two periods that they are frequently spoken of together as the Cambro-Ordovician.[1]

Ordovician time can probably best be said to start with a renewed sinking of both the Appalachian and Cordilleran geosynclines. The

[1] Many of the limestones in the Philadelphia area are of Cambro-Ordovician age.

sea soon spread over most of the interior of the United States. However, several uplifted areas of Cambrian and Pre-Cambrian rocks were not submerged and formed islands in the Ordovician sea. One of these, the Cincinnati Arch, was a narrow strip of land extending northward from Nashville, Tennessee, through the region of Cincinnati, into Ontario. This arch was important in that it acted as a barrier which separated the seas of the Appalachian Trough from those of the west. It thus prevented a complete mixing of the eastern and western faunas, although many species might have migrated around the islands.

Northwest of the Cincinnati Arch was another inland sea, the so-called "Michigan Basin." It connected with the Appalachian Basin through several low regions in the Cincinnati Arch, notably the Chatham Sag near Chatham, Ontario.

Uplift and Deposition of Shale.—During Early Ordovician (Canadian) time it is possible that Appalachia was further uplifted. At first, great quantities of mud were deposited both in the trough and in the open sea east of Appalachia. These muds have now become shales and are found near the eastern edge of the trough, near the shore line of Appalachia. This belt of shales extends from the city of Quebec in Canada southward to eastern New York, and is known as the Levis formation in Canada and as the Deepkill shale in New York. Graptolites, especially *Tetragraptus,* are common fossils in these shales.

Beekmantown Limestone.—While the Levis-Deepkill shales were being deposited near the shore, limestones and dolomites were being formed in the deeper, clearer water in the center of the Appalachian Trough. These carbonate rocks make up the Beekmantown group which extends from Quebec southward to Alabama, which was the southernmost limit of the Beekmantown sea.

The Beekmantown limestone is named for a town in Clinton County, New York, where it is well exposed and where numerous fossils have been found. In New York State, algal reefs (*Cryptozoon*) are common, and are also present in central and southeastern Pennsylvania and near Hagerstown, Maryland. The middle part of the Beekmantown is highly fossiliferous, especially in New York State, and is characterized by the gastropod *Lecanospira* (Figure 88). Beekmantown fossiliferous deposits are present along both sides of Lake Champlain.

In Pennsylvania, the formation is fairly widespread and is found in the Lehigh Valley, in the Chester Valley west of Philadelphia, and near Bellefonte and State College. In New Jersey, the Beekmantown constitutes the upper part of the Kittatinny limestone and is present in Sussex and Warren Counties.

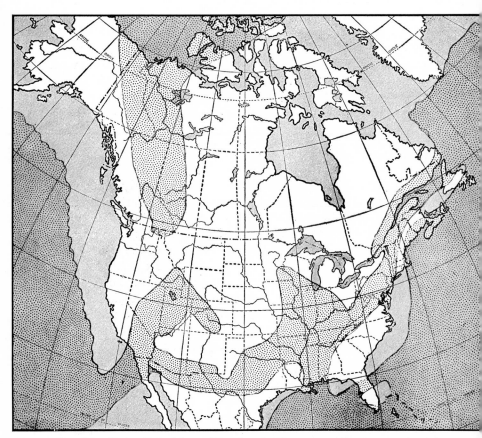

FIG. 79. Early Ordovician. The Appalachian geosyncline was covered by the sea, with shallow water extending as far west as the Mississippi River. Various islands (not shown on the map) existed, notably in New York and Ohio. The Taconic Revolution at the end of the Ordovician temporarily blocked the sea connection in the region of the Gulf of St. Lawrence. Portions of the Cordilleran geosyncline were submerged and were connected with the Appalachian Trough by the Ouachita geosyncline in Texas. The open "Atlantic" sea existed east of Acadia-Appalachia.

Fossils of probable Early Ordovician age (= Beekmantown?) were recently found in micaceous sandstone at the bottom of a well in Dixie County, Florida. This suggests the presence of an Ordovician sea east of the main Appalachian Trough. The continent of Appalachia may have existed still farther east or, as suggested in the previous chapter, it may have been merely a series of islands, in which case the Florida fossils may have been deposited in one of the inter-island channels. Figure 79 indicates that Florida may have been partly submerged by the open Atlantic, east of Appalachia.

Erosion Interval.—The Beekmantown sea completely withdrew from the Appalachian Trough, and probably from the entire North American continent. This period of erosion which followed the withdrawal must have been of considerable length, for when the sea again advanced over the land its marine life had undergone numerous changes that must have taken place when the seas were far removed from the present shore line. Because this erosion interval is thought to have been very long, some geologists regard the Canadian as a separate major period, between the Cambrian and the Ordovician.

Middle Ordovician (Champlainian)

After this period of erosion, it is probable that Appalachia was again uplifted, while the trough sank. The sea invaded the trough along its entire length, from Alabama to the Gulf of St. Lawrence. Beds of sandy or silty clay that have become black shale were deposited in parts of this sea, while in other places a limestone was formed. These shale and limestone deposits are called the Chazy formations from Chazy, New York, and indicate relatively shallow water. It is probable that this sea advanced and retreated several times. The Chazy formations are best developed in New York State, especially along Lake Champlain. The Stones River limestone of southeastern Pennsylvania is probably the equivalent of the Chazy rocks of New York. Fossiliferous shales near Clinton, Hunterdon County, New Jersey, have been assigned to the Chazy by some geologists, but the correlation is by no means certain.

Farther west, the land was above water and extensive deposits of quartz sand were laid down and later smoothed over by an advancing sea. These sands, changed to sandstones, make up the St. Peter formation, well exposed in Minnesota, Michigan, Wisconsin, and elsewhere in the interior of the continent.

Finally, the Chazyan sea withdrew altogether from the Appalachian geosyncline, probably because of a general uplift that also caused the land mass of Appalachia to rise. The sediments carried from this continent again caused or accompanied a sinking of the trough, and the sea advanced once more. This invasion by the sea was very widespread and it is probable that, with the exception of a few islands, notably the Cincinnati Arch, salt water covered North America from Texas to the Arctic Ocean and from Cascadia to Appalachia.

Jacksonburg Limestone (= Trenton).—The deposits of the Appalachian Trough of this period were largely limestone. Many different formations have been described, all dating from this phase of

Fig. 80. Cement quarry in Jacksonburg formation, near Nazareth, Pennsylvania.

the Ordovician, sometimes called the Mohawkian. Among these is the Jacksonburg limestone of New Jersey and Pennsylvania. In the Lehigh Valley this limestone is abundantly quarried as cement rock. Extensive deposits of this rock are to be seen at Nazareth, Martins Creek, Bath, and Fogelsville, in Pennsylvania (Figure 80). The best cement rock consists of an optimum mixture of limestone and shale. The Jacksonburg limestone crops out in a continuous band from the

Delaware River near Belvidere, New Jersey, to Northampton on the Lehigh River, and in local areas farther west in Lehigh and Berks Counties. In southern Pennsylvania, the limestones of this age are known as the Mercersburg and Shippensburg formations, occurring locally in Cumberland, Franklin, and Fulton Counties. They also extend southward into Maryland.

Farther north, in New York State, the counterpart of this limestone is a part of the Trenton limestone, named from Trenton Falls, Oneida County, New York. From this area a great many Ordovician fossils have been collected and described. The presence of so many formations with their few but characteristic fossils suggests that the shallow Jacksonburg sea advanced and retreated several times. During this stage in the earth's history the Adirondacks were probably still an island or an archipelago.

Upper Ordovician (Cincinnatian)

Appalachia continued to rise and, because of the steeper gradient, its rivers began to transport coarser material (Figure 81). As a consequence, the limestones of Middle Ordovician time gave way to the shales of the Martinsburg formation. The transition between the two is not sharp, and it is probable that, for a while at least, shales were being deposited near the shore at the same time that limestones (part of the Trenton limestone) were being formed in the deeper parts of the trough. However, as Appalachia continued to rise, the shales predominated and some of the fine-grained muds from that uplifted continent were transported as far west as the Ohio-Indiana border, where the Cincinnatian formations consist of shales and impure limestones. Fossil invertebrates are exceedingly abundant near Cincinnati, Ohio, and Covington, Kentucky.

Martinsburg shales are well exposed near Branchville, Sussex County, New Jersey, where a few graptolites have been found. In many places these shales were subsequently altered by pressure to slate. The Martinsburg formation extends southwestward from Unionville, New York, across Sussex and Warren Counties, New Jersey, approximately paralleling the Delaware River to Delaware, New Jersey. At Delaware, the shales cross the river and extend southwestward into Pennsylvania. Slates of this age are extensively quarried near Bangor, Slatington, Pen Argyl, and Wind Gap, Pennsylvania. The Reedsville shales of central Pennsylvania are also equivalent to those of the Martinsburg formation.

Various shales deposited in New York, especially the Canajoharie and Utica formations, are probably equivalent, in part, to the Martins-

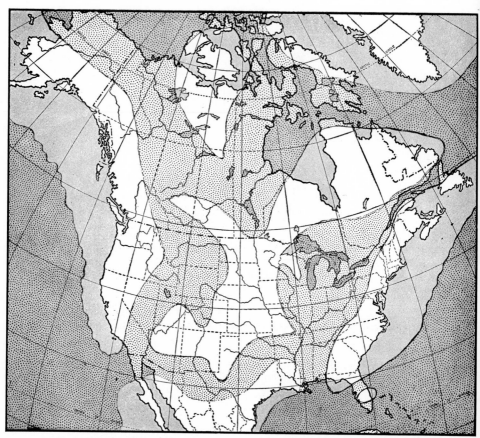

Fig. 81. Late Ordovician. By this time the seas were widespread, covering large portions of North America.

burg shale of Pennsylvania. On the other hand, the upper part of the Trenton limestone is apparently of about the same age as the Martinsburg formation.

The Appalachian basin was probably connected to the open ocean at both its north and south outlets. However, the fauna entering the waters of the basin seem to have come mainly from the north. The fossils of the Late Ordovician seas seem to be modified descendants of Middle Ordovician Arctic species. Many of these species are similar to, or identical with, those of the Late Ordovician of Europe, a fact that can best be explained by the theory that there was a shallow water connection between the continents over which the littoral or shore-dwelling forms could migrate.

Juniata and Bald Eagle Sandstone.—With the continued rise of Appalachia and the consequent increase in the amount of sediment being poured into the trough, the sea gradually became shallower. (It apparently took millions of years for the weight of the sediments to cause the geosyncline to sag.) As the sea became shallower, the deposits of marine shales and limestones were succeeded by sandstones of deltaic or alluvial origin, usually reddish in color. These sandstones occur at many places in Pennsylvania and make up the Juniata and Bald Eagle formations. Since they are of nonmarine origin, and since no land life had yet developed, no fossils have been found in these rocks and it is therefore difficult to determine their age. In fact, some geologists place them at the beginning of the Silurian. However, if these sandstones are traced toward the southwest they appear to interfinger with marine limestones carrying Late Ordovician fossils, representing the marine equivalent of these extensive deltaic deposits. One of the probable marine equivalents of the Juniata and Bald Eagle sandstones is the Richmond series of Indiana and Ohio. Fossils are exceedingly abundant in rocks of this age near Cincinnati.

No rocks of Cincinnatian age are known from New Jersey. It is possible that they were never laid down, but it is more probable that some deltaic sandstones did occur in northern New Jersey, but were eroded as Appalachia continued to rise. In New York, extensive deposits of red sandstone were formed in the Niagara Falls area. These are thought to represent a similar delta of considerable magnitude, known as the Queenston Delta.

In Pennsylvania, the coarser sandstones constitute the Bald Eagle formation. These have withstood erosion and form some of the ridges which exist at the present day. For example, the three eastern tunnels of the Pennsylvania Turnpike (Tuscarora, Kittatinny, and Blue Mountain) are partly in Bald Eagle sandstone.

Taconic Revolution

Ordovician time came to a close with a period of mountain building. This was probably the result of the overloading of the Appalachian basin. To compensate for the sinking of the land in this area, Appalachia had been continuing to rise, a rise which culminated in a period of folding and thrust-faulting from the east. The mountains formed by this revolution probably existed on the western flank of Appalachia, northeast of the Appalachian Trough, and extended from central Newfoundland through New Brunswick and New England at least as far as northern New Jersey.

Fig. 82. Diagram showing evidence of Taconic Revolution. Cambrian and Ordovician rocks were folded and peneplaned before the deposition of the horizontal Silurian formations. (By permission from *Historical Geology*, by Russell C. Hussey. Copyright 1944, McGraw-Hill Book Co., Inc.)

These mountains, called Taconic from the present Taconic Mountains of eastern New York and western Massachusetts, have long since disappeared and we have only indirect evidence of their existence. They can be thought of as the precursors of the northern Appalachian Mountains which were to follow some 265 million years later. In most cases, the evidence of folding and mountain building of this period has been obliterated or confused by the later and much more extensive Appalachian revolution of Permian time. However, in some places the Cambrian and Ordovician rocks were greatly folded during the Taconic revolution, and then leveled off or peneplaned during the erosion interval before the beginning of the Silurian period. The Silurian formations were then laid down horizontally on the folded older rocks, as shown diagrammatically in Figure 82.

Volcanoes of the Ordovician

The only direct evidence of the presence of volcanoes in eastern North America during Ordovician time is the presence of a volcanic plug near Beemerville, Sussex County, New Jersey. We also have indirect evidence of vulcanism in the form of volcanic ash and lava. Volcanic ash, altered to metabentonite, is imbedded in some Ordovician rocks from New York to Alabama. It is probable that the volcanoes which produced this ash occurred along the western slope of Appalachia during Early and Middle Ordovician time.

In thickness, these beds vary from one inch to about 10 feet. There are numerous localities near Bellefonte in central Pennsylvania where metabentonite is conspicuous. It is also interbedded with the Jacksonburg limestone near Nazareth, Pennsylvania. Near Jamestown in Lebanon County, Pennsylvania, there is a lava flow which is definitely associated with Ordovician shales, and there are also (vesicular) lavas of Ordovician age in Michigan.

As we have mentioned in an earlier chapter, many geologists believe that at least some of the intrusive granites and metamorphic rocks of the Piedmont Plateau, such as the Wissahickon and Manhattan formations, were deposited during Ordovician time, and not during the Pre-Cambrian era.

Ordovician History of Western North America

The Cordilleran Trough was intermittently covered by the sea during Ordovician time and by the end of the period there was a continuous seaway from Mexico to the Arctic. The adjoining lands were

Fig. 83. A large, partly coiled Ordovician nautiloid capturing a trilobite (*Triarthus becki*) at the end of its tentacles. At the far right are some crinoids (*Ectonocrinus grandis*) and on the floor of the ocean can be seen trilobites, starfish, coral, and some brachiopods. (J. P. Cowan, Hughes Tool Co.)

ORDOVICIAN FOSSILS

FIG. 84. Gastropods *Maclurites* sp., Cincinnati, Ohio.

FIG. 85. Cephalopoda, *Orthoceras harperi*, Cincinnati, Ohio.

FIG. 86. Graptolites, Fort Ann, New York.

FIG. 87. Brachiopod, *Lingulepis florida*, deep well, Florida.

(Continued on opposite page.→)

apparently low, with relatively little sediment being carried to the inland sea. A widespread deposit of fossiliferous dolomite of Late Ordovician age was formed in this trough.

Ordovician Life

Plants.—Plant life was still restricted to algae (seaweeds). Cryptozoon reefs are present in the Beekmantown formation in New York and Pennsylvania. Certain massive fossils which have been called *Receptaculites,* and were once regarded as sponges or corals, may possibly belong to the plant kingdom.

Protozoa.—Foraminifera and radiolaria are common in a few Ordovician rocks and probably were abundant in all seas. However, their small size and thin shells did not favor their preservation as fossils.

Sponges.—Sponges are represented by a number of types but do not form a conspicuous feature of Ordovician deposits. They are rare in New York, New Jersey, and Pennsylvania, but are fairly common in the southern Appalachian region.

Graptolites.—The graptolites, floating colonial organisms that had made their appearance in the Late Cambrian, reached their climax during the Ordovician. Because of their floating habitat, many graptolites were widely distributed and consequently are valuable for long-range correlation. Many genera from eastern North America are identical with genera from England, Norway, and Sweden. Genera characteristic of the Lower Ordovician (Canadian) are *Tetragraptus* and *Phyllograptus,* which occur in the Deepkill shales of New York (Figure 86). A few graptolites are known from near Clinton, New Jersey.

Coelenterates.—Corals first appeared in Middle Ordovician seas, but formed only a relatively minor part of the marine life. Simple cup corals or horn corals (*Streptalasma*) were locally abundant, as was the large colonial form *Columnaria.* By Late Ordovician time, compound forms such as *Halysites* and *Paleofavosites* had evolved. These relatively small animals were the ancestors of some of the true reef corals that were so conspicuous during the Silurian and Devonian

FIG. 88. Cast of Gastropod, *Lecano-spira.*

FIG. 89. *Rafinisquina alternata,* Cincinnati, Ohio.

FIG. 90. Gastropoda, *Platystoma niagarense,* Cincinnati, Ohio.

periods. A few medusae or jellyfish have been found in Ordovician rocks, and Figure 91 shows one from the vicinity of Troy, New York.

Bryozoa.—These colonial animals first became abundant during the Early Ordovician and developed so rapidly that more than 1,000 species are recorded from the Ordovician rocks. They were especially abundant in limy seas and today make excellent index fossils of certain Ordovician limestones, although they are extraordinarily difficult to study. One of the species of Ordovician bryozoa (*Heterotrypa*) is shown in Figure 92.

Fig. 91. An Ordovician medusa, *Discophyllum pellatum,* from Troy, New York.

Echinoderms.—Most of the major groups of echinoderms such as the cystoids (Figure 93), blastoids, crinoids, starfish, brittle stars, and sea urchins, were present in the Ordovician seas, the most important of these being the cystoids and crinoids. The cystoids reached their climax during this period and are represented by 21 genera, including *Malocystites, Pleurocystites,* and *Agelacrinus.* These are common only in a few places and well-preserved specimens are rare.

The crinoids were so abundant in some Ordovician seas that their stalks, plates, and even perfect heads compose solid layers of rocks. Some of the important genera are *Glyptocrinus, Heterocrinus,* and *Dendrocrinus.* Blastoids, starfish, and sea urchins were just beginning to appear but were relatively rare.

Brachiopods.—Brachiopods were very abundant and, with the trilobites, constitute the most important index fossils of the period. The thin-shelled types of the Cambrian were largely replaced by those whose stronger limy shells had definite hinges. Among the char-

Fig. 92.   The Ordovician bryozoa *Heterotrypa frondosa,* from Cincinnati, Ohio.

Fig. 93.   The cystoid *Pleurocystites elegans* from Ordovician rocks at Coburg, Ontario.   Note the irregular plates.

acteristic genera are *Lingula, Rafinisquina, Resserella, Dinorthis, Platystrophia, Strophomena,* and *Zygospira* (Figures 87 and 89).

Gastropoda.—Gastropods (snails) were more abundant than they had been during the Cambrian, but were still not as important as they were to 'be in later geological periods. Many of the Ordovician gastropods are poorly preserved and it has been thought by some geologists that the shells may have been thin or made of some such material as aragonite, which was not adapted for preservation. One of the significant coiled snails was *Lecanospira,* an index fossil of the Beekmantown limestone. Other important Ordovician genera were *Cyclonema, Trochonema, Raphistoma, Bellerophon,* and *Maclurites* (Figures 84, 88, and 90).

Pelecypoda.—The clams had not yet reached importance and their fossils are rather rare in Ordovician rocks. Characteristic genera are the peculiar *Ambonychia* and *Byssonychia,* with a large wing on one side of the beak. Other mussel-like forms such as *Modiolopsis* made their appearance during the Ordovician, but achieved greater development and prominence in later periods. Most of the Ordovician pelecypods are merely preserved as molds in sandstone, which makes them very difficult to identify.

Cephalopoda (Nautiloidea).—This group was represented in the Cambrian only by some questionable forms which existed during the latter part of the period. By Ordovician time, the cephalopoda had reached a position of great prominence and included some of the largest and most powerful animals of the Ordovician sea. Both coiled and straight creatures formed this group, although the straight kind was dominant and reached its climax during this period. Some characteristic genera were *"Orthoceras"* (= *Michelinoceras*) (Figure 85), *Gonioceras,* and *Oncoceras.* Some species of *"Orthoceras"* reached a length of 15 feet. The coiled types included *Trocholites* and *Eurystomites. Cycloceras* was a curved form midway between the coiled and straight types.

Trilobites.—These animals were still abundant and perhaps reached the height of their development during this period. Just as the Cambrian had its giant *Paradoxides harlani,* so did the Middle Ordovician have the 24-inch *Isotelus gigas,* which was one of the largest trilobites of all time. The head and tail of this enormous creature are similar and each constituted about one third of the length. *Isotelus, Bumastis,* and other related genera had lost many of their marks of segmentation and had a "bald-headed appearance." Other characteristic Ordovician genera are *Illaenus* and *Ceraurus.*

Many Ordovician trilobites had developed the protective habit of rolling up in a ball like a pill bug, and are often found in the rocks in this position.

Ostracodes.—Other crustaceans that made their first appearance during the Ordovician are the ostracodes, small bivalved animals superficially resembling clams. Many of these are microscopic in size, but a few, such as *Leperditia,* are large enough to be seen by the naked eye, and are abundant in certain Ordovician rocks.

Other arthropods present but inconspicuous in Ordovician seas are the Eurypterids (sea scorpions) and the Merostomes (direct ancestors of the king crabs).

Vertebrates.—Sometime during the Cambrian or Early Ordovician, the first primitive vertebrate animals made their appearance in the sea. It is probable that we will never find the earliest forms, but some fossils have recently been discovered in the Ordovician in several parts of the country that apparently represent some very primitive fishes. In 1891, Charles Walcott announced the discovery of some plates and scales near Canon City, Colorado, which he thought belonged to certain ancient fishes known as Ostracoderms. The scales are not like modern fish scales but are covered with an enamel-like substance. Similar scales have been found in Ordovician rocks in Wyoming, Michigan, and South Dakota. So far, no complete specimens have been found, but some idea of their possible appearance can be obtained by studying the better-preserved ostracoderms of the Silurian and Devonian, which are undoubtedly the descendants of these primitive Ordovician creatures.

Economic Resources of the Ordovician

Petroleum.—Oil has been found in rocks of all ages from the Ordovician to the Pleistocene. The limestones and dolomites of the Trenton formation in Ohio, Indiana, and southern Ontario have been producers of oil and gas since 1883. Also, in the mid-continental area, oil is produced from Ordovician rocks in various fields, especially in central Oklahoma.

The exact origin of oil is unknown. It is generally believed to have been formed by the decomposition of marine animals and plants, probably largely of minute forms. It accumulates in suitable porous rocks, sometimes deep beneath the surface, and is usually concentrated in pools in the vicinity of favorable structures such as anticlines or stratigraphic traps.

Limestone.—Ordovician limestones of the Appalachian Valley are quarried for various purposes, such as road metal, flux for smelting iron ore, and for agricultural fertilizer. Chemical lime of high purity is quarried from Ordovician rocks at Bellefonte, Pennsylvania.

Marble.—Certain Ordovician limestones have been metamorphosed to marble and are of considerable commercial value. The Ordovician marble quarries near Rutland, Vermont, are among the most famous in the country, and the Ordovician marbles of eastern Tennessee are also of considerable economic importance.

Cement Rock.—Certain limestones of the Jacksonburg formation are peculiarly adapted for the manufacture of Portland cement. This rock has nearly the right mixture of clay and lime and needs only a slight addition of high grade limestone (generally Franklin limestone) to make it of marketable quality. There are numerous Portland cement plants in the Lehigh Valley near Portland, Nazareth, and Bath, Pennsylvania; while a few were formerly in operation across the Delaware River near Phillipsburg, New Jersey. There are also other sources of cement rock in the southern Appalachian Valley.

Slate.—The Martinsburg formation is an excellent source of roofing slate. Most of the important quarries are in a belt some 7 to 13 miles wide in Northampton and Lehigh Counties, Pennsylvania, in localities such as Pen Argyl, Slatington, and Danielsville. Slate was formerly quarried from the Martinsburg formation in Sussex and Warren Counties, New Jersey, but there are no operations in this state at the present time. Slates occur in other formations of various ages, but, generally speaking, are less important and extensive than those of the Martinsburg formation.

Iron.—The iron deposits near the contact of the Cambro-Ordovician limestones with igneous intrusions of Triassic age have been discussed in a previous chapter. Sedimentary iron deposits are also known in Ordovician rocks in eastern Newfoundland.

FURTHER READING

The references for Chapters 10–16 will be found at the end of Chapter 16.

CHAPTER 12

THE SILURIAN

The term "Silurian" was first used by the English geologist Roderick Murchison in 1835 for rocks in western England and eastern and southeastern Wales, and was derived from the Silures, a tribe of ancient Britons. Murchison's "Lower Silurian" later became the Ordovician.

	Pennsylvania		New Jersey	New York	
UPPER SILURIAN	Keyser		Manlius Rondout Decker	Manlius Rondout Decker	
	Tonoloway Wills Creek	Bloomsburg Red beds	Bossardville	Salina	CAYUGAN
MIDDLE SILURIAN	McKenzie Clinton		Poxino Island High Falls	Clinton	NIAGARAN
LOWER SILURIAN	Tuscarora		Shawangunk	Medina	MEDINAN

Lower Silurian (Medinan)

As was the case with the Cambrian and Ordovician, the Silurian can conveniently be divided into lower, middle, and upper phases. The Lower Silurian is frequently spoken of as the Medinan, named from the town of Medina, New York, where the deposits are well exposed.

At the beginning of the Silurian, Appalachia was still mountainous, while most of the remainder of the continent was relatively level. Sediments from Appalachia continued to wash down into the inland sea between Appalachia and the Cincinnati Arch, and great quantities of sand were trapped in this sea, forming deposits of sandstone perhaps 1,000 feet thick. Toward the east, near the shore line of Appalachia, these sediments were very coarse and formed conglomerates. In northern New Jersey and eastern New York these conglomerates are known as the Shawangunk and Green Pond formations, probably local remnants of a once-extensive conglomerate that covered much of the area. The Shawangunk forms the crest and eastward-facing

143

cliff of Kittatinny Mountain and is well exposed at Delaware Water Gap, where the river cuts a gorge, 1,200 feet deep, through this mountain. The unconformable contact between the Ordovician and the Silurian is shown in Figure 94.

FIG. 94. Unconformity between Ordovician Martinsburg shale (left) and Silurian Tuscarora sandstone at Lehigh Gap, Pennsylvania.

In Pennsylvania, the sediments of the Early Silurian were slightly less coarse and formed the Medina group of formations, the principal formation being the Tuscarora. The Tuscarora and Shawangunk formations were probably built up as a great alluvial fan. The massive Tuscarora sandstone and conglomerates form many of the mountains of the central part of the state and, together with those of the Bald Eagle and Juniata formations of the Ordovician, make up the mountains penetrated by the three eastern tunnels of the Pennsylvania Turnpike.

In New York State, similar coarse sandstones occur from Otisville to Rosendale. Fossils are not common in the Tuscarora and Shawangunk formations, but a few eurypterids were discovered in the Lower Silurian rocks at Otisville, and a few fossils have been found at the Delaware Water Gap. A characteristic fossil of this period is the *Arthrophycus allegeheniensis*, originally described as a plant but now generally regarded as the borings or tubes of a worm (Figure 95).

Fig. 95. *Arthrophycus alleghiensis* from the Silurian Tuscarora formation. Is it algae or worm tube?

West of the Cincinnati Arch, the water was clearer and limestones were deposited at the same time as the sandstones of the Medina group. Highly fossiliferous limestones of Lower Silurian age are found today in Illinois, where they make up the Alexandrian group, named from the town of Alexandria, Illinois.

There is no evidence that the Lower Silurian (Medina) sea had any connection with the Atlantic Ocean to the northeast. An arm of the ocean extended up the St. Lawrence Valley and covered Anticosti Island, but probably did not connect with the waters in the Appalachian basin.

Middle Silurian (Niagaran)

Appalachia continued to be worn down, and by Middle Silurian time must have been relatively low, judging from the shales that were deposited in the Appalachian Trough by the sluggish streams that washed down from the highlands to the east (Figure 96). The shales deposited at this time are known as the Clinton beds, and are very extensive from New York to Alabama. In central Pennsylvania Clinton shales are especially well developed in parts of Huntingdon, Centre, and Blair Counties, and along the Susquehanna River near Allenwood. A phase of the Clinton (Rose Hill sandstone) makes up Kittatinny Mountain, above Harrisburg, Pennsylvania.

Shales of Clinton(?) age (High Falls formation) have been questionably recognized in New Jersey, where they lie on top of the Shawangunk conglomerate at the Delaware Water Gap, and northeast to Rosendale, New York. However, no fossils have been found in these rocks and their age is still uncertain.

Hematite (red) iron ore is common in Middle Silurian shales. At the type locality, near Clinton, New York, iron mines were worked before the Civil War. Near Birmingham, Alabama, shales of similar (Clinton) age are second only to the ores of the Lake Superior region in the production of iron in the United States. It is estimated that more than 600,000,000 tons of ore are still available in the Clinton beds.

It is believed that iron ore was formed as a chemical precipitate in the marshes and lagoons of Middle Silurian time, the iron being originally derived from the igneous rocks of Appalachia, over which the streams flowed on their way to the inland sea. Marine fossils are frequently found in these ore deposits.

Gradually the sea in the Appalachian Trough cleared and limestone deposits were formed in the place of the shales, especially in the deeper water in the western part of the trough. These limestones are known as the Niagara group and contain extensive coral reefs (*Favosites*, etc.). Niagara limestones are represented in southwestern Pennsylvania, Maryland, and West Virginia by the McKenzie formation, but are better developed in western New York near Rochester and Niagara Falls.

Niagara Falls and Gorge.—The Silurian section is excellently exposed in the gorge of the Niagara River separating New York State from Ontario. The lowest formation, the Queenston shale of Ordovician age, is visible in the lower cliffs. Along the railroad track

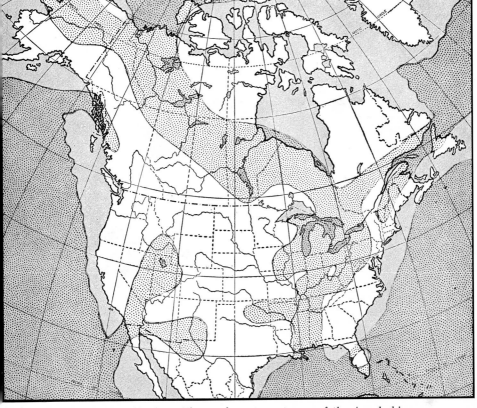

Fig. 96. Middle Silurian. The northeastern entrance of the Appalachian geo-syncline was probably reopened during middle Silurian time. There was also a sea to the northwest, via Hudson Bay and northwestern Canada. The Cordil-leran geosyncline was intermittently filled by this sea during Silurian time.

through the gorge, from Lewiston to Niagara Falls, one encounters formations of decreasing age: Medina (Lower Silurian) through Clinton and Lockport (Salina) of Middle Silurian age. The hard Lockport dolomite at the top of the section forms the edge of Niagara Falls. It is the hardness of this rock, together with the softer character of the underlying formations, which accounts for the existence of these

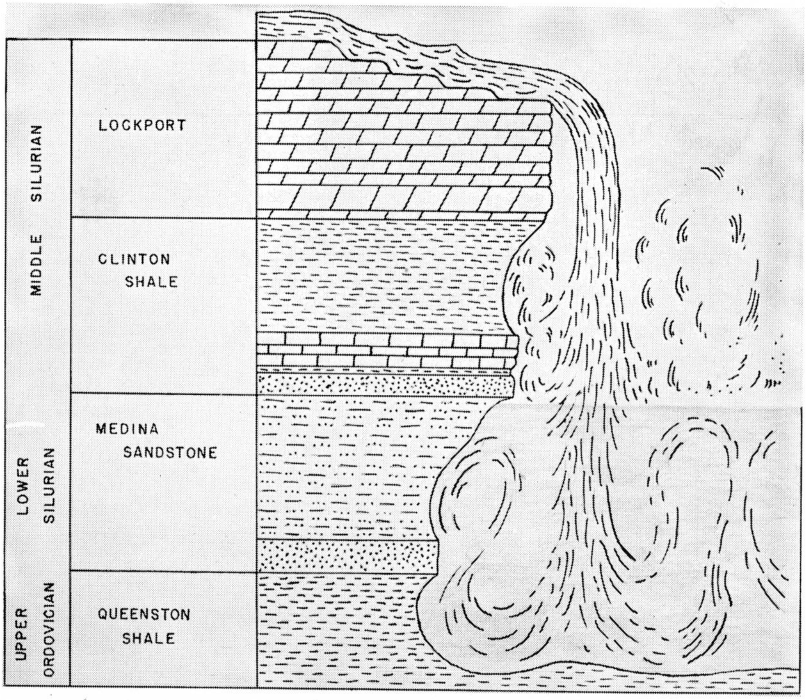

Fig. 97.   Diagrammatic representation of Niagara Falls.

falls. Fossils are found in considerable numbers in various formations in the gorge and may readily be collected along the railroad track on the New York side of the river. (See Figure 97.)

Extent of the Niagara Sea.—During Niagara time, the inland sea spread as far west as Indiana, Illinois, Wisconsin, and eastern Iowa, a fact revealed by the presence of Middle Silurian fossils at Chicago, Illinois; Racine, Wisconsin; and elsewhere. Arms of the sea apparently extended into the Ouachita Trough in Oklahoma and northern Texas. Numerous islands probably existed at that time, including remnants of the Adirondacks in New York. The sea probably extended northeastward, joining the open ocean in Labrador, and another arm of the sea probably extended to the Arctic through New

York State, Ontario, and Hudson Bay. Extensive Silurian deposits occur along the west side of Hudson Bay from the entrance of James Bay to Churchill.

Upper Silurian (Cayugan)

Salina Salt Beds.—By Late Silurian time, the southern part of the Appalachian Trough became dry land, while a sea connection probably persisted from the Arctic Ocean across Canada into Michigan, Ohio, New York, and western Pennsylvania (Figure 98). Arid conditions gradually developed over much of northeastern North America, particularly near the shores of this sea in northern Pennsylvania, southwestern New York, northern Ohio, and parts of southern Michigan and Ontario. Parts of this sea eventually became cut off from the main ocean to the south. The enclosed sea became very salty because of the excessive evaporation of water, and great quantities of salt and gypsum were deposited on its margins and bottom. These beds cover an area of approximately 10,000 square miles, and are known as the Salina salt beds (Figure 99). Near Ithaca and Tully, New York, the salt beds are up to 1,000 feet in thickness, and in southern Michigan they are more than 600 feet thick. The thickest individual bed is about 80 feet thick. Salt is extensively mined today in much of this area.

Some geologists believe that conditions here were not unlike those of the Dead Sea today. The salt ponds in this area must have received occasional supplies of sea water through small channels connecting with the open ocean. This would have caused a continuous supply of brine, thus making possible the great thicknesses of salt.

Bloomsburg Red Beds.—To the southeast, toward Appalachia, the salt deposits merge into red beds of nonmarine origin. These include the Vernon shale of eastern New York and the Bloomsburg red beds, the latter being well exposed near Bloomsburg, Columbia County, Pennsylvania. These red beds are not of exactly the same age in all places, and were probably deposited on land at the same time that the salt formations and other truly marine deposits were being laid down in the sea.

Toward the southwest the Salina salt lake deposits merge into shales and limestones of definitely marine origin. In Pennsylvania the marine equivalent of the Salina is the Tonoloway limestone, which occurs at Mount Union and Lewistown, Pennsylvania, and near Cumberland, Maryland. Northern New Jersey also seems to have been covered by a shallow sea during the latter part of Silurian (Salina)

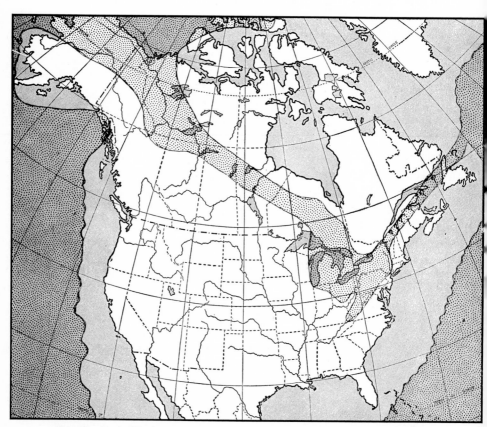

FIG. 98. Late Silurian. Most of North America was above water during the
Late Silurian. Great quantities of salt accumulated in the concentrated seas of
Salina time. These saline bodies of water were bordered on the southeast by
deserts (redbeds) and merged westward into an inland sea of normal salinity.
The connection to the open ocean was probably via the northwest, although
there may have been a temporary seaway to the northeast.

time. Numerous ostracodes are present in the Bossardville limestone, while along the Delaware River near Port Jervis, New York, a more extensive marine fauna is known in limestone of the Decker formation, which overlies the Bossardville limestone.

Close of the Silurian.—The Silurian shore line probably oscillated, for the Decker limestone is nonmarine. However, the sea again ad-

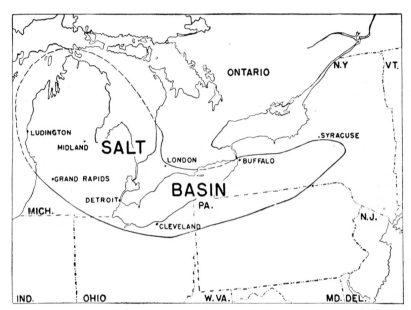

Fig. 99. Map showing the approximate extent of the Salina Salt Basin. (By permission from *Historical Geology*, by Russell C. Hussey. Copyright 1944, McGraw-Hill Book Co., Inc.)

vanced and the final episode of the Silurian was the deposition of the limestones of the Manlius formation.[1]

The close of the Silurian Period was a relatively quiet and inactive time in North America. No extensive mountains were formed in this hemisphere, and the transition to the Devonian was gradual. In Europe, however, the forces of the earth were more active, and the so-called Caledonian Mountains were formed, extending in an arc northeastward from the British Isles to Scandinavia, then westward through Spitzbergen and northern Greenland. The only evidence that we now have for these once majestic mountains is the folded and faulted character of the Silurian and older rocks along the line of this former range. This mountain building, or diastrophism, appar-

---

[1] The Manlius, Rondout, and Decker formations were formerly placed at the beginning of the Devonian.

ently took place after the deposition of the Silurian rocks and before the advance of the Devonian sea.

Volcanic Activity.—Volcanic activity in North America during the Silurian was of local character and, as far as we now know, no volcanoes existed in what is now the Middle Atlantic States. The presence of ash and lava interbedded with Silurian fossiliferous sediments in Maine, New Brunswick, and the Gaspé region indicate the former presence of volcanoes, some of them perhaps marine during this period.

Silurian Life

Plants.—Lime-secreting algae continued to be present, but relatively few records of these exist in Silurian rocks. A few cryptozoon

Fig. 100. The Silurian Period. A large eurypterid (*Eurypterus remipes*), probably a foot and a half long, dominates the scene. Crinoids, cup corals, and chain coral, as well as some brachiopods and trilobites, can be seen in the restoration. The beginning of a land flora is suggested in a hazy background. (J. P. Cowan, Hughes Tool Co.)

reefs occur in the McKenzie formation in Huntingdon County, Pennsylvania. Some small fragments of supposed fossil land plants have been reported from Silurian rocks of England, but they are not definitely identified. A few better preserved fossil plants have been described from the Silurian of Australia. However, indirect evidence of the presence of land plants during the Silurian is afforded by the existence of a well-developed land flora in early Devonian time. These Devonian plants must have had more primitive ancestors and these probably lived during the Silurian. The fact that terrestrial plants and animals are rarely preserved as fossils is the main reason why we have so little positive records of any Silurian land plants. However, it is entirely possible that more will yet be found. The nonmarine deposits of the Tuscarora or Shawangunk formations might contain such fossils, although the nature of the sandstone and conglomerate is not favorable for their preservation.

FIG. 101. Cross section of the Silurian sponge *Hindia,* from Tennessee.

Protozoa.—Formanifera undoubtedly existed, although their record in the rocks is scant.

Sponges.—Various kinds of sponges were present in Silurian seas. Among the most usual genera are the saucer-shaped *Astraeospongium* and the nearly spherical *Hindia* (Figure 101).

Corals.—The corals developed considerably during this period and by Middle Silurian (Niagara) time formed extensive reefs. Characteristic genera were *Favosites* (honeycomb coral), *Halysites* (chain coral), and *Syringopora* (tube coral). In addition to these reef-building corals there were numerous kinds of solitary cup corals.

Graptolites.—The graptolites were on the decline, and are not as common in the Silurian rocks of the United States as in those of Ordovician age. *Monograptus clintonensis* is known from the Clinton shales of New York.

Bryozoa.—Bryozoa are present in both shaly and pure limestones, thereby indicating that they lived in both clear and slightly muddy water. Many varieties are quite similar to those of the Ordovician, while others such as the lace-like *Fenestrellina* and *Polypora* made their first appearance in the Silurian. These genera were to reach greater development in the Devonian and Mississippian periods. Although bryozoa are present in the Silurian rocks of New York and Pennsylvania (for example, at Rochester, New York), they are much more abundant in the limestones of the Mississippi Valley, where they form an important element of the fauna. They are especially characteristic of reef associations.

Echinoderms.—Crinoids and cystoids are relatively common, while the other echinoderms are rare. *Caryocrinus* is a characteristic cystoid known from Rochester, New York; Chicago, Illinois; and elsewhere. Crinoids are so abundant in some places that their stems constitute an important part of some limestones. Although especially common in Wisconsin and Illinois, they also occur in the Silurian of New York, New Jersey, and Pennsylvania.

Brachiopods.—Some Ordovician genera persisted into the Silurian (*Hesperorthis, Girptorthis, Platystrophia*), while many new genera appeared for the first time. *Strophomena* and *Rafinesquina* of the Ordovician were replaced by *Strophonella* and *Brachyprion*. In the Orthid group we find many species of *Dalmanella* and *Rhipidomella*. Other new forms are the smooth *Whitfieldella* and the spire-bearing *Conchidium*. The *Spirifers* appeared in the Middle Silurian (Clinton) and developed many species in the latter part of the Silurian and during the Devonian. Other characteristic Silurian brachiopods are *Pentamerus* and *Atrypa*.

Gastropoda.—There are many types of gastropods, both low- and high-spired, especially in the Middle Silurian (Niagara). Characteristic genera are *Tremanotus, Loxonema, Platyceras,* and *Poleumita*.

Pelecypoda.—Bivalves were rather inconspicuous during the Silurian time. The large clam *Megalomus niagarense* is common in the Niagara of Ohio, while *Pterinea* and *Modiolopsis* occur in the Silurian of New York and Pennsylvania.

Cephalopods.—Both coiled and straight forms were present during the Silurian, although they were much more abundant in Europe than in America.

Worms.—Worm trails have been reported from rocks of various ages from the Pre-Cambrian on, but their identification and correlation is difficult because of the lack of characteristic markings. Certain marking characteristic of the Lower Silurian (Medina = Shawangunk) had been named *Arthrophycus alleghenienses*. Some paleontologists identify this as a worm trail or tube, while others believe it to be an impression of a seaweed. Worm jaws or scolectolonts, generally of minute size, occur in some rocks. They are frequently excellent index fossils. A few actual worm remains have been found (e.g., *Lecathyaus* near Chicago, Figure 32).

Trilobites.—The trilobites had passed their climax and were not as numerous as they had been in the Ordovician. Nevertheless, the

Fig. 102. Restoration of the eurypterid *Pterygotus buffaloensis*. Actual length of the animal about nine feet. (New York State Mus.)

group still formed an important part of the marine life of this period. Many genera had persisted from the Ordovician, although in most cases the species were different. Among characteristic Silurian genera

Fig. 103.   Restoration of Silurian underwater scene showing eurypterids, gastropods, and algae. (New York State Mus.)

are *Calymene, Bumastus,* and *Dalmanites.* Many of the Silurian trilobites were highly specialized, with prominent spines or other ornamentation; among these may be mentioned *Trochurus* and *Deiphon.*

Eurypterids.—The sea scorpions, although never abundant, are of very striking appearance, and reached the height of their development during Silurian time. The average length of these creatures was a little less than one foot, although some giants, such as *Pterygotus buffaloensis*, from western New York, reached a maximum length of nine feet, with spines extended. This unusual animal was possibly the largest and most noteworthy arthropod that ever existed.

Many of the eurypterids are thought to have lived in brackish water, and to have been more or less common during certain phases of Salina time. Their affinity for rivers and brackish water lagoons explains their scarcity in marine deposits and their extremely local distribution. The eurypterids declined abruptly at the close of the Silurian, and are much less common thereafter.

An animal thought to be the most ancient air-breathing scorpion (*Proscorpius*) is known from the Silurian rocks near Buffalo, New York (Figures 102 and 103). This and some possible millipeds from the Silurian of Wales may represent the first animals to breathe air. However, since these are not perfectly preserved, and are associated with brackish-water species, their air-breathing habit is not fully substantiated.

Ostracodes.—These bivalved crustaceans evolved considerably during this period. While many were microscopic, a few reached the great length, for them, of one inch.

Fig. 104. The Silurian ostracoderm fish *Dartmuthia*, from the island of Oesel (or Sarema) in the Baltic Sea.

Fish.—Fish lived in the fresh-water streams during Silurian time, but little is known about them from their fossils (Figure 104). As far as is known, they were limited to primitive armored forms (ostracoderms). The genus *Palaespis* is known from the Bloomsburg beds of Perry County, Pennsylvania, and the genus *Cyathaspis* has been found in rocks of the Shawangunk group near Otisville, New York.

Economic Resources of the Silurian

Iron.—The deposits of the Clinton group have been discussed on page 146.

Salt.—As mentioned earlier in this chapter, great deposits of salt accumulated in the Salina sea during Late Silurian time. Salt is mined today in New York, Pennsylvania, Ohio, Michigan, and Ontario.

Petroleum.—Silurian rocks are not among the chief sources of oil and gas, although some of the Clinton sandstones of central Ohio and Kentucky have yielded limited quantities.

Other Resources.—Gypsum is present in Silurian rocks in New York and Ohio, while cement rock is obtained from Silurian formations in New York and Maryland.

FOR FURTHER READING

The references for Chapters 10–16 will be found at the end of Chapter 16.

CHAPTER 13

THE DEVONIAN

The rocks of this age are very well developed in Great Britain, where they were known to early geologists as the "Old Red Sandstone." The British geologists Roderick Murchison and Adam Sedgwick began to study these rocks in 1836, and after a few years of careful work proposed the name "Devonian," after Devonshire for this series of rocks made up primarily of sandstones and shales. It later became evident that Devonshire was an unfortunate choice for a type locality because rocks of this same age are better exposed and less disturbed in the Rhine Valley of Germany.

	Pennsylvania	New Jersey	New York
UPPER DEVONIAN	Chemung⎤ Portage ⎥ ⎥Catskill Phase	Skunnemunk	Chemung⎤ Portage ⎥ ⎥Catskill Phase
MIDDLE DEVONIAN	Hamilton Marcellus⎦ Onondaga Esopus	— Marcellus Onondaga Esopus	Hamilton Marcellus⎦ Onondaga Esopus
LOWER DEVONIAN	Oriskany Helderberg	Oriskany Helderberg	Oriskany Helderberg

In North America, the Devonian is best developed in New York, and the formations of that state are used to form the standard section of the entire country. In New York, as well as in much of the Appalachian Valley and Plateau, deposition was almost continuous, so that practically all phases of the Devonian are present. In Pennsylvania, practically all of the New York divisions are represented, the Devonian being second only to the Coal Measures (Pennsylvanian) in extent.

Lower Devonian

Helderberg Time.—At the beginning of the Devonian, Appalachia as well as the lands to the west of the geosyncline must have been very low, for only fine-grained sediments were deposited in the trough. ·

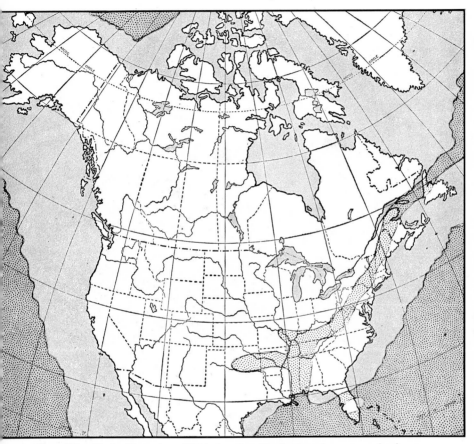

Fig. 105. Early Devonian (Helderberg). North America was a land mass somewhat larger than at present. A narrow seaway filled the Appalachian geosyncline, but the rest of the continent was above water.

The Appalachian Sea filled this trough and extended from the Gulf of Mexico to Newfoundland (Figure 105).

The formations comprising the Helderberg group are almost entirely of limestone, of only a few hundred feet in thickness. Various formations of this group have been described, but the best example is the type locality at the Helderberg Escarpment, southwest of Albany, New York.

FIG. 106. Restoration of Early Devonian sea life of New York state (Helderberg), showing algae, cephalopods, and crinoids. (New York State Mus.)

The earliest phase of the Helderberg group is the Coeymans limestone, which has a thickness of about 40 feet in the Delaware Water Gap area. A few fossils, especially the brachiopod *Gypidula coeymanensis* have been found north of the Delaware Water Gap and across the river at Flatbrookville, New Jersey. In the Nearpass section near Tri-States (New York, New Jersey, and Pennsylvania), the Coeymans limestone is coarsely crystalline and contains many crinoid stems. A coral bed at the base of the formation contains many specimens of *Favosites helderbergiae* (Figure 106).

A later stage of the Helderberg group in the Delaware Valley area is represented by the New Scotland shaly limestone. This occurs in the Water Gap area along the Lackawanna Railroad, just east of Godfrey's Ridge, Northampton County, Pennsylvania. The brachiopod *Eospirifer macropleurus* is characteristic of this formation. A similar formation occurs near Flatbrookville, New Jersey. The shaly lithology of the New Scotland formation indicates a slight shoaling of the water.

In the Delaware Valley region, the New Scotland formation was followed by a limestone, indicating a return to clearer and possibly deeper water. This limestone is found at numerous places along Walpack Ridge in Sussex County, New Jersey. The fauna is not very different from that of the older beds, but the brachiopod *Leptaena rhomboidalis* is especially abundant. These limestones (Becraft formation) are much better developed in New York. For example, at Becraft Mountain, near Hudson, the Becraft limestone is extensively quarried for Portland cement.

Helderberg rocks extend southwestward across Pennsylvania into Maryland (exposed in Washington County) and Virginia (near Woodstock and Clifton Forge). The marine invasion of Helderberg time was largely limited to the Appalachian Trough. The center of the continent and the Cordilleran Trough were probably above water during this stage.

Oriskany Time.—During the next phase of the Lower Devonian, the Oriskany, an extensive deposit of sand accumulated in the Appalachian Trough, from New York to Alabama. Probably some extensive dunes were formed along the shore at about the end of Helderberg time, and the sand from these dunes was carried down into the Oriskany sea to form the extensive deposits of sandstone.[1] At any rate, Appalachia was low lying and was not being eroded very rapidly, for if it were the Oriskany deposits would not have contained such pure quartz sand, because the weathering of crystalline rocks such as made up Appalachia give rise to more mud (shale) than sand.

The Oriskany sandstone is extensively developed in New York, the type locality being at Oriskany Falls, Oneida County. The Oriskany formation is remarkable for its widespread and uniform character. In southeastern New York and in northeastern Pennsylvania, the sandstone gives way locally to shale, while in New Jersey it is mostly limestone. Throughout most of the Appalachian geosyncline the Oriskany consists of sandstone, usually less than 100 feet in thickness. This rock weathers to a quartz sand and is one of the chief sources of glass sand in Pennsylvania and New York.

The early Oriskany sea was first limited to the eastern part of New York (near Albany), but gradually advanced into western New York and Ontario. The relationship of the fauna suggests that there was probably a connection to the open ocean to the northeast, via the Gaspé area.

---

[1] Evidence for these dunes is afforded by the roundness and frosted surfaces of the sand grains.

In Pennsylvania, the Oriskany occurs along a line from Monroe County (near Delaware Water Gap) through northern Northampton, Lehigh, and Berks Counties, and again locally in the central part of the state from Union and Montour Counties to Fulton and Bradford Counties. Good exposures of the Oriskany with characteristic fossils (*Costispirifer arenosus, Platyceras* spp., etc.) can be seen along the Pennsylvania Turnpike near the Midway Station (80 miles east of Irwin, Pennsylvania). The fossils are fairly common, but are usually poorly preserved because of the character of the sand. There are also numerous quarries near Huntingdon and Petersburg, Pennsylvania.

In northwestern New Jersey, the Oriskany contains three well-marked faunal zones, the lowest one characterized by the trilobite *Dalmanites dentatus*, the middle zone by the brachiopod *Orbiculoidea jerseyensis*, and the upper zone by the brachiopod *Acrospirifer murchisoni*. These fossils occur in the Nearpass quarry near Tri-States Rock and at "Trilobite Ridge" east of Port Jervis, New York.

The invasion by the sea must have been fairly extensive at this time, for Oriskany deposits are known from western Maryland, Virginia, and West Virginia, while deposits probably contemporaneous with these are found as far west as southeastern Missouri, western Tennessee, and southwestern Illinois.

Middle Devonian

Onondaga Time.—Oriskany time, with its widespread sand deposits, was followed by the Onondaga stage, when limestone was deposited in the Appalachian Trough. The name is derived from Onondaga County, New York, where these limestones occur about 100 feet in thickness. The sea overflowed the trough and extended westward into the Mississippi Valley and probably northwestward across Canada to the Arctic Ocean near the present Mackenzie River delta. There was also a connection to the Cordilleran Trough.

In northern New Jersey and eastern New York and Pennsylvania, there is a shaly deposit known as the Esopus grit that lies between the Oriskany and Onondaga formations. It does not occur to the south, in Maryland, thus suggesting that the southern part of the trough may have been above water for a short time. Imprints of seaweed are occasionally found in the Esopus grit, for instance near Walpack Ridge, New Jersey. The Esopus formation was given the name "Cauda galli grit" by Vanuxem in 1842 because of the seaweed(?) markings on the bedding planes which resembled the tail of a rooster.

Appalachia must have been low in Onondagan time, for few sediments were washed from it into the trough. The clear water was an excellent habitat for corals, and many reefs are found in these deposits. One of the most extensive coral reefs of Onondaga time crossed the present channel of the Ohio River at Louisville, Kentucky ("Falls of the Ohio"). The characteristic fossils include the corals *Favosites* and *Zaphrentis*, the brachiopods, *"Spirifer," Atrypa,* and *Athyris,* and the trilobite *Odontocephalus.*

Henry Herpers of the New Jersey Geological Survey has recently recorded a fauna of about a dozen corals, crinoids, brachiopods, gastropods, a conularid, and the very abundant fucoid (plant) *Taornus caudagalli* in Sussex County, New Jersey. According to Mr. Herpers, this fauna shows a close relationship between the Esopus grit and the Onondaga formation.

In New Jersey the Onondaga limestone overlies the Esopus grit along the northwestern slope of Walpack Ridge, indicating a gradual transition from grit (shale) to limestone as the water became clearer. This suggests a deepening of the sea as the shore line withdrew farther and farther away. Fossils have been found near Tri-States and Flatbrookville, but are usually fragmentary.

In Pennsylvania, a phase of the Onondaga called the Buttermilk Falls limestone is extensively developed near Stroudsburg. It occurs on the north side of Godfrey Ridge and at various quarries in the vicinity of Stroudsburg. Corals, trilobites, brachiopods, and other fossils are present. Another phase of the Onondaga, the Selinsgrove limestone, is well exposed at its type locality, Selinsgrove Junction, Northumberland County, on the east bank of the Susquehanna River, four miles south of Sunbury.

Marcellus Time.—At the end of Onondaga time, Appalachia began to rise, with the result that the streams stripped off its soil and carried considerable quantities of mud into the trough. Consequently, the deposits from this time to the end of the Devonian are much thicker and coarser than those formed during the early part of that period.

The deposits following those of Onondaga time were muds, since hardened to shales. They constitute the Marcellus formation. Most of the fossils found in these shales are of floating organisms or of forms attached to floating things. It is believed that the deposits of black mud were so extensive and so foul that they killed off the corals and other bottom-dwelling animals that had thrived during Onondaga time. As the Marcellus shales are traced farther east, they appear to thicken and are replaced by a sandy shale, apparently indicating slightly clearer water.

The Marcellus shales were named from exposures found at Marcellus, Onondaga County, New York. The formation occurs in the Hudson Valley and extends across the state, thinning toward the west. Near the base of the black shale are a few layers of limestone which extend from the Schoharie area to Ontario County in New York. They are characterized by the presence of *Goniatites* (cephalopods) and other fossils.

The Marcellus shale occurs in New Jersey only along the bank of the Delaware River, a few miles south of Port Jervis, New York. Black shales of the Marcellus formation occur in various quarries near Stroudsburg and Bushkill, Pennsylvania. Brachiopods, worms, trilobites, bryozoa and other fossils occur in these rocks.

According to Dr. Bradford Willard, of Lehigh University, who has studied this formation extensively, the Marcellus enters Pennsylvania at Matamoras on the Delaware River (opposite Port Jervis, New York), and underlies the low ground bordering the river, its top occasionally showing in the base of bluffs that rise to the northwest.

> Westward to the Susquehanna River, the formation follows a nearly straight line, broken only by minor divergencies. In the Susquehanna and Juniata valleys, the Marcellus outcrop weaves back and forth, skirting the base of the small ridges of Montobello sandstone. It disappears westward beneath the Allegheny Front to reappear no more in Pennsylvania. Southward it passes from the state as several narrow bands of outcrop in Franklin, Fulton and Bedford counties.[2]

Hamilton Time.—In New York, various subdivisions of the Hamilton are recognized, including the Marcellus,[3] Skaneateles, Ludlowville, and Moscow. Rich and distinctive faunas have been described from each. One formation of the Hamilton group, the Cherry Valley limestone of central New York, is especially rich in fossil cephalopods (Figure 107). The formations of the Hamilton group crop out at various places in the Catskill Mountains, along the Hudson River, and in central New York in a wide belt between Albany and Buffalo. In Pennsylvania, the various divisions of the Hamilton group are much less distinct and can best be separated on the basis of a comparison of their fossils with those of the better marked New York formations.

[2] Bradford Willard, *The Devonian of Pennsylvania*. Pennsylvania Topog. and Geol. Surv. Bull. G-1 (1939), pp. 168–69.
[3] Some geologists place the Marcellus in the Hamilton group; others do not.

While sandstone and shale were deposited in the Appalachian geosyncline during most of Hamilton time, there were also local deposits of coral limestone. An especially fossiliferous reef can be seen in a cut along Highway 90 on the west side of Broadhead Creek, three miles north of Stroudsburg (Figure 108). Other outcrops of this reef can be seen north of the Wind Gap, at Lehighton, and at Rockville quarry, near the railroad bridge, five miles north of Harrisburg.

FIG. 107. Slab of Cherry Valley limestone with characteristic cephalopods; much reduced. (New York State Mus.)

Recent work by Dr. Willard has demonstrated that there was probably a cape, which he calls Cape Cumberland, extending across central Lebanon County, across Dauphin and Cumberland Counties, and then turning southward through Franklin County into Maryland. The approximate position of this cape is shown in Figure 109. The deposits north of this cape are mainly sandstone and apparently represent deltaic material washed into the Marcellus and Hamilton seas from this land mass. The Marcellus and Hamilton deposits elsewhere in Pennsylvania are mainly marine, and were deposited in deeper water farther away from the land. The body of water in which these marine sediments were deposited has been called the Penn-York embayment by Willard.

FIG. 108. Field party collecting fossils from "Centerfield Coral Reef" near Stroudsburg, Pennsylvania.

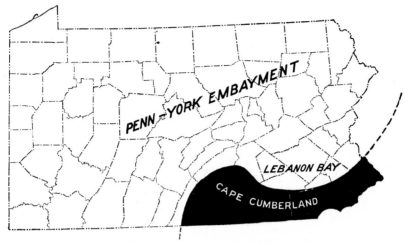

Fig. 109. Paleogeographic map of Middle Devonian time in Pennsylvania showing the supposed extent of the Penn-York embayment. (Bradford Willard, Pennsylvania Geol. Surv.)

Late Devonian

Early Portage Time.—Appalachia, as well as Acadia to the north, had been rising during most of Middle Devonian time. About the climax of that stage, this uplift had progressed with such vigor that it culminated in a period of mountain building, called the "Acadian disturbance" because its influence was especially felt in northern New England and Nova Scotia (Acadia). However, the uplift also affected the entire mass of Appalachia at least as far south as present-day Cape Hatteras (Figure 110). The Devonian and older rocks of the northern part of the Appalachian geosyncline were strongly folded and were intruded by igneous material. This resulted in a permanent destruction of the trough, with the result that never again was there a northeastern outlet to the open sea. From southern New England southward, the effect of the Acadian disturbance was felt mainly east of the geosyncline. The main evidence for the disturbance, from New York southward, is the increased amount of sediment washed into the inland sea.

Volcanoes.—At this time volcanoes were numerous in southern Quebec, Gaspé, New Brunswick, and Maine, where great thicknesses of lava are preserved. In some places the lavas have been eroded away, exposing the granites and other deeper igneous rocks. Such "granitic batholiths" make up the Little Megantic Mountains of New Brunswick, the granites of Nova Scotia, and the granitic cores of the

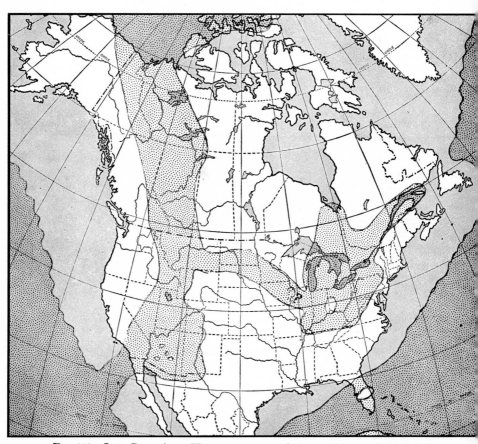

FIG. 110. Late Devonian. The seas were much more widespread than during Early Devonian time. Streams flowing westward from the mountains, which had been recently uplifted by the Acadian disturbance, formed great deltas (notably the Catskill) at the western edge of the Appalachian embayment. By the end of Devonian time the Acadian uplift had probably broken the sea connection to the northeast. A seaway still existed to the Arctic Ocean.

White Mountains of New Hampshire, Mount Katahdin, and other mountains of northern Maine. If any volcanoes were present south of New England, they were on the continent of Appalachia and all evidences of their existence have long since been destroyed with the weathering of that former extensive land mass.

Tully Limestone.—During early Portage time, the Tully limestone was deposited in the eastern part of the geosyncline (Figure 111). It is best developed in New York and is named from the town of Tully

Fig. 111.   Restoration of Late Devonian sea life of New York state (Portage). Note sponges (*Hydnoceras*), coiled nautiloid (*Manticoceras*), straight nautiloid ("*Orthoceras*"), as well as crinoids, starfish, and fishes.   (New York State Mus.)

in Onondaga County, where it is well exposed. This limestone carries a considerable quantity of iron pyrites. The fauna is essentially a modification of the Hamilton (Middle Devonian), although there are some characteristic species. The brachiopod *Hypothyridina venustula* is characteristic of early Upper Devonian and occurs in the Tully limestone in New York and Pennsylvania. Also, the trilobite *Scutella tullius* is an index fossil of the formation in New York. In some parts of the Tully of New York, where the iron pyrites are most abundant, there is a dwarf fauna indicating adverse conditions for marine life.

In Pennsylvania, Willard believes that the Tully "is confined to the sweep of Devonian formations which follow the curve of the Allegheny Front between Bedford and Lycoming Counties. In northeastern Bedford County, eastern Perry, east central Northumberland, Columbia, Luzerne, Carbon and Schuylkill Counties the fauna occurs, usually in a shaly strata." [4]

[4] Willard, *op. cit.,* pp. 220–21.

Late Portage Time.—Although the Tully limestone is usually regarded as part of the Portage group, it is distinct from the other formations of the group mainly because it is a limestone while the later formations are predominately shales and sandstones. During Portage time, at least after the deposition of the Tully limestone, the Appalachian geosyncline was gradually becoming filled by the tremendous amounts of sediment washed into it from Appalachia. Consequently, there was a regression of the sea from the trough. This was not a rapid process, and there were probably slight readvances along with the gradual retreat, but the tendency during the Upper Devonian was toward a withdrawal of the sea from the Appalachian basin.

Devonian Delta.—The streams flowing into the sea from Appalachia formed an immense delta. The landward part of the great delta formed "red beds," composed of sandstones and shales with a characteristic red color and with a great abundance of mud cracks. These represent the portion of the delta where the sediments were exposed to the atmosphere. To the west, these red beds are found to interfinger with marine fossiliferous sandstones and shales that represent the littoral or shore deposits. This delta began forming at least as far back as Marcellus time, for the marine shales of that formation grade eastward to nonfossiliferous red beds. The red beds advanced gradually westward as the delta grew and the sediments accumulated.

These extensive red beds in New York and Pennsylvania were once mapped as the Catskill formation. However, this designation is somewhat misleading because it does not represent a single time unit. Some red beds interfinger with the Marcellus and with other Middle Devonian formations; other red beds somewhat farther west can be traced to the Portage and other Upper Devonian formations. It seems better, therefore, to regard the Catskill red beds as a phase or facies of various formations of Middle and Upper Devonian age. This relationship is shown diagrammatically in Figure 112. This relationship is similar to the Bloomsburg red beds of the Silurian, which represent the landward phases of several different marine formations. (See page 149.)

The Portage group represents the marine phase of the retreating Upper Devonian sea. It has a wide distribution in Pennsylvania. The beds enter Pike County above Matamoras as a relatively broad band which, narrowing as its dips steepen, continues west to the Susquehanna River. The outcrop winds back and forth in the central part of the state, largely in the Susquehanna Valley, then swings into a long curve, east of the Allegheny Front, to Maryland. Lesser areas are found in Bedford, Fulton, Huntingdon, Blair, and western Juniata

Counties.[5] Conditions similar to those of Pennsylvania existed in Maryland during Portage time. Part of the Jennings formation of western Maryland is probably equivalent to the Portage group.

New Jersey was probably dry land during Portage time, for no marine deposits are known equivalent to the Portage group. The nonmarine Skunnemunk conglomerate of the Green Pond Mountain area, with its layers of red sandstone alternating with the conglomerate, may represent a terrestrial deposit near the shore line, with the

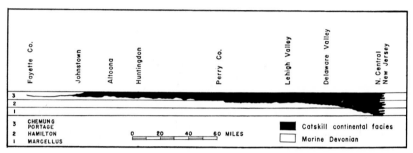

Fig. 112. Idealized section showing relationship of the continental Catskill phase with marine stages of the Devonian. (After Bradford Willard.)

interfingering of the marine (Portage) and nonmarine (Catskill). Plants found by Prosser at Monroe, Orange County, New York, suggest that the Skunnemunk formation is of the same age as the Portage.

Chemung Time.—The sandstones and shales of the Portage group were followed by those of the Chemung group. In many places in New York and Pennsylvania it is exceedingly difficult to differentiate these two groups, and the separation must be based on a careful study of the fossils.

The marine beds of the Chemung overlie those of the Portage in much of central Pennsylvania, between the Allegheny Front and the Susquehanna River south through Bedford and Fulton Counties to the Maryland line. In Maryland, the Chemung is represented by the upper beds of the Jennings formation. Their thickness is as much as 3,000 feet along the Allegheny Front between Altoona (Horseshoe Curve) and Lock Haven. The Chemung formations also crop out sporadically along the north branch of the Susquehanna River to the New York line, especially in Susquehanna County and westward.[6]

Fossils are present at many localities and consist largely of crinoids, brachiopods, and mollusks. A characteristic fossil is *Cyrtospirifer disjunctus*. Recently, a plate of the large fish *Dinichthys* was found in a road cut at Franklin Narrows, near Franklindale, Bradford County.

[5] *Ibid.*, p. 207.   [6] *Ibid.*, p. 247.

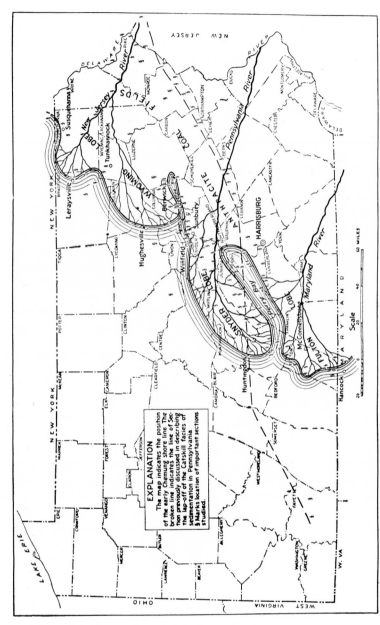

Fig. 113. Paleogeographic map illustrating hypothetical position of the Chemung shore line in Pennsylvania. Note rivers flowing into the Chemung Sea. (Bradford Willard, Pennsylvania Geol. Surv.)

Although this fish has been reported from the Devonian of New York and Ohio, this is the first record from Pennsylvania.

As mentioned previously, the marine Chemung shales grade eastward to the nonmarine Catskill facies. The shore line, or contact between the Chemung and Catskill, has been very carefully traced in Pennsylvania by Willard, and is shown in Figure 113.

> The Chemung shore line crossed Pennsylvania in a southwesterly direction from Susquehanna County, not far from Susquehanna village near the northeastern corner of the State to Fulton County on our south-central border. The line is irregular. Three river deltas or delta lobes are recognized, separated by two embayments. . . . Upon crossing from New York State to Susquehanna County, the shore line turns immediately west to east-central Bradford County (near Leraysville), where it swings southeast rather sharply into northwestern Wyoming County, makes a small embayment north of the Tunkhannock and passes southwestward into Sullivan County. . . .[7]

As can be seen in Figure 113, a narrow bay (Luzerne Bay) extended eastward through Montour and Columbia Counties into western Luzerne County. A prominent peninsula (Snyder Lobe) extended southwest to Huntingdon County. East of the peninsula, the narrow Perry Bay extended northeastward to Perry County. The three rivers, New Jersey River, Pennsylvania River, and Maryland River are, of course, hypothetical. However, evidence for them is found in the great amount of sediment poured into the Chemung sea.

Post-Chemung Devonian.—Three Upper Devonian groups later than the Chemung have been recognized in southwestern New York and northwestern Pennsylvania: the Canadaway group, the Conneaut group, and the Conewango group. They are somewhat similar to the deposits of the Chemung group and are often included with them. The rocks of these groups occur in northern and northwestern Pennsylvania, from Bradford County to Lake Erie. Various formations of the Post-Chemung Devonian are important because of their oil and gas, one of the most significant being the Venango formation of the Conewango group. Incidentally, the *Dinichthys* from Franklin Narrows, mentioned on page 171, may have come from the Canadaway group rather than from the Chemung proper.

Catskill Phase

As has been made clear in this chapter, the Catskill red beds, once regarded as a separate formation, are now thought to be the landward phase or facies of the great Upper Devonian delta that was formed

[7] *Ibid.,* p. 272.

throughout this period. Parts of the red beds are equivalent to the marine Marcellus of early Upper Devonian age, while others, farther west, are equivalent to the Chemung, or Post-Chemung formations of late Upper Devonian age. In other words, the delta was gradually advancing westward as the geosyncline became filled with the sands, shales, and other deposits brought into it by the rivers flowing from Appalachia.

FIG. 114. Outcrop of Catskill redbeds along the Pennsylvania Turnpike.

Various formations of sandstone and shale have been recognized in the Catskill facies of Pennsylvania and New York. However, their recognition and correlation with their marine equivalents are extremely difficult and will not be attempted here. Suffice it to say that shales and sandstones of the Catskill facies cover essentially all of northeastern Pennsylvania, and extend south into Maryland (Figure 114). These shales and sandstones are relatively resistant to weathering and frequently form the crests of hills. They occasionally occur with some conglomerate at various places along the Pennsylvania Turnpike up to five miles east of Sideling Hill Tunnel. (The tunnel itself is dug through Pocono sandstone of Mississippian age.)

As can readily be inferred from its name, the Catskill rocks occur in the Catskill Mountains of New York. These rocks, being non-marine, contain few fossils. Fossil plants have been found at a few places, especially a fern of the genus *Archaeopteris*. Ostracoderm (fish) plates are known at a few places along the Pennsylvania Turnpike.

Another delta, similar to the Catskill, was formed about the same time in the Gaspé region of eastern Quebec. Extensive nonmarine beds with fossiliferous fresh-water fish and land plants are common at certain localities in that area, especially near Escuminac at the head of the Bay of Chaleur.

Other Devonian Rocks of North America

Outside the Appalachian geosyncline, the Devonian deposits of North America are relatively thin and no complete sections are represented. In Middle Devonian time there was a marine basin in Michigan separated from the Appalachian geosyncline by the northward extension of the Cincinnati Arch. Coral reefs were especially abundant in this embayment, which is called the "Michigan Basin." The possible presence of a Devonian sea east of Appalachia is suggested by the presence of some fossils, questionably of Devonian age, found in well cores from Levy County, Florida.[8]

Cordilleran Geosyncline.—The sea invaded this trough during Middle and Upper Devonian times. Extensive fossiliferous deposits have been found in Utah, Nevada and along the Mackenzie River, near the Arctic Circle.

Eria Land Bridge.—It is probable that a land bridge connected northern North America with Europe during most of Devonian time. It is assumed that it started from Nova Scotia and Newfoundland and continued across Greenland and Iceland toward Ireland. The evidence for the existence of this "bridge" is indirect and of two types: (1) The rugged mountains apparently once extended farther out to sea, and the Caledonian Mountains of Scotland, formed during the Silurian (see page 151), extended to the west. It is highly probable that these ranges joined in a connecting link between the two continents; (2) the great similarity in the land plants and fresh-water fish of the Devonian of Europe and North America strongly suggests that they were able to migrate across such a land bridge. For convenience, geologists call this hypothetical bridge "Eria."

End of the Devonian.—The Acadian Disturbance (see page 167) continued throughout Devonian time. The eastern part of the Appalachian sea had been completely filled by the Catskill red beds, but

---

[8] Horace G. Richards, "Studies on the Subsurface Geology and Paleontology of the Atlantic Coastal Plain," *Proc. Acad. Nat. Sci. Phila.* (1948), p. 70.

open sea did exist farther west in Ohio, Indiana, and Illinois. The sea connection to the northeast ceased to exist, owing to the presence of the Acadian Mountains. The connection to the northwest through the Great Lakes and western Canada to the Arctic was, however, still open.

Devonian Plant Life

As we have brought out in previous chapters, records of land plants before Devonian time are fragmentary and we can assume that there was no abundance of vegetation until the Devonian. Plants developed very rapidly and became abundant during the Devonian, and representatives of many phyla are found in the rocks laid down during this period. One of the most primitive land plants is *Psilophyton princeps*, found in the Lower Devonian rocks of the Gaspé Peninsula. The plant probably lived in the marshy bogs of the period. It had slender stems with regular Y-shaped branches, at the tips of which were small pendant spore sacs. Related types of fossil plants have been found in the Devonian rocks near Rhynie in northeastern Scotland, one of these being described under the generic name *Rhynia*. While the exact position of these primitive plants in the classification is still unsettled, they are generally placed in a separate phylum, Psilopsida (see page 85). Some botanists place them in the phylum Bryophyta. (See Figure 53, page 84.)

Primitive ancestors of the calamites or horsetails (arthrophyta) are known from some Devonian rocks, but their exact classification is uncertain.

The Lepidophyta (scale trees), which were to assume massive proportions in Pennsylvanian time, were represented in the Devonian by various ancestral forms. One of the most ancient representatives of this group is the genus *Archeosigillaria*, which consisted of a trunk about 25 feet in height. The best specimen was found in rocks of Portage age near Naples, New York, and is now on display in the New York State Museum at Albany. A related tree, *Protolepidodendron*, grew to an even larger size.

Both the true ferns and seed ferns were features of the Devonian landscape of Pennsylvania, New York and elsewhere, the most representative genus being *Archaeopteris*. The seed ferns (Pteridospermatophytes) were, like the Lepidophytes, to assume much more massive size in the Coal Periods. However, ancestral forms are found in Devonian rocks. The best representative of the group is *Eospermatopteris textilis*, of which a large group of stumps was discovered at Gilboa, New York, during the excavations for the Schoharie Reservoir. These plants consisted of cylindrical stems 30 to 40 feet in height and up to three feet in diameter. The top of the plant bore fronds, some of which reached nine feet in length. A fine exhibit of these plants can be seen in the New York State Museum, where they have been restored under the direction of Dr. Winifred Goldring. (See Figure 115.)

FIG. 115. An Upper Devonian forest at Gilboa, New York, consisting mainly of the seed fern *Eospermatopteris* and the lycopod *Archeosigillaria*. (New York State Mus.)

Ancestral gymnosperms (conifers) of the genus *Callixyon* have been found in Devonian rocks of Oklahoma, Michigan, Indiana, New York, and Pennsylvania (?). Although only trunks or pieces of the branches have been recovered, a study of the wood structure makes it clear that these plants belonged to the same group as our modern conifers. The largest trunk found has a diameter of five feet. Pieces of large trunks of *Callixyon* have been found in Devonian rocks of Ellesmere Island in the Canadian Arctic, indicating a remarkable difference in climate from that prevailing in that region today.

Devonian Marine Life

The marine life of the Devonian was not very different from that of the Silurian, except for the great increase in fishes. Some genera ranged from the Silurian into the Devonian, although many new ones

Fig. 116. Devonian marine life. In the foreground can be seen a large ostracoderm (*Pterichthys*), above which is the smaller ostracoderm (*Cephalapsis*). At the upper right are some primitive bony fish (ganoids), and on the floor of the ocean can be seen some cup corals, crinoids, and brachiopods. (J. P. Cowan, Hughes Tool Co.)

appeared at the beginning of the Devonian, and practically all species underwent a change (Figure 116).

Protozoa.—Foraminifera were present, but their fossil remains are not abundant in Devonian rocks today.

Sponges.—Sponges were a conspicuous element of the Devonian seas. The siliceous or glass sponges were particularly abundant in the Chemung rocks of New York, where *Hydnoceras* (Figure 121) was a characteristic genus. Sponges are rare in the Devonian rocks of Pennsylvania or New Jersey.

Corals.—Although many Silurian genera continued into the Devonian, many additional species also appeared. Reef corals were exceedingly abundant in the Devonian, especially the honeycomb coral (*Favosites*) (Figure 117), the organ pipe coral (*Syringopora*) and the chain coral (*Halysites*) (Figure 118). Cup corals (*Heliophyllum, Zaphrentis, Streptalasma*) (Figures 119 and 120), etc., were also very conspicuous. Corals are abundant in the Onondaga and Hamilton limestones, but less so in the Marcellus shales and sandstones. This distribution reflects their preference for clear water, as opposed to muddy or sandy habitats.

Silicified corals, especially *Favosites*, frequently occur in pebbles found in the Tertiary and Pleistocene formations of New Jersey and other Coastal Plain states. These are thought to have been carried down from the Devonian outcrops by ancient streams and spread out over the coastal plain.

Other Coelenterates.—Stromatopors, other coral-like reef builders, were present in some Devonian seas. The graptolites, which had been so abundant in the Ordovician shales, were diminishing in numbers during the Silurian and were almost extinct by the Devonian, only a few species being known from this period.

Bryozoa.—Colonial bryozoa are often found among the coral reefs of the Onondaga and Hamilton formations, especially in the outcrops of the Centerfield Reef near Stroudsburg, Wind Gap, and Lehighton, Pennsylvania. Many genera have been identified, the most conspicuous being the lace-like *Fenestrellina* (Figure 125) and related forms.

Echinoderms.—The cystoids were almost at the point of extinction. The blastoids were increasing in importance, but were not to reach their peak until the next period (Mississippian). Crinoids flourished in clear water. They were important inhabitants of the limy seas and did much to build up these extensive Devonian limestone deposits. While few perfect specimens are known from Pennsylvania or New Jersey, fragments of stalks are very abundant in many Devonian rocks, especially those of the Onondaga and Hamilton groups.

Starfish were also increasingly abundant. Because they do not preserve well as fossils, they are rarely found in Devonian rocks. However, a slab was found in the Hamilton formation near Mount Marion, New York. The slab contained the remains of over 400 starfish, some of them actually preserved in the process of eating clams, as is their habit today. This slab is in the New York State Museum at Albany (Figure 126).

SILURIAN AND DEVONIAN FOSSILS

FIG. 117. Silurian coral *Favosites*.
FIG. 118. Devonian coral *Halysites*.
FIGS. 119, 120. Silurian coral *Streptelasma*.
FIG. 121. Devonian sponge *Hydnoceras*.
FIG. 122. Devonian trilobite *Calymene*.

FIG. 123. Devonian brachiopod *Gypidula*.
FIG. 124. Devonian brachiopod *Spirifer medialis*.
FIG. 125. Devonian bryozoa *Fenestrellina*.

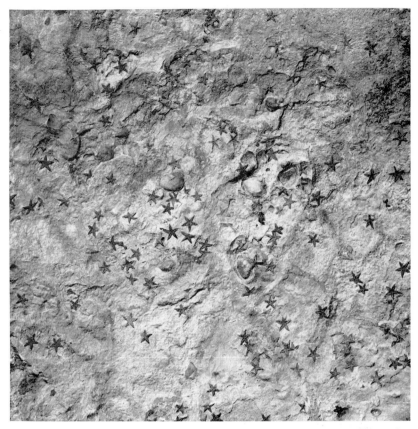

Fig. 126. Slab of starfish (*Devonaster eucharis*) from the Hamilton formation at Saugerties, New York. The slab measures 4 feet 9 inches square. (New York State Mus.)

Brachiopods.—These animals probably reached their zenith during the Devonian, and formed the most abundant faunal element of Devonian seas. They are most useful as index fossils, many species being characteristic of certain formations. Many genera are represented, the most important being *Stropheodonta, Chonetes, Atrypa, Athyris, Gypidula* (Figure 123), and the *"Spirifers"* (Figure 124). The last-mentioned brachiopods are perhaps the most characteristic fossils of Devonian time, many genera and hundreds of species being known from North America.

Pelecypods.—The clams were larger and more conspicuous than they had been during earlier periods. In contrast to the crinoids and corals, they preferred a muddy location for their habitat and consequently are found in the shales, especially those of the Hamilton and

Marcellus formations. Winged forms such as *Pterinopecten, Leptodesma,* and *Aviculopecten* were present, while other genera included *Cypricardella, Orthonota, Nuculites,* and *Modiomorpha.*

Gastropoda.—The snails were not as common as the clams. Both rounded and elongate forms are present, some of them possessing numerous spines. Some of the more usual genera are *Platyceras, Loxonema,* and *Ptomatis.*

Pteropoda.—A minute mollusk, *Styliolina fissurella,* makes up solid masses of limestone in the Upper Devonian in New York.

Cephalopoda.—Both straight and coiled types were present in the Devonian, and a new group of cephalopods, the ammonites, made their appearance. These show a distinct evolution in that the ends of the septa are angularly bent into lobes and saddles. Although this group of cephalopods was to attain an extraordinary degree of complexity in the Mesozoic, the ammonites of the Devonian are relatively simple. The most important Devonian genus is *Goniatites,* and other ammonites known from Pennsylvania and New Jersey are *Gomphoceras, Agoniatites,* and *Manticoceras.* An interesting "missing link" is the genus *Bactrites,* which has a straight *Orthoceras*-like shell, but which shows its ammonite relationship by its complex suture lines. (See Figure 107.)

Trilobites.—The trilobites had begun their decline by the Devonian, but were nevertheless an important part of the marine life of the period. Some Silurian genera carried over into the Devonian, among which should be mentioned *Phacops, Trimerus,* and *Calymene* (Figure 122). Among the new Devonian genera are *Cryphaeus* and *Terataspis.* Some species of *Dalmanites* and *Terataspis* reached a very large size, one of them (*T. grandis*) reaching the all-time record length of 29 inches. The development of spines and frills was a feature of certain Devonian trilobites.

Eurypterids.—Many large eurypterids lived during the Devonian, but were usually limited to brackish or fresh waters. Most of the genera are similar to those of the Silurian (*Eurypterus, Stylonurus,* etc.), but the species are different. Some of the Devonian eurypterids reached the extreme length of six or eight feet.

Ostracodes.—Devonian ostracodes, although small, are very beautiful creatures and make excellent index fossils.

Insects and Other Arthropods.—Although no fossil insects or arachnids have been found in Devonian rocks from eastern North

FIG. 127. The Devonian placoderm fish *Bothriolepis* from the Gaspé Peninsula.

FIG. 128. Devonian spiny sharks. (Univ. of Kansas Nat. Hist. Mus.)

America, a few primitive wingless insects and some fossils questionably identified as mites have been found associated with land plants in the Devonian rocks of Scotland.

Fishes.—Although fishes were not the most abundant animals of the Devonian, various kinds present during this period represent a

FIG. 129. Primitive armored fish, *Coccosteus,* with some ostracoderms in the foreground. (Univ. of Kansas Nat. Hist. Mus.)

great advance over the more primitive Silurian ancestors. In fact, they constitute the most important faunal advance of the period and give their name to the Middle Paleozoic (Age of Fishes). Fossils of Silurian fish are absent, or are very rarely found.

Ostracoderms, descendants of Ordovician and Silurian forms, are present in small numbers in some Devonian rocks, especially in the Gaspé region of eastern Canada, where the water was fresh or brackish. A few ostracoderm plates are occasionally found in the Catskill red beds of Pennsylvania. The placoderm *Bothriolepis* (Figure 127) is also one of the common fish fossils from the Gaspé region.

Sharks were present in great numbers in some Devonian seas but, because of their soft cartilaginous skeletons, only their teeth and fin spines are normally preserved as fossils (Figure 128). These are especially abundant near Cleveland, Ohio. Some of these Ohio specimens are exceptionally well preserved, with not only their teeth and fin spines, but with many of the soft parts as well, including muscle segments and kidneys, being recorded in the rocks.

The arthrodires (armored fish) were also conspicuous in some Devonian seas and were represented by some rather large and powerful individuals (Figure 129). One genus, *Dinicthys* (Figure 130), reached a length of 20 feet and had hard body plates over the head and forepart of the body. Individual plates of *Dinicthys* have occasionally been found in Pennsylvania and New York, while perfect specimens are fairly frequent in Ohio, especially near Cleveland and Columbus.

The primitive bony fish (ganoids), which are related to our modern sturgeons and gar pike, were represented in Devonian seas by *Cheirolepis* and several other genera. Finally, there were the lungfish (*Dipterus, Scaumenacia*) which, like their modern descendants, were physically adapted for air breathing. Although fossils of these Devonian fish are very rare, and are unknown

FIG. 130. Restoration of the large arthrodire *Dinicthys*. (Amer. Mus. Nat. Hist.)

from eastern North America, they are exceedingly important from the evolutionary point of view. From a comparison with the several genera of lungfish that are living today (for instance, *Protopterus* now living in the Nile River) one can obtain a concept of the evolutionary tendency away from water breathing to air breathing, and consequently from an aquatic existence onto the land. Another interesting lungfish which was well on its way to a terrestrial habit is the genus *Eusthenopteron* (Figure 131), from the Devonian rocks at Escuminac, Quebec, on the Bay of Chaleur. This fish had a fin skeleton remarkably like that of a limb of a land vertebrate.

The only important group of fish absent from Devonian rocks is that comprising the bony fish or teleosts, which constitutes the most important group today.

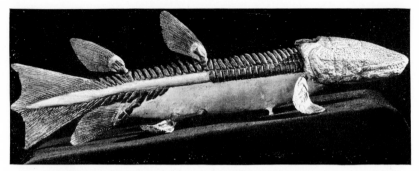

FIG. 131. Restoration of the crossopterygian fish *Eusthenopteron*. Possibly the ancestor of the amphibians and higher vertebrates. (Amer. Mus. Nat. Hist.)

Amphibia.—A footprint thought to have been made by an amphibian was found many years ago near Warren, Pennsylvania, in Upper Devonian rocks. It was named *Thinopus antiquatus*, although there has been considerable doubt whether it was actually a footprint, or merely a concretion of inorganic origin. Dr. Willard has described some tracks which he observed near Lanesboro, Pennsylvania, as belonging to a new order of Amphibians which he called the Ichthyopoda. He referred these tracks to two species of a new genus *Paramphibius*. Subsequently, Dr. Kenneth Caster found additional material at this locality, and concluded that the tracks were not made by amphibians but by a Devonian xiphosuran, or king crab, *Protolimulus*. So, again, we find a difference of opinion as to the presence of amphibians during the Devonian period of America.

A Danish expedition led by Lauge Koch found some undoubted amphibian skeletons in the Upper Devonian rocks of eastern Greenland. These specimens are known as the Stegocephalia, or roof-headed animals, and were so called because their skulls were covered by a heavy armor of bony plates, thus suggesting a fighting quality for self-protection. Other paleontologists call this order the Labyrinthodontia. It may be noted in passing that the age of these Greenland amphibia is somewhat uncertain. The Swedish workers, especially Stensiö and Jarvik, favor the view that they are of Devonian age, while the English workers, especially Watson and Westoll, regard them as of early Mississippian age.

Economic Resources of the Devonian

Petroleum.—The first commercial oil in the United States was obtained in 1858 from Devonian rocks at Titusville, Pennsylvania, and western Pennsylvania still produces a considerable quantity of high-

Fig. 132. A fire in the Leduc Oil Field. The field is one of western Canada's important new oil discoveries and is located (some) 25 miles south of Edmonton, Alberta. The oil is produced from buried Devonian coral reefs.

grade oil. Far more important today, however, is the oil production from Devonian rocks in Michigan, and especially those in Oklahoma and west Texas. Natural gas is also obtained in great quantities from Devonian rocks of western Pennsylvania, New York, and West Virginia. During the past few years new and important sources of oil have been discovered in Devonian coral reef rocks at Norman Wells (the former headquarters of the Canol project) on the Mackenzie River in northwestern Canada, and at the Leduc, Redwater, and many other fields near Edmonton, Alberta (Figure 132).

Sand.—Sand is found in practically all geological formations and is generally omitted from these discussions. However, the pure quartz sand of the Oriskany formation deserves special mention because of its importance in the manufacture of glass. The lens of the great 200-inch telescope at Mount Palomar in California was made from sand obtained from the Oriskany formation.

FURTHER READING

The references for Chapters 10–16 will be found at the end of Chapter 16.

CHAPTER 14

THE MISSISSIPPIAN

The deposits lying next upon those of the Devonian were at one time termed the Carboniferous ("carbon-bearing") because of the extensive coal measures deposited in these formations in many parts of the world. Late investigation has indicated the necessity of dividing the Carboniferous of North America into two major periods: the Mississippian, sometimes called the "Sub-Carboniferous," and the Pennsylvanian, or Carboniferous proper.[1] The majority of the coal deposits were formed during the latter period. The Mississippian Period derives its name from the Mississippi Valley, where marine deposits of this age are extensively developed.

	Pennsylvania	New Jersey	New York
UPPER MISSISSIPPIAN	Mauch Chunk —Loyalhanna—	—	—
LOWER MISSISSIPPIAN	Pocono	—	Cattaraugus beds

Lower Mississippian

The continent of Appalachia was still rugged and continued to be eroded, its streams carrying tremendous quantities of sediments, mostly sand and mud, into the Appalachian geosyncline (Figure 133). The Appalachian Trough continued to subside, possibly because of the great weight of the sediments. However, the sinking was largely counteracted by the amount of sediment being poured into the trough. The result was that the land remained near sea level during most of Mississippian time. At times, the sinking would be more rapid than the sedimentation and the sea would invade the trough; at other times, the land was above sea level. In other words, the shore line fluctuated during this period.

The northeastern entrance to the Appalachian Trough had been permanently blocked during the Devonian by the uplift of the Acadian Mountains. During the early part of the Mississippian time, the in-

[1] European geologists do not recognize these divisions of the Carboniferous.

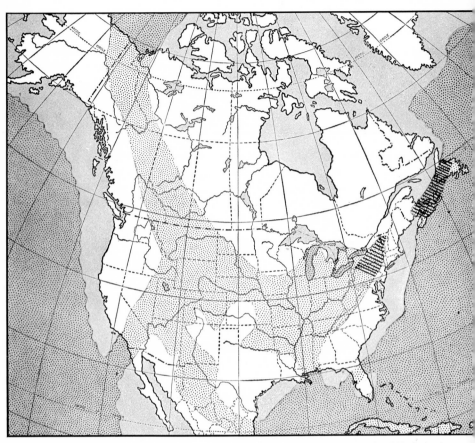

FIG. 133. Early Mississippian. A broad seaway extended up the Mississippi Valley, northward to the Arctic Ocean. The Appalachian geosyncline was largely filled and great delta deposits were formed along the western slope of Appalachia. The sea connection to the northeast was permanently broken. Areas of swamps or fresh-water deposits are indicated by darker shading.

land sea continued to occupy the southern part of the trough, in Alabama, Georgia, and Tennessee. The sea probably advanced periodically to the northeast, but most of the deposits of Maryland and Pennsylvania of this period form the nonmarine Pocono sandstones and shales (see below). Farther west, marine conditions existed in the Mississippi Valley during most of Mississippian time. An arm of this sea probably extended eastward to western Pennsylvania, where its sediments merged with the nonmarine Pocono beds.

Pocono Group.—The muds and sands washed into the Appalachian Trough during the early Mississippian time gradually hardened to sandstones and shales and now form the Pocono formation of Pennsylvania and adjacent states. Their resistance to erosion is responsible for the relief of the Pocono Mountains of Pennsylvania. These mountains, in contrast to those of the central and west central part of the state, are mainly an eroded portion of the great Appalachian Plateau. Rocks of the Pocono group, however, are also found in the highly folded Valley and Ridge Province of Pennsylvania. The Sideling Hill and Rays Hill tunnels of the Pennsylvania Turnpike are largely or entirely dug through rocks of Pocono age.

West of Pennsylvania the rocks of the Pocono group blend into the marine sandstones of the Waverly group of Ohio. Similarly, in Allegheny and Cattaraugus Counties of western New York, there are marine shales probably contemporaneous with the Pocono rocks. The remainder of New York, as well as most or all of New England, probably stood above sea level at this time, for no deposits of this age are known from that region. In the northeastern part of the Appalachian geosyncline there was a similar nonmarine basin, in which the shales and sandstones of the Horton group were deposited. These rocks are present today in localities in New Brunswick and Nova Scotia.

If any Mississippian deposits existed in New Jersey they have since been eroded away, for none are known from this state. The Pocono formation, however, does extend south of Pennsylvania into Maryland and Virginia. Near Roanoke and Blacksburg, Virginia, and elsewhere in the Shenandoah Valley, there are a few coal beds (the "Valley Field"). Coal has also been mined from Pocono rocks in Pennsylvania, for example, near Peters Mountain, 12 miles north of Harrisburg.

Loyalhanna Limestone

There is a conspicuous gap, or unconformity, between the rocks of the Pocono group (Lower Mississippian) and those of the Mauch Chunk (Upper Mississippian). During this interval eastern Pennsylvania was probably being eroded. However, in southwestern Pennsylvania and West Virginia, the Loyalhanna marine limestone was formed. This formation is sometimes dated as Early Mississippian and sometimes as Late Mississippian. The generally accepted correlation based on the marine deposits of the Mississippi Valley does not recognize any "Middle Mississippian."

Upper Mississippian

By Late Mississippian time a rise of the southern part of the Appalachian geosyncline probably produced a barrier which prevented the entrance of marine waters from the Gulf of Mexico (Figure 134). This blockade was almost the final chapter in the long career of the great geosyncline, which had been in existence and receiving sediments intermittently ever since the beginning of the Cambrian. It will be recalled that the northeastern entrance had been blocked during the Devonian by the uplift of the Acadian Mountains, and the southwestern entrance was closed by this uplift. The new land mass which comprised parts of Georgia, Alabama, Mississippi, and Louisiana and at least part of the present Gulf of Mexico, has been called Llanoria. During part of this stage Llanoria was probably continuous with Appalachia. However, Llanoria was not entirely effective as a barrier, for another sea entrance was formed farther west, through Mexico, Texas, Arkansas, and Tennessee, and connected the Mississippian ocean with the waters in the remaining part of the Appalachian geosyncline.

Mauch Chunk Formation.—In Late Mississippian time, sediments somewhat similar to those of Pocono time were deposited in the Appalachian basin in Pennsylvania and adjacent Maryland and New York. These sediments are the dull red sandstones and shales of the Mauch Chunk formation and are about 2,000 feet thick. Like the Pocono rocks, they are fairly resistant and form the crests of many hills. In Pennsylvania these rocks are especially conspicuous near Mauch Chunk in the Lehigh Valley. The Laurel Hill and Allegheny Mountain tunnels of the Pennsylvania Turnpike were dug through rocks of Mauch Chunk age.

Farther south, the nonmarine rocks of the Mauch Chunk formation grade into marine sandstones and shales. As mentioned above, the sea probably entered the southern part of the Appalachian geosyncline. How far east this sea extended is not known, but rocks, possibly of Mississippian age, have been found in deep wells in Georgia and northern Florida, suggesting that this region was also covered by the sea during Mississippian time.

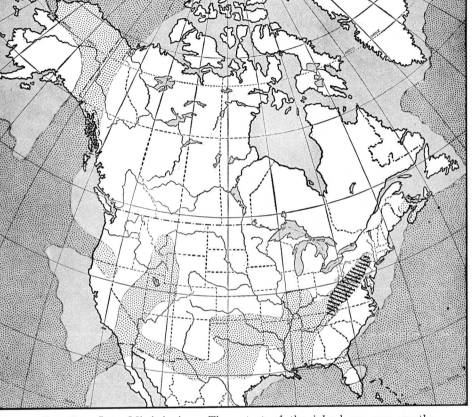

FIG. 134. Late Mississippian. The extent of the inland sea was greatly
reduced. Swamp or deltaic deposits (indicated by darker shading) continued
to form in the old Appalachian geosyncline, and there were occasional short
periods of marine submergence. Some coal was formed in these swamp deposits.

Windsor Formation.—In the extreme northern part of the geosyncline, in parts of New Brunswick and Nova Scotia, nonmarine shales and sandstones somewhat similar to the Mauch Chunk were deposited where the Upper Mississippian Windsor group overlies the Horton. Locally extensive deposits of salt and gypsum were also formed. A well drilled in Hillsboro Bay, nine miles from Prince Edward Island, encountered upwards of 12,000 feet of nonmarine Mis-

FIG. 135. Contact between Mauch Chunk formation (Mississippian) and overlying Pottsville (Pennsylvanian) near Pottsville.

sissippian and Pennsylvanian deposits. A few fossils of Late Mississippian time have been found in Nova Scotia and on the Magdalen Islands, and indicate local marine enbayments in the Acadian region. This fauna shows a closer relationship to the Mississippian of Europe than to that of other parts of North America. The Mauch Chunk rocks of Pennsylvania contain very few fossils, only a few plants and amphibians having been found there.

Mississippian Time in Central and Western North America

Mississippi Valley.—During much of Mississippian time the sea flooded the present valley of the Mississippi River, depositing immense quantities of limestone. These limestones can be seen exposed in bluffs along the Mississippi River from Missouri to Iowa. At many places they are very fossiliferous, Keokuk and Burlington, Iowa, being especially famous for crinoids. Slightly farther east, the "Indiana Lime-

stones" of Mississippian age are extensively quarried for building
stone. East of the Cincinnati Arch, these limestones and other marine deposits interfinger with the nonmarine Mississippian deposits of
the Appalachian Trough (Pocono and Mauch Chunk).

Mountain Building.—While no new mountains of major importance were formed in eastern North America during most of Mississippian time, there was a marked uplift of Appalachia at about the
end of the period. The material carried down from the re-uplifted
land mass formed some of the sediments of Late Mississippian and
Early Pennsylvanian times. As mentioned earlier, the Llanoria uplift
during Mississippian time formed a land mass along the north coast
of the Gulf of Mexico. There is also indirect evidence of an uplift
in Colorado during this period, a mountain-building disturbance which
continued into Pennsylvanian time.

Mississippian Life

Fossils are very rare in Mississippian rocks in eastern United
States. Therefore, in discussing the life of the period, it will be necessary to draw on material from other areas, especially from the Mississippi Valley region which was covered by the sea during much of
the period.

Plants.—Plant life of the Mississippian was undoubtedly abundant,
but fossils are not common and are poorly preserved. A few plants
are known from the Pocono beds, one characteristic form being *Tri-
phyllopteris*. Mississippian plants were apparently very similar to
those of the Pennsylvanian period to be described in the next chapter.

Protozoa.—For the first time, foraminifera formed an important
part of the sea fauna. The most common genus was *Endothyra* which
made up great masses of limestone in Indiana (Salem limestone) and
in other parts of the Mississippi Valley. These forms were microscopic in size and must have occurred in tremendous numbers to form
such extensive deposits.

Sponges.—Apparently rare. A few have been described from
Lower Mississippian rocks near Titusville, Pennsylvania. One genus
has been appropriately named *Titusvillia*.

Corals.—The extensive reef-building tabulate corals of the Silurian
and Devonian (*Favosites*, etc.) completely disappeared from the
scene. Other types were present during Mississippian time but were
not abundant. They were usually solitary in habitat or else lived in
small groups. The large compound tetracoral *Lithostrotionella*, which

formed heads up to two feet in diameter, lived in the seas occupying the present Mississippi Valley.

Bryozoa.—The lacy forms (*Fenestrellina* = "*Fenestella*," etc.) reached their climax. Another important Mississippian genus is *Archimedes*, characterized by its spirally twisted axis.

Echinoderms.—Crinoids were very abundant in both species and numbers. Crawfordsville, Indiana, and Keokuk and Burlington, Iowa, are world-famous localities for these fossils. Blastoids, hitherto not

Fig. 136. Mississippian echinoid *Melonechinus*, from St. Louis.

common, reached their peak of development during the Mississippian period. The bud-shaped *Pentremites* was characteristic and made up the bulk of certain limestone deposits. Starfish were rare, but echinoids for the first time became relatively common. One of the most interesting forms was *Melonechinus* (Figure 136), which resembled a small cantaloupe. It is especially common near St. Louis, Missouri (St. Louis limestone).

Brachiopods.—These were very much like those of the Devonian and made up a large part of the marine life of the period. The family Productidae was especially common and made its first appearance at that time. Other important Mississippian genera include *Dictyodostus, Mesolobus, Chonetes,* and "*Spirifer.*"

Pelecypods and Gastropods.—These were locally common; a few occur in the Pocono sandstone.

Cephalopods.—The ammonites (*Goniatites,* etc.) which had appeared during the Devonian, increased in numbers and in the complexity of their suture lines. They were, however, more abundant in Europe than in North America.

Trilobites.—These were practically extinct, only a few small forms being known from this period.

Ostracodes.—In contrast, the ostracodes were abundant, although the majority of the species were very small.

Insects.—Although only a very few fossil insects have been found in Mississippian rocks, the presence of a few of these fossils in the Devonian, and the great complexity of insect life on the Pennsylvanian tell us that insects must have been present during the Mississippian. The Pocono, Mauch Chunk, and other sandstones of this age are not favorable for the preservation of delicate insect fossils, which probably accounts for their absence.

Fishes.—These were locally abundant, but were less varied than in the Devonian. Fossils of at least 300 species of cestraciont or "shell crushing" sharks have been found. These are usually represented merely by their teeth and fin spines. The Port Jackson shark of Australia is a lineal descendant of these fossils.

Amphibia.—Until recently, these were known in America only by footprints. However, in 1940, some disarticulated amphibian bones were discovered in shales of Mauch Chunk age near Hinton, West Virginia. Other skeletal material is known from the Mississippian of Europe.

Economic Resources of the Mississippian

Petroleum.—Mississippian rocks, notably in Illinois and west Texas, are among the important producers of petroleum. A relatively small percentage of the oil and gas from Pennsylvania, Ohio, West Virginia, and Kentucky comes from buried sands of the Pocono, Ste. Genevieve, or Mauch Chunk formations. The Berea sandstone of Ohio was formerly an important producer. The recently (1951) discovered fields in the Williston Basin of North Dakota produce from Mississippian rocks.

Salt.—In Michigan, brines from deeply buried Devonian and Mississippian rocks produce large quantities of salt, bromine, and magnesium.

Coal.—The "Valley Field" of the Shenandoah Valley of Virginia produces coal from Mississippian rocks, important mines being located at Wytheville. Coal was formerly obtained from Mississippian rocks in Pennsylvania.

Other Minerals.—Gold, silver, and lead are obtained from Mississippian limestone near Leadville, Colorado, while zinc and lead are obtained from Kansas, Missouri, and Oklahoma, where they were introduced by later igneous activity. Carnotite (uranium-vanadium) occurs in noncommercial quantities in a gravel conglomerate in the Mauch Chunk formation at Mauch Chunk, Pennsylvania.

FURTHER READING

The references for Chapters 10–16 will be found at the end of Chapter 16.

CHAPTER 15

THE PENNSYLVANIAN

The upper part of the Carboniferous strata has been designated as the Pennsylvanian because it is exceptionally well developed in the coal fields of western Pennsylvania.

	Pennsylvania	New Jersey	New York
UPPER	Monongahela Conemaugh Allegheny	— — —	—
LOWER	Pottsville	—	Pottsville, including Olean conglomerate and Sharon shale

General History.—At the beginning of Pennsylvanian time, the land surface in the Appalachian geosyncline was largely at, or slightly above, sea level. The sediments that washed in from Appalachia filled the basin faster than its floor subsided. The connection to the open sea was, as it had been during Mississippian time, from the southwest.

Most of the rocks of Pennsylvanian age in eastern North America were deposited near the western part of the Appalachian geosyncline and were only slightly affected by the crustal movements that took place during the Appalachian Revolution of Permian time, when the present Appalachian Mountains were formed. Accordingly, these rocks have been much less folded and faulted than those in the eastern part of the trough. The change between the highly folded rocks of the Appalachian Ridge and Valley Region and the more or less horizontal strata of the Allegheny Plateau is very apparent as one drives along the Turnpike between Harrisburg and Pittsburgh.

The rate at which sediments from Appalachia were poured into the Appalachian Trough was so great that three immense deltas were created along the western flanks of Appalachia, one in east-central Pennsylvania, one in West Virginia, and the third in northern Alabama. At least once during Pennsylvanian time these deltas were submerged by the sea, but during most of the period they were immense swamps. At the end of Pennsylvanian time most of Penn-

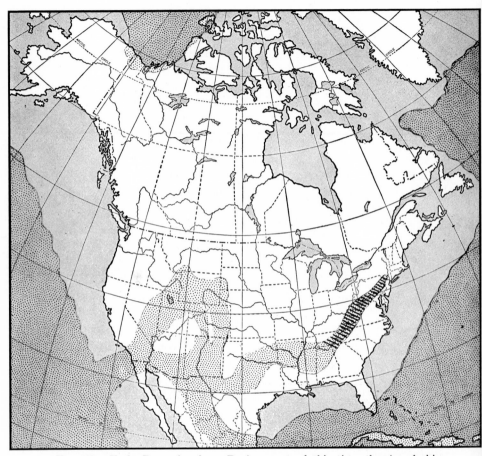

FIG. 137. Early Pennsylvanian. During most of this time the Appalachian Trough was slightly above sea level, with the result that immense coal swamps (indicated by darker shading) existed in the area. There were occasional inroads of the shallow sea into the trough. The connection to the open ocean was probably via the southwest.

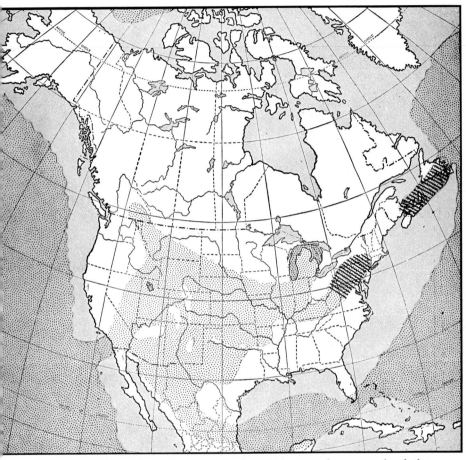

Fig. 138. Middle Pennsylvanian. The inland sea spread over much of the continent at the same time that the coal swamps (indicated by darker shading) increased in extent. As during the Early Pennsylvanian, there were occasional inroads of the sea into these swamps. See Figure 157 for the distribution of these swamps.

FIGS. 139, 140. Highly eroded red sandstone of Pennsylvanian age. Magdalen Islands, Gulf of St. Lawrence.

sylvania and possibly parts of northern New Jersey were probably covered by bituminous coal.

Not all the deposits of Pennsylvanian time were coal bearing. As shown in the maps (Figures 137 and 138), large parts of the North American continent were covered by a sea. There were also extensive deposits of nonmarine sandstone near the northeast entrance of the old Appalachian geosyncline. Some of these Pennsylvanian sandstones on the Magdalen Islands are constantly being eroded by the waters of the Gulf of St. Lawrence (Figures 139 and 140).

What is Coal?—"Coal," says Ashley, "is a rock, lying in beds in the earth, derived from the partial decomposition of masses of vegetable matter. Chemically it consists principally of carbon, hydrogen, oxygen, nitrogen, and some other substances. By heating, it may be broken up into moisture, combustible volatile matter (gas), fixed or free(?) carbon, and ash."

Theoretically, coal could have accumulated during any geological period when plants were sufficiently abundant. Local deposits of coal are known in formations both older and younger than the Carboniferous, but it was in this period, particularly during the Pennsylvanian, when coal formation was especially widespread. The many freshwater swamps, the mild climate, and the luxuriant vegetation, combined to form perfect conditions for the formation of coal. The vegetation of the Pennsylvanian swamps accumulated so rapidly that tremendous quantities of peat were formed, which were later covered by thick layers of sedimentary rocks. The heat and pressure caused by this load eventually changed the peat to lignite, and finally to bituminous coal.

The change of the plants into the mineral product is a slow and complicated process which occurs under water or any other covering that will protect the dead fibers from the air. Peat, the first step in the formation of coal, was formed very rapidly in the three deltas of the Appalachian basin, Pennsylvania, West Virginia, and Alabama. West of the Cincinnati Arch, which still persisted at this time, there were similar swamps which gave rise to the coal beds of the Illinois basin and the Mid-Continent region. Farther north, there was the smaller isolated Acadian Basin which produced the coal fields of New Brunswick, Nova Scotia, and Cape Breton Island.

Comparison is often made between the coal swamps of Pennsylvania and the present Dismal Swamp of Virginia and North Carolina. The analogy is good if one disregards the differences in vegetation between that of the coal swamps and that which exists in the present

Dismal Swamp. In both cases we have luxuriant vegetation with the rapid accumulation of peat.

The following geological period, the Permian, was a time of diastrophism or mountain building in the region of the former Appalachian geosyncline. The additional heat and pressure caused by this crustal movement was sufficient to change the bituminous (soft) coal to anthracite (hard) coal. During this process, many of the gases present in bituminous coal escaped, which is one of the main differences between the two kinds of coal. The anthracite coal beds of eastern Pennsylvania are remnants of swamp deposits of this period that have been folded and metamorphosed and which, fortunately for our modern industry, were not completely eroded away.

Lower Pennsylvanian

Pottsville Group.—During Early Pennsylvanian (Pottsville) time the Appalachian Trough in Pennsylvania was slowly but intermittently sinking. This sinking was very pronounced in the eastern part of the state and to the south, while in western Pennsylvania the land was somewhat higher. Then the whole region sank. The result was that the lower eastern portion was covered by sediments 1,000 feet thick, while the higher western part only had sediments between 100 and 300 feet thick. Most of these sediments were of swamp or freshwater origin, but occasionally, during short intervals, the subsidence was relatively faster and resulted in local invasions of the sea. This accounts for the layers of marine fossils interbedded with the coal and shale of terrestrial origin. Some Pottsville shales and sandstones form crests in the Allegheny Mountains.

The extensive coal swamps of Pennsylvanian time which probably extended across eastern Pennsylvania into northern New Jersey have been removed during the long periods of erosion that followed Carboniferous time. No deposits occur today in New Jersey between the Upper Devonian and the Triassic. In New York, a few deposits of Pennsylvanian age are known from the southwestern portion of the state. These consist of the Olean conglomerate and the Sharon shale, both equivalent in age to the Pottsville group of Pennsylvania. A few thin streaks of coal have been reported in the Sharon, but these are of no commercial value. Extensive coal swamps, however, did exist in New England and Nova Scotia. The coal in the former is of little or no commercial value, while the deposits of Nova Scotia constitute eastern Canada's main supply of coal.

Southward from Pennsylvania, the Pottsville deposits are much thicker, reaching a thickness of about 5,000 feet in Virginia and 7,000 feet in Alabama. It does not follow that the coal is thicker and better in the south; many of the rocks of Pottsville age are sandstones and shales of no commercial value.

The Pottsville formation is named from Pottsville, in the anthracite region of Pennsylvania. A great many individual coal layers have been mapped and named, and in many cases correlations have been made with the zones of the bituminous fields of western Pennsylvania. The Lykens (#2 Lykens Valley) coal beds of the anthracite region were deposited while dry land existed in the western (bituminous) part of the state; otherwise, there are probably equivalent coal formations in the two regions.

Upper Pennsylvanian

Allegheny, Conemaugh, and Monongahela Groups.—Deposition of coal, shales, sandstones, and occasional limestone continued throughout Pennsylvanian time. Three groups younger than the Pottsville have been recognized in both the anthracite and bituminous fields of Pennsylvania, although they are more conspicuous in the western part of the state.

The Allegheny or "Lower Productive Coal Measures" are 300 feet thick with about 12 coal beds, of which seven are important. Above the Allegheny is the Conemaugh or "Lower Barren Coal Measures," 600 to 900 feet thick, with 75 beds of sandstone, shale, coal, clay, and limestone. The coal, however, is only of local value. The uppermost Pennsylvanian group in the state is the Monongahela or "Upper Productive Coal Measures," from 300 to 460 feet in thickness. The important Pittsburgh coal seam is at the base of this group. Other coal beds in the Monongahela group are interbedded with shales and limestones, some of which contain marine fossils. This is further evidence of the fluctuation between swamp and marine conditions during Pennsylvanian time.

Principal Coal Fields of North America

Pennsylvania Anthracite Field.—Anthracite occurs in four irregular basins in northeastern Pennsylvania. "The basins are the bottoms of folds into which the coal beds and adjoining rocks were thrown at the end of Carboniferous time. The upper parts of the folds were carried away during the long period of erosion that followed the folding." [1] As a rule the coal beds are thicker than those of the

---

[1] George Ashley, *A Syllabus of Pennsylvania Geology and Mineral Resources,* Pennsylvania Topog. and Geol. Surv. Bull. G-1 (1931), p. 92.

bituminous fields. The Mammoth bed averages between 35 and 40 feet in thickness, and at one place is as much as 114 feet thick because of folding.

Although this field covers less than 500 square miles, it has produced to date about one fourth of the coal mined in the United States. Unfortunately, more than half of the coal of the anthracite beds has now been mined, and the field will probably be exhausted in about 300 years. The most important anthracite mines are in the vicinity of Mount Carmel, Shamokin, Carbondale, Scranton, and Hazelton.

Appalachian Bituminous Field.—This field underlies the Allegheny Plateau from northern Pennsylvania to Alabama. The most important coal mines are in Pennsylvania and West Virginia, but other important mines occur in Ohio, Kentucky, and Alabama. In contrast to the anthracite region, the strata are flat and have not been folded. The coal usually occurs in thin seams, of which the most important is the Pittsburgh. It is a seam about 10 feet thick that underlies an area of 6,000 square miles in western Pennsylvania, eastern Ohio, and northwestern West Virginia. This is one of the most important mineral beds of the world.

Illinoian Field.—This coal was formed in a shallow basin in central Illinois, southwestern Indiana, and western Kentucky. It usually occurs in thin seams.

Mid-Continent Field.—This field covers parts of Missouri, Iowa, Kansas, Oklahoma, and Texas. Although covering a greater area than the Appalachian field, it is of much less importance because of the thinner seams of coal (less than 4 feet).

Rhode Island and Massachusetts.—There is a small coal basin in Rhode Island, near Narragansett Bay. However, extreme metamorphism has in most cases altered the coal to graphite of very little fuel value. A very poor grade of graphitic coal was formerly obtained near Worcester, Massachusetts.

New Brunswick.—Coal is mined at Minto, New Brunswick. However, because it contains excess amounts of sulphur, it is not extensively used commercially.

Nova Scotia.—Although the Acadian beds are small in extent, they are very thick, up to 13,000 feet. Of course, this is not entirely coal, and the various layers are interbedded in the sandstones and shales. The average thickness of the coal layers is five feet. A coal mine at Spring Hill, near Amherst, Nova Scotia, has shafts 13,000 feet in length to a maximum depth of 4,000 feet, the deepest coal mine in North America. Near Sydney, Cape Breton Island, the mines extend some three miles beneath the bottom of Cabot Strait. The maximum depth of these mines is 2,500 feet.

Coal Fields of Other Ages.—Coal was formerly mined from the Triassic (Newark group) in Virginia and North Carolina; a rather inferior grade of coal is mined from Jurassic rocks in Greenland, while fairly extensive deposits of coal are known from Cretaceous and Eocene formations in western United States and Canada. We have already mentioned the important deposits of coal in Mississippian (Pocono) rocks in Virginia, and that coal was formerly mined from Mississippian rocks in Pennsylvania.

Pennsylvanian Life

As was the case with the Mississippian, examples of the marine life of the period have to be taken, in general, from the Mississippi Valley.

Fig. 141. A Pennsylvanian coal swamp. In the right foreground is a large scale tree or *Lepidodendron*. Other characteristic coal plants such as *Calamites,* the fern *Pectopteris,* and *Cordaites* can be seen. A stegocephalian amphibian is in the foreground. (J. P. Cowan, Hughes Tool Co.)

On the other hand, examples of the flora of the time are largely taken from the coal beds of Pennsylvania and adjacent states (Figure 141).

Protozoa.—Foraminifera continued to be important. The fusilinids, relatively large bottom-dwelling forms about the size and shape of a

FIG. 142. *Fusilina* sp., characteristic foraminifera of Pennsylvanian age.

wheat grain, were so abundant that they formed limestones in many areas (Figures 142 and 143). Smaller types of foraminifera were also present, and these, together with the fusilinids, are good index fossils.

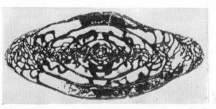

FIG. 143. Enlarged cross section of *Fusilina* sp.

They are frequently used by oil geologists to spot subsurface formations.

Sponges.—These were common in Kansas and Texas.

Corals.—Corals were not conspicuous in Pennsylvanian seas. Those that were present were mostly small, solitary types (Figures 144 and 145). For some reason which is not entirely clear, the climate in Spitsbergen in the Arctic Ocean must have been relatively mild, for extensive coral reefs were developed there during this period. Other coelenterates included the conularids of uncertain affinity, but probably related to the jellyfish (Figure 146).

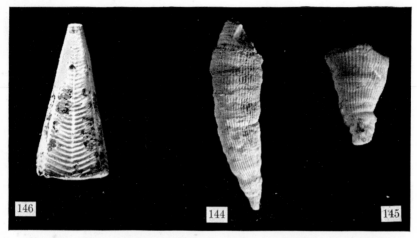

Fig. 144. Pennsylvanian coral *Lophophyllum profundum* from Texas.
Fig. 145. Pennsylvanian coral *Lophophyllum radisceum* from Texas.
Fig. 146. *Conularia crustula* from the Pennsylvanian of Texas.

Bryozoa.—These existed in great numbers, especially in Kansas.

Echinoderms.—Crinoids are abundant in Pennsylvanian rocks but are usually represented merely by fragments, especially stalks. The echinoids were more numerous than they were in the Mississippian, but are represented mainly by broken plates and spines. The blastoids, which had reached their peak during the Mississippian, were now on the road to extinction. In America they vanished during the Early Pennsylvanian, although in the East Indies they lived into Permian time.

Brachiopods.—Various genera of the family Productidae, of which were many species ornamented with spines, were the dominant brachiopods of the period.

Pelecypods and Gastropods.—Marine species were common, especially in the Mississippi Valley. Some land snails have been found associated with fossil wood at Joggins, Nova Scotia, and Braidwood, Illinois. Some fresh-water clams have also been found in the non-marine rocks of Nova Scotia and Illinois.

This is the first period in which mollusk shells were abundant and well preserved. Pennsylvanian shells were of calcite, and well suited for preservation, while the older species were probably composed of unstable aragonite.

Cephalopods.—The goniatite-like ammonites continued to exist and become more complex in structure, although they were not to reach any great complexity until the Permian and later periods. Nautiloids were present but were not conspicuous.

Trilobites.—The once-flourishing trilobites became almost extinct in Pennsylvanian time.

Ostracodes.—These small bivalved crustaceans were fairly abundant and their fossil remains exist today in many shales of this age. They make good index fossils, especially for the subsurface geologist.

Insects.—Fossil insects are fairly abundant in the coal measures of Belgium, and have occasionally been found in the United States, espe-

Fig. 147. Wing of Pennsylvanian insect from near Pottsville, Pennsylvania. (John Rehn.)

cially at Mazon Creek, Illinois. Many of these insects are of archaic types which are not living today, while others belong to existing groups such as the dragonflies and cockroaches. Some dragonflies of this period were exceptionally large, one species with a wingspread of 29 inches being known from the coal measures of Belgium. Some of the cockroaches reached a length of four inches. A collection of fossil insects from the Pennsylvania coal fields is now in the Natural History Museum at Reading, Pennsylvania (Figure 147).

The fact that the insects were represented by so many different families indicates that they must have had their origin in some earlier period. Very few insect fossils are known from Mississippian rocks, although a few fragments have been found in the Devonian of Rhynie, Scotland. Probably these more primitive insects were not composed of hard parts which would make them suitable for preservation as fossils.

Other Arthropods.—Eurypterids, king crabs (Limuloids), scorpions, spiders (Figure 148), and millipedes, have been found in concretions at Mazon Creek. One of the millipedes reached a length of 12 inches.

Fig. 148. Pennsylvanian spider, *Cleptomartus platus,* from England. (A. Petrunkievitch.)

Fish.—Fresh-water sharks, ganoids, and other fish are known from Linton, Ohio, Mazon Creek, and a few other places.

Amphibia.—Some eighty-eight species of amphibia belonging to extinct groups of Stegocephalia (Labyrinthodontia) and Lepospondyli have been described from the Pennsylvanian rocks of North America; of these, fifty species were from the shales at the base of the Freeport coal at Linton, Ohio. The majority of these amphibia were small, only a few inches in length. A few Pennsylvanian amphibia were much larger and may have reached a length of 10 feet. What was probably the largest of the group is *Onychopus gigas,* known only from its footprints in Mid-Pennsylvanian sandstone near Lawrence, Kansas. These footprints are five inches long, and it is thought that the animal may have weighed several hundred pounds.

Reptiles.—A few small reptiles are known from Pennsylvanian rocks near Linton, Mazon Creek, and in Texas, but the group did not reach any importance until the Permian.

Plants.—Vegetation was very luxuriant in the jungle-like swamps of this age. Although some of the plants reproduced by seeds, the majority were spore-bearing types. Since cannel coal consists of the remains of spore cases, these structures must have been very abundant at certain times. Among the various kinds of plants present in the Pennsylvanian swamps were the following:

Ferns (Pteridophyta). Some of these were very large, reaching a height of 50 feet, with fronds measuring five or six feet. Probably the most common genus was *Archaeopteris* (Figure 151).

Seed Ferns (Pteridospermatophyta). These fern-like plants reproduced by seeds instead of spores. They were more common than the true ferns, and can only be distinguished from them when the fruiting fronds are present. *Pecopteris, Neuropteris,* and *Alethopteris* are probably the most abundant genera from the Pennsylvania coal fields (Figures 152 and 154).

Rushes (Arthrophyta). These plants reached the size of trees, probably three feet in diameter and 100 feet high. They were characterized by their jointed stems and vertical ribbing. Whorls of leaves called annularia (Figures 149 and 155) were developed at each joint. These annularia are frequently detached and found as fossils away from the stalks, as if they had blown away. The most common genus of this plant is *Calamites* (Figure 150) which is very abundant in the shales between the coal beds, in both the anthracite and bituminous fields of Pennsylvania. The modern descendant of these rushes is the small horsetail or *Equisetum.*

Scale Trees (Lepidophyta). These were the giants of the coal swamps, some having trunks six feet in diameter and a height of 100 feet. Although not true trees in the botanical sense, they took the place of trees in the association. The leaves of these trees were attached closely to the trunk; when the leaves fell off, permanent scars were left on the trunk. These leaf scars give a scaly appearance and amateur collectors have brought to museums specimens which they thought were fossil snakes or fish, only to find that they were trunks or branches of these scale trees.

The most common scale tree was *Lepidodendron* (Figures 153 and 156). It had a small slender trunk, branching frequently near the crown, which contained leaves like large pine needles. *Sigillaria,* another common genus, was usually unbranched, and possessed a thicker trunk, with vertical ribbing and leaf scars arranged in vertical rows. A third conspicuous genus is *Cordaites,* named after the Bohemian botanist Corda. This plant had a slender trunk with branches only near the top. The blade-like leaves were often six feet long and as much as 15 inches in width.

Plants of Pennsylvanian age are frequently world wide in distribution, indicating that they may have migrated from continent to continent over ancient land bridges.

PENNSYLVANIAN COAL PLANTS

Fig. 149. *Annularia.*
Fig. 150. *Calamites.*

Fig. 151. Fern.
Fig. 152. Seed fern (*Alethopteris*).

PENNSYLVANIAN COAL PLANTS

Fig. 153. *Lepidodendron.*
Fig. 154. True fern.

Fig. 155. *Annularia.*
Fig. 156. *Lepidodendron* branches.

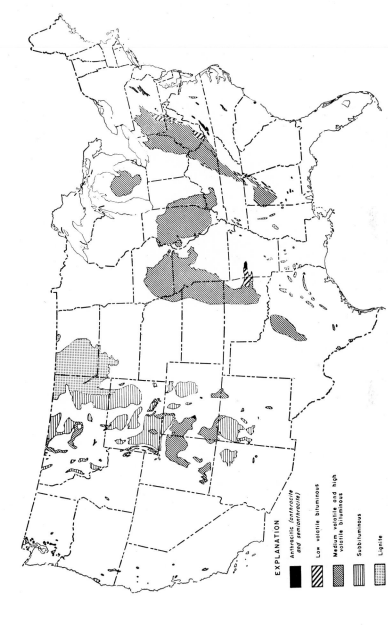

FIG. 157. Coal fields of the United States. Except for the small Triassic fields in Virginia and North Carolina, the fields in the eastern part of the country are all of Carboniferous age. The fields in the west are of Cretaceous and Eocene age, and the lignite area in the Dakotas and Montana is of Eocene age. (U.S. Geol. Surv.)

EXPLANATION

Anthracitic (anthracite and semianthracite)

Low volatile bituminous

Medium volatile and high volatile bituminous

Subbituminous

Lignite

Economic Resources of the Pennsylvanian

Coal.—This most important of all Pennsylvanian economic resources (Figure 157) has been fully discussed in the main part of this chapter.

Petroleum.—Petroleum is obtained in great quantities from rocks of this age, especially in Kansas, Oklahoma, Texas, and Wyoming. A small amount of oil and gas is obtained from Pennsylvanian rocks in western Pennsylvania and West Virginia.

Other Products.—Pennsylvanian rocks are locally important for Portland cement, plastic clay, iron ore, and gypsum. Clay suitable for firebrick is frequently found below coal beds, the result of the action of the swamp waters of Pennsylvanian soil.

FURTHER READING

The references for Chapters 10–16 will be found at the end of Chapter 16.

CHAPTER 16

THE PERMIAN

The name "Permian" was proposed in 1841 by the British geologist Sir Roderick Murchison, who took the name from the province of Perm, on the west flank of the Ural Mountains in Russia. It was here that Murchison found marine deposits of this age overlying the coal measures in a horizontal plane.

	Pennsylvania	New Jersey	New York
UPPER	—	—	—
LOWER	Dunkard	—	—

With the exception of those of the Southwest, most Permian deposits of the United States were, until relatively recently, included with the Pennsylvanian. In many places, particularly in the eastern United States, there is no break between the Pennsylvanian and the Permian deposits.

Early Permian History of Eastern North America

At the beginning of the Permian, Appalachia still extended from Newfoundland to Mexico, but had been eroded considerably and was no longer the extremely high continent it had been during the early and middle Paleozoic (Figure 158). The Appalachian geosyncline was also near the end of its existence. It consisted of a broad alluvial plain, from which westward flowing streams brought sediment toward a retreating sea. The Permian sediments deposited in this sea constitute the Dunkard group of southwestern Pennsylvania, southeastern Ohio, and northwestern West Virginia. These deposits probably extended over a wider area, but later erosion has restricted them to their present limited distribution.

The Dunkard group is largely alluvial, and contains some coal beds with numerous fossil plants, as well as a few fossil insects. Some brachiopods and shark spines have been found in Monongalia County,

217

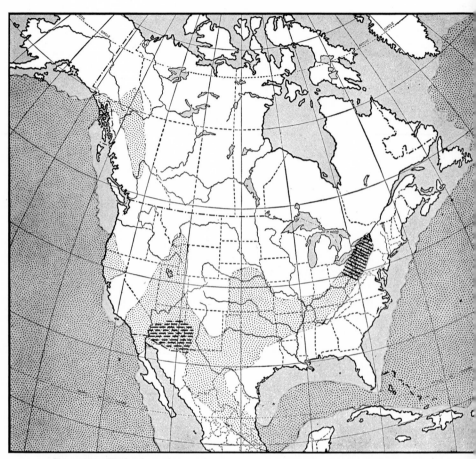

FIG. 158. Early Permian. The sea covered portions of the interior of the continent, notably the "Kansas Dead Sea." A narrow arm of salt water extended northeastward to Ohio and Pennsylvania, although during most of Early Permian time the region was swampy and above sea level. The Appalachian Revolution took place at the end of Permian time.

West Virginia. These indicate that there was probably marine or brackish water in the geosyncline, at least temporarily.

There are no records in eastern North America of any Permian history after the deposition of the Dunkard group. We can therefore assume that the Appalachian Trough was entirely filled and that Appalachia was so thoroughly eroded that no more material was deposited along its western edge.

The Appalachian Revolution

By far the most important event that took place in eastern North America during Permian time was the formation of the Appalachian Mountains. Ever since the beginning of the Paleozoic, sediments carried from the highlands of Appalachia on the east and from the continental area on the west had been accumulating in the Appalachian geosyncline. Over the 400 million years from the Cambrian to the Permian, it is estimated that more than 25,000 feet of limestone, sandstone, shales, and other sediments accumulated in this trough! As we have stated in previous chapters, this tremendous load, estimated by Ashley as 250,000 cubic *miles*, frequently caused the floor of the trough to sink. The total sinking of the floor of the trough has been estimated at between five and eight miles. At this depth the originally hard rocks encountered temperatures which were high enough to melt some of them.

Whether it was because of the melting of some of the lower formations in the former trough, or because of some other less-understood reason or reasons, the beginning of the Permian was a period of great uplift and folding. The pressure to form this folding apparently came from the southeast and moved slowly toward the northwest, causing the rocks to rise into more and more folds as the movement gained headway. As the pressure increased, these folds became higher and steeper and many rocks which originally had been laid down in a horizontal plane were now vertical. Some rocks were even overturned by a series of thrust faults of apparently great intensity, and Cambrian and Pre-Cambrian rocks were carried many miles to the west where they came to rest on rocks of much later age. The Blue Ridge Thrust Fault can be traced for 700 miles from Pennsylvania to Alabama. Here Cambrian or Pre-Cambrian rocks overlie younger Paleozoic rocks. A somewhat more local thrust fault can be seen at Birmingham, Centre County, Pennsylvania, where Cambrian rocks overlie the Ordovician.

Granite and other igneous rocks were intruded during this period of mountain building. In most cases it is difficult or even impossible to differentiate between these Permian intrusions and those of the Pre-Cambrian. The granites of the Piedmont region of eastern Pennsylvania are generally thought to be mainly of Pre-Cambrian age, while the somewhat similar granites in the Piedmont area of North Carolina, Georgia, as well as in parts of New England, may be of Permian or Late Carboniferous age.

Ashley gives a rather striking analogy to explain the Appalachian Revolution by comparing the state of Pennsylvania to a series of long rugs laid down on a floor.

> Imagine 20 or 30 long rugs on the floor, one on top of another, and then getting down on your knees and beginning to push one end of the pile, and the other end being against a wall. The folds made in the rugs would resemble those made in the rock strata of the earth's crust.
>
> The folding, at first all at the east, gradually spread westward. As folds became vertical, the pressure acted across the folds and not with the bedding and some of the folds broke and one part overrode another, sometimes for several miles. In places, soft beds, like shales, simply crumpled up.[1]

The intensity of the folding gradually died out as it progressed westward and the folds almost disappear in the western part of Pennsylvania. We have noted in a previous chapter how the Pennsylvanian rocks west of the Allegheny escarpment are horizontal in contrast to the folded rocks of eastern and central Pennsylvania.

This mountain building caused a lineal shortening. To return to Ashley's analogy: "Just as when you push on the end of a pile of rugs, until they take up less floor space, the Appalachian Revolution greatly shortened Pennsylvania possibly by 100 miles, according to rough estimates. The rocks under Philadelphia may have originally underlain what is now the Atlantic Ocean."[2]

No accurate estimate of the height of these Permian Appalachian Mountains can be given. If some of the folds were restored they would probably project five miles or more above sea level. However, it is probable that this folding process was very gradual, requiring millions of years, so the folds may never have reached their full height, but were eroded into a series of rugged mountain peaks, not unlike the Alps or Himalayas of today. A series of diagrams illustrating the geological history of the Appalachian Mountains is shown in Figure 159.

The great pressure that was at least partly responsible for the Appalachian Revolution, caused considerable metamorphism to take

[1] George Ashley, *A Syllabus of Pennsylvania Geology and Mineral Resources.* Pennsylvania Topog. and Geol. Surv. Bull. G-1 (1931), p. 70.
[2] *Ibid.,* p. 71.

place, particularly in eastern Pennsylvania. Many of the shales (for instance, those of the Martinsburg formation of Ordovician age) were changed to slates, the limestones to marble, and the sandstones to schists. The coal deposits in the region affected by the mountain building were distilled and the gases driven off, with the result that the coal of eastern Pennsylvania is now anthracite, while that of an

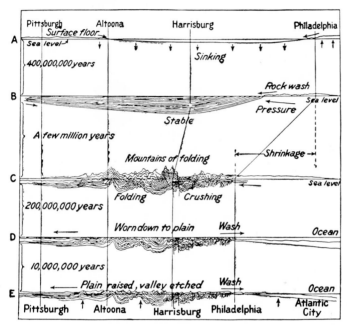

Fig. 159. Chart showing principal events in the history of the Appalachian Mountains of Pennsylvania. (Penna. Topog. and Geol. Surv.)

equivalent age in the western part of the state is bituminous. Any oil or gas formed in Devonian (or older) rocks in eastern Pennsylvania was completely distilled and destroyed, which explains the absence of such materials in the eastern part of the state.

In New Jersey, the effect of the disturbances was greatest in the southeastern part of the folded area, as shown by the fact that the Paleozoic rocks are more distorted southeast of the Highlands than in the Kittatinny Valley. In New England and the Maritime provinces of eastern Canada, earlier disturbances, especially the Taconic (Ordovician) and Acadian (Devonian), had already distorted the rocks of the northeast end of the geosyncline. This folding and uplift was further complicated during the Permian uplift, with the result that it is extremely difficult to separate the various crustal movements. We do know, however, that in New Jersey, Pennsylvania, and the southern Appalachian region the mountain building dates entirely from the Appalachian Revolution. It is possible that some of this folding actually took place during the Late Pennsylvanian, but since the Dunkard deposits of southwestern Pennsylvania actually show a slight folding, it seems probable that most of the mountain building took place after Early Permian time. It may have continued into the Early Triassic, although this is doubtful since there was a very long period of erosion before the deposition of the Newark beds of Late Triassic age. It is generally believed that the climax of this mountain building took place at the end of the Permian.

Permian History of Central and Western North America

Mid-Continent Area.—During Early Permian time, the sea covered the Mid-Continent area. As was the case with the Dunkard group, here also there was a gradual transition between the Pennsylvanian and Permian. This inland sea seems to have been very extensive, and, judging by the presence of some remnants of Permian rocks, may have extended eastward to join the alluvial deposits of the Dunkard. This connection, if it existed, may account for the presence of the brachiopods in West Virginia. The outlet of this sea was probably to the southwest across Oklahoma and Texas and then southeast to the present Gulf of Mexico. As far as we know at present, there was then no outlet from the Dunkard basin except to the west. At any rate, the southern part of the Appalachian Trough had been elevated, blocking the sea connection to the southeast.

The Ouachita and Arbuckle mountains of Arkansas and Oklahoma are thought to have been folded and uplifted at about the same time that the Appalachians were being formed in the East. Probably some other local uplifts and folding took place at this time.

During the course of Permian time, deltaic material washed from the recently elevated Ouachita and Arbuckle mountains into the Mid-Continent arm of the sea, reducing the width of the seaway to a strait. The oceanic waters could not flow freely to and from this inland Permian sea.

The climate became arid and the inland sea too saline for marine life. Great deposits of salt accumulated in the basin, frequently spoken of as the "Kansas Dead Sea." An occasional break through the barrier probably allowed more salt water to enter, but it was quickly evaporated, forming increasing amounts of salt and gypsum. The basin gradually filled with salt and mud, and later with red muds and sands spread out by fresh-water streams. These form the "redbeds" that overlie the salt. By the middle of the Permian, this Mid-Continent sea became extinct.

Permian Basin of Texas and New Mexico.—Long after the Mid-Continent sea (Kansas Dead Sea) had dried up, deposition continued in the so-called Permian Basin of west Texas and southeastern New Mexico. Almost continuous records of the Permian can be found in this area, and sediments (mostly marine) 14,000 feet in thickness are known. The history was very complex and need not concern us further here. The deposits of the Permian Basin are important sources of oil and potash salt. It is worthy of note that the Carlsbad Caverns of southeastern New Mexico were formed by solution or dissolving of limestone deposits of this Permian sea.

Far West.—Marine waters existed in part of the Cordilleran Trough during the Early Permian, and in Middle or Later Permian a new trough extended across British Columbia into Washington and Oregon. There was also a Permian sea in portions of Alaska. Volcanoes were active during the Permian in eastern California, western Nevada and Idaho, and eastern Idaho.

Climate

Although little evidence is available from eastern North America, studies in other parts of the world reveal a wide variation in climatic conditions during the Permian period.

Deserts.—Desert conditions existed during part of Permian time, causing tremendous accumulations of salt from Kansas to New Mexico. These deposits are not continuous, and the salt dates from various parts of the Permian. Similar Permian salt deserts existed in Germany and in Russia. These three regions contain the world's greatest deposits of salt.

Glaciation.—The Permian was a period of great contrasts. Although vast areas of the world had an arid climate, other parts were covered with immense ice sheets. The strange thing about the Permian glaciations is that they were largely distributed in southern land masses, rather than in the polar regions. Permian tillite and other evidences of glaciation are known from South Africa, Australia, Brazil, Argentina, and India. The reasons for this remarkable distribution of ice sheets is not clear. At least some of these glaciers may have been connected with newly uplifted mountains. At Squantum, near

Boston, Massachusetts, there is a deposit of tillite that is thought to have been brought by a valley glacier from the rising Appalachian Mountains.

Gondwana Land Bridge

The wide distribution of certain Permian plants, especially *Glossopteris*, in South America, Africa, and India, has been taken as an indication that there was a land bridge connecting these proto-continents during this period. This bridge, sometimes enlarged in theory to a sunken continent, has been called Gondwana. Evidence for the existence of a large continent in the South Atlantic is difficult to obtain, but it is entirely possible that there was a temporary isthmus or island arc connecting Africa with South America.

Permian Life

As was the case with the Mississippian and Pennsylvanian, most of our examples of Permian life (Figure 160) will of necessity be drawn from outside of eastern North America, since the records of the Permian life of this region are very limited and consist chiefly of land and brackish water species.

Plants.—Because of the increased aridity during much of Permian time, the flora, as a whole, declined. However, the plants of the Early Permian (Dunkard) of Pennsylvania, West Virginia, and Ohio were not very different from those of the Pennsylvanian. As Permian time progressed, the large species of *Lepidodendron, Calamites, Sigillaria,* and other characteristic coal plants disappeared from the scene, and their place was taken by more modern types of vegetation.

In contrast to the above-mentioned flora of the warm coal forests that prevailed in certain regions during part of Permian time, the flora characteristic of the Southern Hemisphere was quite possibly a response to the cooler climate caused by local glaciation. This group of plants, known as the *Glossopteris* flora, named from the fern-like leaves of the genus *Glossopteris* (phylum Pteridospermatophyta) was characteristic of Late Permian time. The importance of the *Glossopteris* flora as an indication of a possible Permian land bridge between South America and Africa has already been discussed.

Protozoa.—Foraminifera, particularly the spindle-shaped fusilinids, continued to flourish in the Permian seas of the Mid-Continent and Texas area. They differed not too greatly from their Pennsylvanian ancestors and, like them, are valuable today as markers of subsurface formations. They thus play an important part in the petroleum geology of the country.

Corals.—Conditions during the Permian were generally unfavorable for coral reefs, with the result that corals were not very abundant.

Fig. 160. The Permian Period. The reptile *Noasaurus,* a close relative of *Dimetrodon,* is shown devouring a small amphibian. The ferns and calamites are survivors from the Carboniferous period that had adjusted themselves to the Permian aridity. (J. P. Cowan, Hughes Tool Co.)

The average Permian corals were small solitary animals, while several groups, including the tetracorals and honeycombs (*Favosites*), became extinct.

Echinoderms.—The blastoids were now extinct, and the crinoids were reduced in numbers.

Bryozoa.—These were common, and closely related to their Pennsylvanian ancestors.

Brachiopoda.—The family Productidae, which had been so plentiful during the Mississippian and Pennsylvanian, was still present at the beginning of the Permian, but became extinct during this period. Some highly specialized and ornamented types of brachiopods were present in the Permian seas. One very aberrant genus was *Richthofenia*, which closely resembled a cup coral. Although the Permian is frequently thought of as a time of limited life because of the arid and otherwise unfavorable climates, the life of the Permian seas, when normal conditions existed, was exceedingly rich, and brachiopods made up a large portion of the fauna. A few specimens of *Lingula*, a brackish-water genus, are known from the Dunkard rocks of Ohio and West Virginia.

Mollusks.—Gastropods and pelecypods were present in the Permian seas, especially in those which covered what is now west Texas

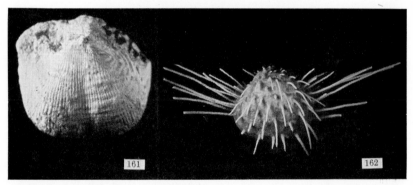

Fig. 161. Brachiopod *Dictyoclostus burlingtonensis,* Quincy, Illinois.
Fig. 162. Pelecypod etched from Permian limestone. (G. A. Cooper.)

and New Mexico. An extensive Permian fauna has been obtained from the vicinity of the Glass Mountains in west Texas. Here the shells are embedded in a dense limestone but can be obtained in perfect condition by a process of etching the rock with acid (Figures 161 and 162). The ammonites showed a marked advance during Permian time. More and more elaborate sutures were developed. In fact, it might be said that the first typical ammonites made their appearance during this period.

Crustacea.—The trilobites, as we have learned, became extinct during Permian time, very few forms having been reported from the rocks of this period. While other crustaceans were present in Permian time, their fossil remains are rare.

Why did the trilobites become extinct? Perhaps it was because many large cephalopods devoured great quantities of these crusta-

ceans, who lost out in the struggle for the "survival of the fittest."
Or their extinction may have been due to the ascendency of the fishes
which also undoubtedly made great inroads into the numbers of trilobites. On the other hand, the trilobites may have died out merely because of the age of the race. A study of the geological history of almost any group of animals shows that they are rare when they make
their first appearance on the scene. They gradually increase in numbers and species until they reach a peak of evolution. Then the group
as a whole goes into a decline, becoming less and less abundant both
in numbers of individuals and species until they finally disappear entirely. Undoubtedly, the trilobites were declining by the end of the
Devonian, and the advent of the voracious cephalopods and fish may
only have served to hasten their inevitable doom.

Insects.—Insects were fairly common during the Permian, although
there were none of the gigantic types of the Pennsylvanian. Because
of the delicate structure of the wings and other parts of their bodies,
their fossil remains are rarely found. In one layer near Elmo, Kansas,
however, more than 10,000 specimens have been found, including May
flies, dragonflies, cockroaches, and several other groups. A few fossil
insects have been found in the rocks of the Dunkard series in West
Virginia and Ohio.

Fish.—Both fresh- and salt-water fish lived during Permian time.
Sharks are known by their innumerable teeth found in the Permian
rocks of Texas, and from this same area we have some good examples
of the crossopterygian *Megalichthys.*

Amphibia.—Skeletal remains of stegocephalians (labyrinthodonts)
and lepospondyls (ancestors of the salamanders) have been found in
"fossil waterholes" in the red beds of Texas and Oklahoma. These
ancient amphibians probably were caught when these waterholes dried
up during droughts of Permian time. The stegocephalians had heavy
bodies, broad flat skulls, and rather weak legs. They were probably
sluggish in habit and rarely exceeded 10 feet in length.

Reptiles.—Although they had not yet reached their evolutionary
climax, reptiles were the undisputed rulers of the land during Permian
time. Many and varied kinds of reptiles lived during this period,
judging from the fossils found in the Permian rocks of Texas, New
Mexico, and Oklahoma. Many other Permian fossil reptiles have been
found in South Africa, India, and northern Russia. Some of them
were well on their way to the bizarre shapes that were to be so prominent during Triassic, Jurassic, and Cretaceous times. The Permian

reptiles of North America are mainly pelycosaurs and cotylosaurs, while those from the old world are mainly therapsids.

The North American cotylosaurs include *Seymouria* and *Limno-scelis,* and among the pelycosaurs are *Dimetrodon* (Figure 163) and *Edaphosaurus.* Footprints of *Dimetrodon* and *Baropus* have been found in rocks of the Dunkard series in West Virginia, and a skeleton of *Dimetrodon* was found many years ago on Prince Edward Island.

Fig. 163.   Restoration of the Permian reptile *Dimetrodon.*

While the majority of these reptiles crawled on the ground, a few became adapted to an aquatic existence.

Ancestors of the Mammals.—One interesting and important group of Permian reptiles is the theriodonts. These strange animals, known only from South Africa, are thought to represent a "missing link" between the reptiles and the mammals. Although they still possessed many reptile characteristics, they may be regarded as the ancestors of the mammals because their leg bones, teeth, and skulls had certain characteristics suggestive of mammals. Very little is known of these primitive animals. Their fossils are rare and they have only been found in the Karroo series of South Africa, which dates from Late Permian and Early Triassic times. It seems possible that the favorable Permian climate of South Africa was responsible for the evolutionary advance of the reptiles to the mammals.

Economic Resources of the Permian

Petroleum.—The oil fields of the "Permian Basin" in southern Oklahoma and the Texas Panhandle are of great economic importance. Oil is also obtained from other Permian fields in Kansas and Wyoming.

Potash.—This product is obtained from Permian rocks of west Texas and southeastern New Mexico.

Coal.—The Dunkard beds of western Pennsylvania and West Virginia are important for their deposits of coal. (See Chapter 15.)

Salt and Gypsum.—Extensive Permian salt deposits are known in Kansas, Oklahoma, Texas, and New Mexico, while gypsum beds occur in Iowa, Oklahoma, Kansas, New Mexico, Texas, Colorado, and South Dakota.

Phosphate.—This is obtained from the Phosphoria limestone of Idaho and Wyoming.

FURTHER READING FOR CHAPTERS 10–16

ASHLEY, GEORGE H. *A Syllabus of Pennsylvania Geology and Mineral Resources.* Pennsylvania Topog. and Geol. Surv. Bull. G-1 (1931).

BONNINE, C. A., and HONESS, A. P. "Bentonite in Pennsylvania," *Proc. Penn. Acad. Sci., III* (1929), pp. 18–25.

BUTTS, CHARLES. *Geology of the Appalachian Valley in Virginia.* Virginia Geol. Surv. Bull. 52 (1940).

———. "Geology of Alabama (Paleozoic)," *Geol. Surv. Ala. Special Report* 14 (1926), pp. 40–230.

CAMPBELL, M. R. *The Coal Fields of the United States.* U.S. Geol. Surv., Prof. Paper 100-A (1917).

CHENEY, M. G., *et al.* "Classification of Mississippian and Pennsylvanian Rocks of North America," *Bull. Amer. Assoc. Petrol. Geol.,* XXIX (1945), pp. 125–69.

CLEAVES, A. B., and ASHLEY, G. H. *Guidebook to the Geology of the Pennsylvania Turnpike.* Pennsylvania Topog. and Geol. Surv. Bull. G-20 (1942).

COLEMAN, A. P. *Ice Ages, Recent and Ancient.* New York: The Macmillan Co., 1929, Chs. 5–12.

COOPER, G. ARTHUR. "Correlation of the Devonian Sedimentary Formations of North America," *Bull. Geol. Soc. Amer.,* LIII (1942), pp. 1728–84.

DUNBAR, CARL O. *Historical Geology.* New York: John Wiley & Sons, Inc., 1949, Chs. 7–13.

EARDLEY, A. J. *Structural Geology of North America.* New York: Harper & Bros., 1951.

EMERSON, B. K. *Geology of Massachusetts and Rhode Island.* U.S. Geol. Surv. Bull. 597 (1917).

HOWELL, B. F. *Revision of the Upper Cambrian Faunas of New Jersey.* Geol. Soc. Amer. Memoir 12, 1945.

HOWELL, B. F., *et al.* "Correlation of the Cambrian Formations of North America," *Bull. Geol. Soc. Amer.,* LV (1944), pp. 993–1003.

Howell, B. F., Roberts, Henry, and Willard, Bradford. "Subdivision and Dating of the Cambrian of Eastern Pennsylvania," *Bull. Geol. Soc. Amer.,* LXI (1950), pp. 1355–68.

Kay, Marshall, et al. "Appalachian Basin Ordovician Symposium," *Bull. Amer. Assoc. Petrol. Geol.,* XXXII, No. 8 (1948), pp. 1395–1657. (Also published as a book by Amer. Assoc. Petrol. Geol., Tulsa.)

King, Philip B. *The Tectonics of Middle North America.* Princeton: Princeton University Press, 1951.

La Forge, L. *Geology of the Boston Area, Massachusetts.* U.S. Geol. Surv. Bull. 839 (1932).

Leighton, Henry. *Guidebook to the Geology about Pittsburgh.* Pennsylvania Topog. and Geol. Surv. Bull. G-17 (1939).

Lewis, J. V., and Kummel, H. B. *The Geology of New Jersey.* Geol. Surv. New Jersey, Bull. 50 (1940).

McGlothlin, T. "General Geology of Mississippi," *Bull. Amer. Assoc. Petrol. Geol.,* XXVIII (1944), pp. 29–62.

Miller, B. L. *Guidebook to Places of Geologic Interest in the Lehigh Valley, Pennsylvania.* Pennsylvania Topog. and Geol. Surv. Bull. G-16 (1939).

Moore, Raymond C. *Introduction to Historical Geology.* New York: McGraw-Hill Book Co., Inc., 1949, Chs. 5–12.

———. "Correlations of Pennsylvanian Formations of North America," *Bull. Geol. Soc. Amer.,* LV (1944), pp. 657–706.

Moore, Raymond C., and Thompson, M. L. "Main Divisions of Pennsylvanian Period and System," *Bull. Amer. Assoc. Petrol. Geol.,* XXXIII (1949), pp. 275–302.

Moodie, Roy L. *The Coal Measure Amphibia of North America.* Carnegie Inst. of Washington, Pub. 238 (1916).

Resser, C. E. *Cambrian System of the Southern Appalachians.* Geol. Soc. Amer., Special Paper 15 (1938).

Resser, C. E., and Howell, B. F. "Lower Cambrian Olenellus Zone of the Appalachians," *Bull. Geol. Soc. Amer.,* XLIX (1938), pp. 195–248.

Schuchert, Charles, and Dunbar, Carl O. *Stratigraphy of Western Newfoundland.* Geol. Soc. Amer. Special Paper 1 (1934).

Schuchert, Charles. *Stratigraphy of the Eastern and Central United States.* New York: John Wiley & Sons, Inc., 1943.

Tilton, John L. "Permian Vertebrate Tracks in West Virginia," *Bull. Geol. Soc. Amer.* XLII (1931), pp. 547–56.

Weiss, Judith. "Wissahickon Schist at Philadelphia, Pennsylvania," *Bull. Geol. Soc. Amer.,* LX (1940), pp. 1689–1726.

Weller, J. Marvin, et al. "Correlation of the Mississippian Formations of North America," *Bull. Geol. Soc. Amer.,* LIX (1948), pp. 91–196.

Weller, Stuart. *The Paleozoic Faunas.* Geol. Surv. New Jersey. Paleontology Vol. 3, 1903.

Willard, Bradford. *Highway Geology Philadelphia to Pittsburgh.* Pennsylvania Topog. and Geol. Surv. Bull. G-12, 1939.

———. *The Devonian of Pennsylvania.* Pennsylvania Topog. and Geol. Surv. Bull. G-19 (1939).

———. *Pennsylvania Geology Summarized.* Pennsylvania Topog. and Geol. Surv. Prog. Rept. 113 (1948).

CHAPTER 17

THE TRIASSIC

The name Triassic was first used by the German geologist F. von Alberti in 1834 for those deposits in Germany which were equivalent to the New Red Sandstone of England. This group of rocks occurs as a single unit in England, but becomes separated into three prominent units in Germany, hence the name "Trias." Although this threefold characteristic does not apply elsewhere in the world, the name Triassic has been universally used for all rocks of the earliest division of the Mesozoic era.

	Pennsylvania	New Jersey	New York
UPPER TRIASSIC	Newark group	Brunswick Lockatong Stockton	Newark
LOWER TRIASSIC		—	—

Lower Triassic

Little is known about the early Triassic history of eastern North America. Presumably the entire region, including at least part of the continental shelf, was above sea level. The Appalachian Mountains were probably high and majestic. At the same time, mountain remnants of Appalachia existed toward the east. Whatever sediments were deposited in the region between the two mountainous areas have apparently long since been eroded away, for we can find no records of their presence today. Apparently the Lower and Middle Triassic of eastern North America were largely periods of erosion.

Upper Triassic

About the middle of Triassic time, a widespread earth movement took place in this region (Figure 164). The old highlands of Appalachia to the east and the newer mountains to the west were both broadly uplifted, while even the region between the two mountainous

231

FIG. 164. Middle Triassic. Marine submergence was limited to the western part of the continent. See Figure 165 for distribution of continental and lake deposits of the Newark group.

areas may have risen slightly. This earth movement, probably accompanied by a series of normal faults, may have been a late or final phase of the Appalachian disturbances which had taken place during Permian time. This uplifting and faulting created a series of intermontane basins, or grabens, that lay between these two mountainous regions. Several such basins, probably not continuous, existed from

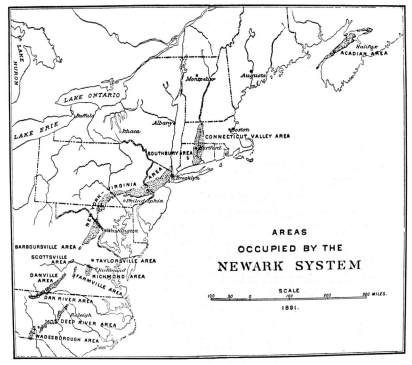

FIG. 165. Distribution of rocks of the Newark group. (U.S. Geol. Surv.)

Nova Scotia to North Carolina, and probably farther south. The distribution of these basins is shown in Figure 165.

The northernmost basin lay along the northwest coast of the Bay of Fundy in the present Province of Nova Scotia. Another important basin, whose width averaged about 25 miles, existed in the present Connecticut River valley. It extended from the northern edge of Massachusetts to Long Island Sound, a distance of about 100 miles. A third basin, and the one most thoroughly studied, extended from the mouth of the Hudson River near New York City southwestward across New Jersey into Pennsylvania, Maryland, and northern Virginia. There are several basin areas in Virginia that may or may not have been continuous, the most important being in the vicinity of

Richmond and Danville. Similar basins occur in North Carolina, and it is probable that they also occurred farther south, although much of the evidence for them is now deeply buried. The Triassic rocks of this entire group of basins make up the Newark group, named for the city of Newark, which is located in the New Jersey-Pennsylvania basin.

The New Jersey-Pennsylvania Basin.—Since this basin includes the type locality, it will be discussed first. Sediments began washing into this basin from both the northwest and southeast. Because of the quantities of mica and other minerals in the rocks of the Newark basin, it is generally thought that the majority of the sediments were carried into it from the Pre-Cambrian highlands to the southeast, the final remnants of ancient Appalachia. Other streams entered this basin from the northwest and brought down material from the up-lifted Paleozoic rocks that bordered the depression. It is generally believed that these streams were short and steep, with a powerful current. Their great carrying power enabled them to transport some fairly coarse boulders.

Three formations of Triassic age have been recognized in this basin. From the oldest to the youngest, they are the Stockton (2,300–3,100 feet thick), Lockatong (3,500 feet thick), and the Brunswick (6,000–8,000 feet thick). It is highly probable, although not entirely certain, that there were periods of erosion between the deposition of these formations. It is also possible that the sources of these three formations were slightly different. The Stockton consists primarily of light-colored sandstones and conglomerates, with interbedded red sandstones and shales; the Lockatong is largely hard black shale and argillite, while the Brunswick is chiefly soft red shale with some interbedded sandstone. However, there is considerable variation in the three formations. MacLaughlin and Willard have recently (1949) expressed the opinion that these three formations indicate facies changes rather than time units.

Igneous Action.—During the existence of these Triassic basins, igneous or volcanic activity occurred at least three times. There were two types of flows, extrusive and intrusive. The extrusive flows reached the surface of the land and then flowed quietly along the ground for some distance before they cooled and hardened. Such igneous rocks are conformable, or parallel, to the sedimentary rocks. At the close of the Triassic, when the rocks of the Newark Basin were titled, many of the softer sedimentary shales were eroded away, leaving the harder igneous rocks which form the Watchung Mountains today.

Whether or not there were actual volcanoes in the region at that time is not known, although it seems likely that some did exist; nevertheless, many of the extrusive flows reached the surface of the land through small vents or openings in the ground. The type of igneous rock extruded by these flows was chiefly basalt. Both diabase and basalt are locally known by the general name "trap," and are frequently quarried for concrete or road metal. Thin deposits of copper ore are occasionally found in these igneous rocks, one group of abandoned copper mines being located near Somerville, New Jersey.

The other type of igneous rock of Triassic age, the intrusive flows, are probably better known because of the prominence of the so-called Palisades along the Hudson River. These magmas were coarser grained because they cooled at lower temperatures and at greater depths below the surface. Both dikes and sills were intruded during Triassic time. The dikes frequently stand out as hills or ridges today because the sedimentary rocks into which they were intruded have subsequently been removed by erosion. In many cases the Triassic shales were altered by heat from the intrusive magma, and are said to have been baked. Baked shales are common today near the contacts with dikes. Triassic sills, usually of diabase, are well illustrated by the Palisades along the Hudson River, from Haverstraw, New York, south to Bergen Point, New Jersey. Sills also occur as isolated ridges in Mercer and Hunterdon Counties (Rocky Hill and Sourland Mountain), New Jersey.

Not all of these intrusions were confined to the intermontane basins; some occurred many miles to the west and cut rocks of a geological age considerably older than the Triassic. For example, a small Triassic diabase dike which cuts rocks of Devonian age can be seen along the Juniata River, on Route 22, near Amity Hall, Pennsylvania.

It is sometimes said that the presence of so much red shale indicates a very arid climate in Pennsylvania and New Jersey during Triassic time. This conclusion, however, is not necessarily valid. True, there must have been periods of aridity, but the presence of fossil fish and other aquatic animals in the Triassic shales of the region suggests that there must have been numerous lakes in the basin. The evidence seems to point to a dry climate, with occasional torrential rains bringing down debris from the higher land and spreading it out in broad alluvial plains. The many slabs of sandstone and shale with mud cracks suggest such alluvial plains that were periodically exposed to the air for long times. These slabs frequently contain the footprints of dinosaurs and other reptiles. The fragmental conditions of the fossil plants found in the Lockatong formation at Gwynedd, Pennsylvania, and the presence of a small reptile *Gwyneddosaurus,* together with the scarcity of fish and fresh-water mollusks, suggests that this material was transported by rivers and spread over the plain.

The presence of more perfect plant fossils at Carversville, Bucks County, Pennsylvania, suggests that those plants actually lived in the region where their fossils were found. Excavations near Boonton, Morris County, New Jersey (now covered by the Jersey City Reservoir), yielded a large collection of fossil fresh-water fish, especially of the genus *Semionotus*. Some fossil remains of fresh-water mussels have been found near Phoenixville and York, suggesting that these places were also under water.

Connecticut Basin.—This basin was very similar to the one in New Jersey and Pennsylvania, but the strata were tilted to the east instead of the west. It is estimated that the sediments in this basin are between 10,000 and 13,000 feet in thickness. After the tilting, many of the softer shales were eroded away, leaving the more resistant igneous rocks which today form the Hanging Hills near Meriden, Saltonstall Ridge, near New Haven, as well as East Rock and West Rock near New Haven. Some volcanic bombs near Mount Holyoke, Massachusetts, tell us that at least some of the volcanic activity during Triassic time must have been violent, and suggest the presence of actual volcanoes, in contrast to the quiet lava flows that were more characteristic of New Jersey and Pennsylvania. Many dinosaur footprints have been found in the Triassic shales of the Connecticut Valley, especially near South Hadley, Massachusetts, and a few imperfect skeletons have been found. While the footprints indicate the presence of large dinosaurs, it is interesting to note that the few skeletal remains thus far found are all of relatively small species.

Connection with the Ocean.—No undoubted marine fossils have been found in any of the rocks of the Newark group anywhere along the Atlantic Seaboard. The presence of a few fossil sharks (*Carinacanthus jepseni*) found in the shales at Gwynedd, Pennsylvania, suggests brackish water, although the evidence is not conclusive. Some tracks or trails observed near Princeton, New Jersey, are thought to have been made by king crabs or closely related animals living in brackish water. Furthermore, a fossil worm, *Spirorbis*, found at York, Pennsylvania, is usually associated with marine rocks, although both it and the king crab could conceivably have lived in fresh-water lakes.

On the other hand, it is highly probable that the Newark and Connecticut basins did have some connection with the open sea. Possibly the Connecticut Basin extended south under what is now Long Island, and thus connected with the ocean. Unfortunately, no wells deep enough to reach any Triassic rocks have yet been drilled on Long Island. Similarly, the New Jersey Basin may have connected with the sea near the present site of New York City.

Salisbury Embayment.—In 1944, The Ohio Oil Company drilled an unsuccessful oil well near Salisbury, Wicomico County, Maryland. After drilling through the Tertiary sediments and a 3,000-foot section of Cretaceous sands and clays, they encountered a red shale which was very similar to that of the Brunswick formation of the Newark group. This shale alternated with sandstone between the depths of 5,360 and 5,529 feet, at which depth the "basement" (Pre-Cambrian?) was reached. These shales and sandstones have tentatively been correlated with the Newark group of Triassic age. The following year, the Socony-Vacuum Oil Company drilled a well near Berlin, Worcester County, Maryland, and encountered the same Triassic(?) rocks between the depths of 6,486 and 7,157 feet.

Further work on the subsurface of Maryland has demonstrated the existence of an ancient channel or trough in the bedrock. The trough extends approximately from Washington, D. C., to Salisbury and Berlin, Maryland, and probably farther east. It is possible that this channel was present during Triassic time and marked an inlet from the ocean through the remnants of Appalachia to the lakes and lowlands of the Newark basin. This channel, deeply buried under Maryland, is still imperfectly known and its existence can perhaps best be demonstrated when and if more wells are drilled in the region. (See Figure 198, page 268.)

It must also be borne in mind that these basins were probably much more extensive than is shown today by the rocks. If so, the Salisbury Embayment may merely be an eastward extension of the New York-Virginia Trough. In this case, the open ocean may have been still farther to the east, separated from the embayment or basin by the remnants of Appalachia.

Southern Basins.—Several basins existed in Virginia and North Carolina, as shown in Figure 165. Some of these basins may have been connected, although it seems more probable that the Deep River and Wadesboro basins of North Carolina were distinct from the Dan River and Richmond basins of Virginia. The climate here was more equable than farther north, for coal beds occur near Richmond, Virginia, and Durham, North Carolina. These beds have been mined at various times, but the grade of coal is inferior to that of Pennsylvanian age. Both vertebrate fossils and plant remains have been found in these coal beds.

Wells drilled at Florence and Summerville, South Carolina, have revealed the possible presence of deeply buried Triassic rocks. These well records, together with geophysical evidence, suggest the existence of at least one Triassic basin in South Carolina. Recent exploratory drilling has suggested the presence of additional deeply buried Triassic sedimentary and igneous rocks under Georgia and Florida.

Late Triassic Folding and Faulting.—At the end of Triassic time, or possibly during the Jurassic, there was a period of faulting which caused the deposits of the Newark basins to be tilted to their present angular position. In New Jersey and Pennsylvania, the beds were tilted to the northwest, while in the Connecticut Valley, as we have seen, the tilt was toward the east. Some of the southern basins were tilted to the east and others to the west. There was some local folding, as shown in the Passaic Valley west of the Watchung Mountains in New Jersey.

Triassic of Western North America

Continental Triassic rocks occur in Idaho, Wyoming, and southward across Utah, Colorado, Arizona, and New Mexico to west Texas.

FIG. 166. Petrified Forest, Arizona.

Fossil plants occur at many places and fresh-water mollusks are occasionally found. Vertebrate fossils are locally common, especially in Arizona. The Painted Desert of Arizona was formed by the erosion of continental Triassic deposits, while the Petrified Forest of the same state is made up of many Triassic trees which have undergone mineral replacement (Figure 166).

Marine Triassic deposits existed only in troughs that were near the present Pacific Ocean and near the eastern shore of the Gulf of California. Such deposits are known from California, Nevada, and Sonora, Mexico.

Triassic Life

Marine Invertebrates.—Since no marine formations of Triassic age are known from eastern North America, and since only relatively few such deposits occur in the western part of the continent, very little

Fig. 167. Marine fossils of Triassic age from El Antimonio, Sonora, Mexico. Belemnites (above) and ammonites (below).

is known about the marine fauna of North America during this period.

Along the Pacific coast there are some deposits of Triassic coral reefs, associated with occasional starfish and echinoids. Relatively few brachiopods were present in these seas, but the gastropods and pelecypods were much more abundant than they had been during the preceding periods. The cephalopods, especially the ammonites, showed a marked increase in numbers. There were also a number of squid-like animals known as belemnites which were to become much more conspicuous during the Jurassic and Cretaceous periods.

The marine Triassic rocks at El Antimonio, Sonora, Mexico, contain an excellent fauna of ammonites and belemnites, especially the former. A few of these are shown in Figure 167. The first lobsters appeared during this period, but were rare and of small size.

Although the marine Triassic fauna of North America is very meager, owing to the scarcity of such deposits, the marine Triassic fauna of South America is very rich. It contains representatives of most of the major groups of invertebrate animals. Because of the close relationship of this South American Triassic fauna with that of Europe, it has been largely studied by European paleontologists and has only recently received much attention on the part of students from the United States.

Fig. 168. A Triassic phyllopod *Estheria*. (W. Bock.)

Fresh-Water Invertebrates.—Various kinds of Crustacea are known from the Triassic rocks of the Newark group. These include shelled forms (phyllopods) such as those of the genus *Estheria* (Fig-

Fig. 169. A Triassic fresh-water mussel, *Antediplodon pennsylvanica*, from Phoenixville, Pennsylvania.

ure 168), some very minute ostracodes, and a shrimp-like animal recently described by Bock from Gwynedd, Pennsylvania, as *Gwyneddocaris parabolica*. Mollusks are very rare in the Triassic shales, although a few fossil fresh-water mussels have been found near York and Phoenixville, Pennsylvania, and in a few localities in other parts of the country (Figure 169). Some peculiar markings in the shales are sometimes considered to have been made by worms, but no positive identification has been made.

Fig. 170. Skeleton of the Triassic fish *Coelacanthus,* from Gwynedd, Pennsylvania.

Fish.—Numerous types of fish existed in Triassic waters including the sharks, dipnoids (lungfish), holosteans (primitive bony fish), and a few teleosts (true bony fish). Fossil fish are not infrequent in the Triassic shales of the Newark group, the majority belonging to the holostean genus *Semionotus.* A few coelacanths (*Diplurus newarki*

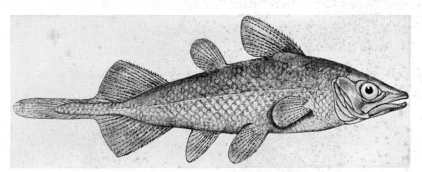

Fig. 171. Restoration of the Triassic coelacanth fish *Osteopleurus.* (G. L. Jepsen, New Jersey State Mus.)

and *Diplurus longicaudatus*) and a shark (*Carinacanthus jepseni*) have also been found near Gwynedd, Pennsylvania, and Princeton, New Jersey (Figures 170 and 171).

Amphibians.—Stegocephalians continued to exist, while the first primitive frogs, known from fossils in Madagascar, made their appear-

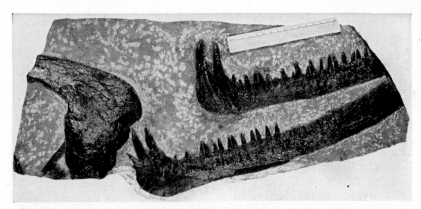

FIG. 172. Jaw of the phytosaur *Clepsysaurus* from Blue Bell, Pennsylvania. (Acad. Nat. Sci., Phila.)

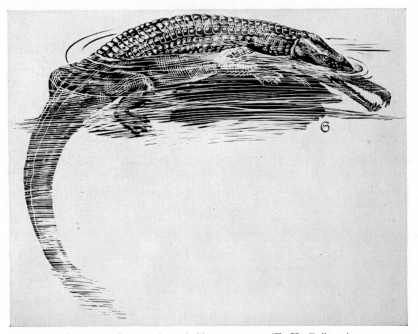

FIG. 173. Restoration of *Clepsysaurus*. (E. H. Colbert.)

ance during this period. Amphibian tracks have been found in rocks of the Newark group.

Reptiles.—*Phytosaurs.* These crocodile-like animals lived among the streams and lakes of Triassic time. Although they closely resembled crocodiles, the phytosaurs were not their ancestors, but belonged to an entirely different group of reptiles that existed only dur-

Fig. 174. A Triassic scene showing the carnivorous dinosaur *Plateosaurus*. (J. P. Cowan, Hughes Tool Co.)

ing Triassic time. Their bodies often reached a length of 25 feet, and they must have been as ferocious and dangerous as the later-day crocodiles. The fossil remains of two genera, *Clepsysaurus* and *Rutiodon*, have been found in the Newark rocks of Pennsylvania, New Jersey, North Carolina, and Connecticut. A very fine lower jaw of *Clepsysaurus pennsylvanicus* was recently found in a quarry near Blue Bell, Montgomery County, Pennsylvania (Figures 172 and 173).

Dinosaurs. The word "dinosaur" is often loosely applied to any large, ancient reptile. In scientific language, however, dinosaurs are restricted to two orders of reptiles, the Saurischia and the Ornithischia, sometimes combined into the single order Dinosauria. The Saurischia, which means "reptile hips" are those dinosaurs whose hip bones resembled those of the typical reptile, while the Ornithischia or "bird hips," are those with hip bones resembling the pelvis of a bird.

The Triassic dinosaurs were relatively small, when compared with those of the Jurassic and Cretaceous (Figure 174). The Triassic rocks of the Connecticut Valley as well as those in Pennsylvania and New Jersey frequently contain dinosaur footprints (Figures 175 and 176),

Fig. 175. Dinosaur footprints in Triassic shales of New Jersey. (Rutgers University.)

and a few incomplete skeletons of small dinosaurs have also been found. The most complete of these skeletons was found near New Haven, Connecticut, and was given the appropriate name of *Yaleosaurus* by the German paleontologist F. von Heune. The reptile measured about six feet in length. Dinosaur tracks are especially common along the Connecticut River near South Hadley, Massachusetts, and along the highway between Springfield and Holyoke. The largest footprint observed measures 23 inches. In Pennsylvania, some eight-inch tracks have been found at Gwynedd and near York. Some small primitive dinosaur fossils belonging to the genus *Coelphysis* were recently found in lower Triassic rocks of New Mexico.

Ichthyosaurs. These fish-like reptiles made their first appearance during Late Triassic time and were to become much more conspicuous during the Jurassic and Cretaceous. No fossil remains of ichthyosaurs have been reported from the Triassic rocks of eastern North America, probably because these animals lived in the ocean while the eastern Triassic rocks are of fresh-water origin. Species up to 25 feet in

Fig. 176. Footprint of Triassic dinosaur *Chirotherium* from Pennsylvania. (After W. Bock.)

length are known from the Upper Triassic rocks of Oregon and California.

Plesiosaurs. These, like the ichthyosaurs, were reptiles that were adapted to life in the ocean. A primitive form, the genus *Pistosaurus*, has been tentatively assigned to the plesiosaurs, although its exact position is uncertain. The plesiosaurs were to become much more abundant during Jurassic and Cretaceous times.

Theriodonts. These mammal-like reptiles of the Upper Permian and Triassic rocks of South Africa have already been discussed. Some of the animals of this group are thought to have been the evolutionary connecting link between the reptiles and the mammals.

Turtles. Turtles were present in Triassic waters, fresh and salt(?), but are not common.

Other Triassic Reptiles from Pennsylvania and New Jersey. Two specimens of a cotylosaur, *Hypsognatus fenneri,* a primitive kind of reptile, have been found in the Triassic rocks near Clifton, New Jersey (Figure 177). These reptiles were survivals from a type that was more characteristic of Permian time and which died out at the end

Fig. 177. Restoration of the cotylosaur *Hypsognathus fenneri,* from the Triassic of New Jersey. (Restoration by John C. German, Amer. Mus. Nat. Hist.)

of the Triassic. A partial skeleton of a small thecodont armored reptile, *Stegomus arcuatus jerseyensis,* was recently found near Neshanic Station, in Somerset County, New Jersey. From the fragment described, it is estimated that the animal was about three feet in length. Finally, the very broken skeleton of a small reptile was found near Gwynedd, Pennsylvania, and described as *Gwyneddosaurus,* a primitive dinosaur, although its exact relationship is uncertain.

Mammals.—The first true mammals appeared during the Triassic period, probably having evolved from the Theriodont reptiles. Our knowledge of these primitive mammals is unfortunately very incomplete, being based only on a few jaws and teeth. Apparently these primitive animals were very small and belonged to an extinct order unrelated to modern forms. There is a difference of opinion as to whether they should be considered mammal-like reptiles or reptile-like mammals. Lower jaws of two animals known as *Dromatherium,* once thought to be very primitive mammals, were found many years ago in a coal mine in the Triassic of North Carolina. Present opinion, however, classifies this genus with the theriodont reptiles.

TRIASSIC PLANTS FROM NEWARK GROUP (after W. Bock)

FIG. 178. Arthrophyte, *Equisitales*.   FIG. 181. Fern, *Mertensites*.
FIG. 179. Cycad, *Otozamates*.   FIG. 182. Conifer, *Araucarites*.
FIG. 180. Fern.   FIG. 183. Gingko, *Neoginkoides*.

Plants.—Algae lived in both fresh and salt water during Triassic time. The marine forms were largely of the calcareous type, although some resembled our present fucoids. Fresh-water algae were abundant in the lakes and ponds of the Newark group, and numerous fossil remains of the family Dasycladaceae have been found near Gwynedd and Carversville, Pennsylvania, and near Durham, North Carolina.

Several relatively large examples of arthrophytes have been found in Newark rocks in Virginia, Pennsylvania, and New Jersey. The best represented genera are *Neocalamites* and *Equisetales* (Figure 178). A few cycads such as *Pterophyllum* and *Otozamites* (Figure 179) and ferns, including *Clathropteris* and *Mertensites,* have been found near Gwynedd, Pennsylvania, and Midlothian, Virginia (Figures 180 and 181). The conifers are represented by various genera including *Cheirolepis, Araucarites* (Figure 182), and *Taxites.* In western North America the conifers formed extensive forests, as witnessed by the fossil remains in the Petrified Forest of Arizona (Figure 166).

Leaves of a gingko were recently found at Carversville, Pennsylvania (Figure 183). This marks the first record of this genus from the Triassic of North America.

Fig. 184. Triassic coal mines near Midlothian, Virginia. The first coal mined in the United States came from this vicinity.

FIG. 185. Iron mine at Cornwall, Pennsylvania. The iron was formed by contact metamorphism between Cambro-Ordovician limestone and Triassic igneous intrusions. (Bethlehem Steel Corp.)

Economic Resources of the Triassic

Coal.—Coal has been mined from the rocks of the Newark series near Richmond and Danville, Virginia, and near Durham, North Carolina. In fact, the oldest coal mines in America are in this vicinity. At the present time operations are limited to exploratory drilling. Figure 184 shows one of the abandoned coal mines near Midlothian, Virginia.

Copper.—Copper ores have been mentioned as occurring in Triassic shales and sandstones in the Piedmont region of New Jersey. Native copper occurs in sheets and stringers throughout the shale and occasionally in the adjacent trap rock, for example, near Somerville. Also, chalcocite (black copper sulphide) occurs in veins distributed throughout the shale and sandstone at Griggstown, Somerset County, and Arlington, Hudson County. Copper was formerly mined from Triassic rocks of Pennsylvania and New Jersey.

Lead.—Lead was formerly mined from Triassic rocks near Phoenixville, Pennsylvania.

Iron.—The extensive iron deposits near Cornwall, Pennsylvania, were formed by contact metamorphism of Triassic igneous intrusions with limestone of Cambro-Ordovician age (Figure 185). The abandoned iron mines at French Creek near St. Peters, Chester County, Pennsylvania, are also near a contact of the Cambro-Ordovician limestone and the Triassic intrusives.

Stone.—Quarries in Triassic rocks of Pennsylvania and New Jersey frequently yield building stone, especially argillite. The traprock quarries produce crushed stone for road building and ballast.

FURTHER READING

The references for Chapters 17–19 will be found at the end of Chapter 19.

CHAPTER 18

THE JURASSIC

The period was named by A. Brongniart and A. von Humboldt for the Jura Mountains of eastern France and northwest Switzerland. Deposits of Jurassic age are much better developed in Europe than in America, where the Jurassic was primarily a period of erosion.

New Jersey to Georgia	Florida	Gulf Coast (Ala., Miss., Ark.)
Buried in extreme eastern North Carolina	Possibly in deep wells	Cotton Valley Buckner Smackover Eagle M'lls

The Jurassic of Eastern North America

At the end of Triassic time, the mountains formed by the tilting and folding of the rocks of the Newark group were being rapidly eroded. It is probable that there were extensive gravel deposits east of these "block mountains," somewhat similar to the gravel plains near the eastern edge of the Rockies today. By the latter part of the Jurassic, these mountains had practically or entirely disappeared, and in their place was a plain which sloped eastward to the Atlantic Ocean. This Jurassic peneplanation smoothed off the upturned Triassic rocks and then, to the east, roughly followed the configuration of the "basement rocks" of the eroded remnants of Appalachia. By this time the ancient continent of Appalachia had been completely eroded, or had sunk beneath the sea.

This gently sloping plain (Figure 186) extends from Long Island to the Mississippi River and has been called the "Fall Zone Peneplane." The slope of the bedrock, and presumably that of the Fall Zone Peneplane, varies from 100 feet per mile near Washington, D. C., in the vicinity of the Salisbury Embayment, to less than 20 feet per mile in parts of North Carolina. In most cases there is a decided increase in the slope near the present coast. The shallow valleys of this plain were filled by gravel transported by rivers.

Fig. 186. Late Jurassic. Submergence was largely limited to the western and southern part of the continent. The Sundance Sea is shown extending from the north into Montana and Wyoming, while the Mexican Sea reached from the south into New Mexico without reaching the Sundance. Marine inroads in the east were limited to Mississippi, Alabama, southern Florida, and extreme eastern North Carolina.

Prior to the Jurassic, the rivers of Pennsylvania and New Jersey had flowed from the east to the west into the Appalachian Trough or the Newark Basin. With the leveling of Appalachia, the majority of the rivers, from Jurassic time to the present, flowed eastward to the Atlantic Ocean. The Fall Zone Peneplane was apparently so level that these rivers flowed toward the east with little or no regard to the position or strike of the upturned edges of the folded and eroded mountains. As we will see in Chapter 25, differential erosion caused a change in the river's position at a later stage.

At the climax of the Jurassic, this plain was uplifted and the gravels on its surface were eroded and redeposited as Lower Cretaceous delta deposits in eastern Pennsylvania, New Jersey, Delaware, and Maryland.

Salisbury Embayment.—If, as suggested in the previous chapter, the channel from Washington, D. C., through Salisbury, Maryland, to the coast was cut or downfaulted during the Triassic or earlier, some sediments of Jurassic age may have been deposited in this region and may still be present far beneath the surface. Figure 187 is a diagrammatic representation of the Salisbury Embayment between Washington and Ocean City, Maryland. Perhaps the deepest parts of the non-marine Potomac sands and clays in the wells at Salisbury, Berlin, and Ocean City, Maryland, may be of Jurassic age. Since no fossils have been found in the material directly overlying the Triassic in these wells, their age is in doubt, although they have tentatively been correlated with the Potomac group of the Lower Cretaceous. The sands and clays of the Potomac group were once called Jurassic on the basis of their vertebrate fossils. However, more recent work on the fauna, and especially the flora, favors a Lower Cretaceous dating. Quite recently (1946) some Lower Cretaceous marine foraminifera were found in the deep oil test at Ocean City, Maryland. However, there is still the possibility that there are some Jurassic rocks between the bottom of the Lower Cretaceous and the top of the Triassic.[1]

Gulf of Mexico Invasion.—The Jurassic sea covered southern Florida, western Cuba, and much of western Mexico. It has recently been demonstrated by a study of deep wells that this sea also covered much of eastern Texas, Louisiana, southern Arkansas, southern Mississippi and Alabama, and possibly southwestern Georgia. The fossils of this sea have been studied by Ralph Imlay and other paleontolo-

[1] Swain (1950) has reported Jurassic ostracodes from the well at Cape Hatteras, North Carolina. This suggests that the Jurassic seas covered extreme eastern North Carolina.

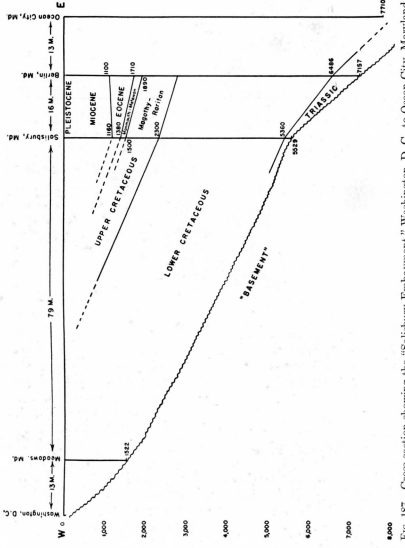

Fig. 187. Cross section showing the "Salisbury Embayment," Washington, D. C., to Ocean City, Maryland.

gists and several Jurassic formations have been recognized. The Jurassic rocks are deeply buried in the eastern Gulf region, but correlations have been made with the surface outcrops in Mexico. The history of the Gulf invasion suggests several advances and retreats of the sea with the greatest advance, that of the Eagle Mills formation, occurring near the end of the period. The climate must have been arid during part of Jurassic time, for salt was deposited extensively and is found in deep wells in Alabama, Mississippi, and Arkansas. It is also possible that the salt domes of coastal Louisiana are of Jurassic age and were uplifted some 20,000 feet or more during much later periods. The extensive "red beds" found in some of the wells offer further evidence for an arid climate during part of the Jurassic.

The Jurassic of Western North America

Marine waters covered parts of western North America during the Jurassic and it is from this region that we best obtain our knowledge of the marine life of the period. The "Sundance Sea" extended south from the Arctic just east of the present line of the Rocky Mountains. At approximately the same time another sea, called the "Mexican Sea," extended north from Mexico, not quite meeting the northern marine invasion. Furthermore, it is thought that the sea inundated much of the land now adjoining the Pacific Ocean, from Lower California to British Columbia.

In addition to the above-mentioned marine deposits in western North America, there are also extensive continental Jurassic formations. For example, Zion Canyon and Rainbow Bridge in Utah are beautiful examples of the erosion of continental Jurassic rocks.

After the retreat of the Sundance Sea, extensive alluvial and continental deposits, known as the Morrison Formation, were formed over a wide area in Colorado, Montana, Utah, Wyoming, and New Mexico. The shales of this formation are world famous for their excellent dinosaur fossils, some 69 species being known throughout the area. In addition to the dinosaurs, some primitive mammals, crocodiles, freshwater mollusks, and plants are known from this formation.

There was extensive igneous action along the Pacific coast during parts of the Jurassic. Associated with this there were uplift and mountain building in a number of places, notably in the vicinity of the present Sierra Nevada, Coast Ranges, and Cascades. The series of disturbances which produced these mountains is generally called the Nevadan Revolution.

Jurassic Life

Because of the lack of Jurassic fossil localities in eastern North America, it is necessary to turn to the western part of the country and to Europe for information on the plant and animal life of that period (Figure 188). The most famous Jurassic locality is at Soln-

Fig. 188. A Jurassic scene showing the carnivorous dinosaur *Antrodemus* (right) and the herbivorous dinosaur *Polacanthus* (left). Note the luxuriant forest of cycads, ferns, etc. (J. P. Cowan, Hughes Tool Co.)

hofen, Bavaria, where some unusually fine-textured limestone was formerly quarried and widely used for lithographic stone. This limestone is especially suitable for the preservation of fossils, and frequently shows many minute details of structure and ornamentation. The Solnhofen locality probably represents a near-shore deposit, for the fossils are both those of marine and nonmarine forms and life. A total of 450 species of animals have been obtained from these quarries, probably the most famous being *Archaeopteryx*, the primitive reptile-like bird.

Marine Invertebrates.—The invertebrate life of the sea was becoming more like that of modern times. Many of the Jurassic corals,

FIG. 189. Jurassic ammonite from Bavaria.

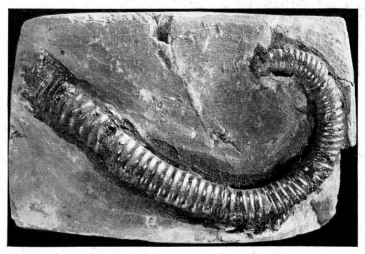

FIG. 190. Jurassic ammonite from Bavaria.

mollusks, echinoderms, and crustacea belong to the same families as their modern descendants. Probably the most important group of Jurassic invertebrates was that of the cephalopods, especially the ammonites. This group of animals had almost reached extinction at the end of the Triassic. However, a few types managed to survive into the Jurassic, and then underwent a great diversification in form and size. They varied in size from very minute creatures to giants several feet in diameter, and constituted an important part of the fauna of Jurassic seas. Pyritized remains of ammonites are fairly common

FIG. 191. Slab of Jurassic ammonites from Bavaria.

in the Jurassic rocks on Germany (Figures 189, 190, and 191) while some less spectacular forms are known from the western part of the United States.

The belemnites, or squid-like cephalopods, also reached their zenith during the Jurassic period. Like the ammonites, they were to persist until the end of the Mesozoic era. Fossil belemnites found in Württemberg, Germany, show that these ancient squid-like animals possessed ink sacs similar to those of the modern squid.

Insects.—Many insects were present during Jurassic time, including representatives of such modern groups as the dragonflies, grasshoppers, flies, and ants.

Fish.—Various kinds of fish were present in the Jurassic seas including sharks, primitive bony fish, and teleosts.

Amphibia.—The labyrinthodonts had died out by Jurassic time, while the frogs, toads, and salamanders were beginning to appear.

Reptiles.—DINOSAURS. As a rule, the Jurassic dinosaurs were considerably larger than those of the Triassic. However, not all dinosaurs were "terrible lizards"; some were small and entirely inoffensive. Some dinosaurs walked on four legs, while in others the front legs were small and practically useless. Their food habits also varied; the teeth of some species indicate quite clearly that they were carnivores, while other dinosaur species were herbivorous. A few may have been omnivorous.

FIG. 192. Restoration of *Stegosaurus* in the Zoological Gardens at Calgary, Alberta. (Calgary Chamber of Commerce.)

Dinosaur skeletons have been found in numerous localities in the West, especially in the Morrison formation of Wyoming, Colorado, Montana, Alberta, and New Mexico. Among the more spectacular dinosaurs were *Stegosaurus, Brontosaurus, Diplodocus,* and *Allosaurus.*

Stegosaurus was a typical armored dinosaur of this period (Figure 192). One of the most interesting features of this creature was the small size of its brain, which weighed approximately 2½ ounces while the entire animal may have weighed 10 tons. There was a noticeable enlargement of the spinal cord in the hip region, which probably served to control the movements of the hind legs and tail. This structure is considerably larger than the true brain and is sometimes, although not too accurately, spoken of as a second brain.

Brontosaurus (thunder lizard) is one of the best known of the dinosaurs. Its picture appears in numerous books and advertisements and life-sized reconstructions or restorations can be seen in many of the large museums of the country. Striking life-sized models of Brontosaurus, as well as of other dinosaurs, can be seen in parks at Rapid City, South Dakota, and Calgary, Alberta (Figure 193). This was a plant-eating dinosaur, some 70 or 80 feet in length, including a long tail. Its fossils are known from Wyoming and other western states.

Fig. 193. Restoration of Jurassic dinosaur *Brontosaurus* at Rapid City, South Dakota.

Diplodocus, while not as long as *Brontosaurus,* attained a length of some 50 feet, and was exceedingly slender. *Allosaurus* was a large carnivorous dinosaur, some 30 to 35 feet in length. While not as large as some of the Cretaceous carnivores, *Allosaurus* must have been a truly ferocious monster.

Ichthyosaurs. These marine reptiles reached the climax of their development during the Jurassic period. They were rarely longer than 20 feet, and most were considerably smaller. The best-known American Jurassic ichthyosaur belongs to the genus *Opthalmosaurus* from the Sundance formation of Montana. The fossil remains of ichthyosaurs are more abundant in European than American rocks. Some especially fine skeletons have been found in the famous quarries near Holzmaden, Württemburg, Germany, in some cases with the carbonized skin completely outlining the shape of the body. Other well-preserved ichthyosaur remains have been found at Lyme Regis, England (Figure 194).   These marine reptiles apparently ate quantities of belemnites (cephalopods), if we may judge from the fossil remains found within the skeletons of many of these large sea monsters.

Fig. 194. Jurassic Ichthyosaur from Lyme Regis, England. Actual length 7 feet. (Acad. Nat. Sci., Phila.)

PLESIOSAURS.   These were the sea serpents of Jurassic time and were characterized by long necks.   Some of these animals reached a length of 20 feet, while even longer ones were to appear during the Cretaceous. The occurrence of a number of rounded and polished gastroliths (gizzard stones), in association with plesiosaur fossils, suggests that these

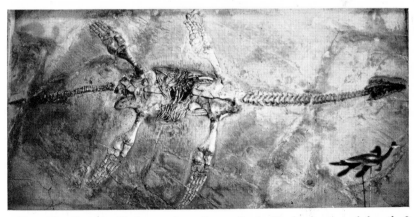

Fig. 195. Jurassic Plesiosaur from Lyme Regis, England. Actual length 8 feet. (Acad. Nat. Sci., Phila.)

marine reptiles did not depend entirely upon their teeth to grind their food.   A fossil plesiosaur from Jurassic deposits at Lyme Regis is shown in Figure 195.

PTEROSAURS.   The flying reptiles appeared at the beginning of Triassic time and flourished during the Jurassic and Cretaceous.   Flight was accomplished by a wing membrane composed of skin, which stretched from the elongated joints of the fourth finger and attached to the body near the hind legs. The first three fingers were not enlarged, and were equipped with claws which were probably useful in climbing. Pterosaurs probably flew over the sea, for their remains are generally found in marine deposits.

Birds.—The quarries at Solnhofen, Bavaria, have yielded two skeletons of primitive birds that have been called *Archaeopterix* and

Fig. 196. Restoration of Jurassic bird *Archaeopterix*. (Rutgers University.)

Archaeornis. These birds had retained many of the features of their reptilian ancestors. There must have been other and more primitive "connecting links" between the reptiles and the birds but, so far, their fossil remains have not been found. Restorations of two Jurassic birds are shown in Figures 196 and 197.

Mammals.—Jurassic mammals were very rare and only a few fragmentary fossils have been found. These consist only of a few jaws and teeth, one incomplete skull, and some leg bones. Because of the fragmentary nature of these fossils little can be said about the general appearance of these primitive mammals except that they were apparently no larger than a rat or a small dog. The best American fossils of this group have been found in the Morrison formation at Como Bluffs, Wyoming.

Fig. 197. The most primitive of birds, *Archaeornis*, in a grove of cycads and palms. (Acad. Nat. Sci., Phila.)

Plants.—The principal groups of plants of Jurassic time included ferns, horsetails, ginkgos, conifers, and cycads. This latter group—the cycadophyta—was undoubtedly the dominant form of plant life of the period. Consequently, the Jurassic is sometimes called the "age of cycads." Many of these species were of world-wide distribution.

Economic Resources of the Jurassic

Coal.—Coal occurs in Jurassic rocks in many parts of the world, but not on the mainland of North America. A limited amount of coal has been mined from Jurassic rocks on the east coast of Greenland.

Gold.—The placer gold discovered in California in 1849 had been carried down by rivers during Cenozoic times from the gold quartz veins (the Mother Lode) in the western slope of the Sierra Nevada. This gold had been brought to the surface of the earth during Jurassic time, in connection with the Nevadan Revolution.

Petroleum.—Because of the absence of Jurassic formations in most parts of the United States, these rocks are not a major source of oil or gas, although some deeply buried Jurassic sands in northern Louisiana and southern Arkansas have recently yielded considerable quantities of oil and gas.

Salt.—One of the conspicuous geological features of coastal Louisiana and southeastern Texas is the presence of buried salt domes. Salt deposits of Pre-Cretaceous age were pushed upwards through later formations, sometimes—as in the case of Weeks Island and Avery Island, Louisiana—actually above the surface. The age of this salt is uncertain, some geologists calling it Permian and others Jurassic, with the weight of the argument being slightly in favor of a Jurassic age. The salt is mined from domes exposed near or above the surface, and is also obtained by deep drilling.

FURTHER READING

The references for Chapters 17–19 will be found at the end of Chapter 19.

CHAPTER 19

THE CRETACEOUS *

THE LOWER CRETACEOUS

The name Cretaceous, derived from the Latin word *creta* meaning chalk, was first used by O. d'Halloy in 1822 for the chalk cliffs on both sides of the English Channel. Later, the term was expanded to include all sediments laid down between the end of the Jurassic and the close of the Mesozoic era. Therefore, while it is true that there

		New Jersey	Del.–Md.	Va.	N. C.–S. C.	Zones	Gulf Coast
UPPER CRETACEOUS	MONMOUTH	Tinton Red Bank Navesink Mount Laurel } Monmouth	—	—	Peedee	Exogyra costata E. cancellata	Navarro
	MATAWAN	Wenonah Marshalltown Woodbury Merchantville } Matawan	—	—	Black Creek	E. ponderosa	Taylor
		Magothy	Magothy	—	"continental Black Creek" marine in wells (subsurface only)	E. upatoiensis	Eutaw Austin
		Raritan	Raritan	Raritan or Tuscaloosa (subsurface only)	Tuscaloosa	E. woolmani	Woodbine
LOWER CRETACEOUS		Potomac (subsurface only)	Potomac marine down dip (subsurface only)	Potomac	part of Tuscaloosa marine down dip (subsurface only)		Washita Glen Rose Travis Peak

are extensive chalk deposits in Cretaceous formations in both Europe and America, and that most of the world's chalk was formed during the Cretaceous, the name is somewhat of a misnomer because the

* SUGGESTION TO INSTRUCTOR. If this chapter and the following ones on the Cenozoic Era are in too great detail for an elementary course in Historical Geology, it is suggested that the material be summarized in lectures, and that the text be used as a reference, and as an example of how more detailed geological history can be worked out.

major part of the Cretaceous deposits of the world are not chalk, but limestone, shale, and sandstone.

Because the Cretaceous period is of fairly long duration, geologists have divided it into two or three parts. While there is no general agreement on the exact divisions, most American geologists use two subdivisions, the Lower Cretaceous or Comanchean, named from the Comanche Indian territory of Texas and Oklahoma, and the Upper Cretaceous, frequently called the Gulf, named from the Gulf of Mexico because such deposits are well developed on the Gulf Coastal Plain. In general usage, the two divisions are generally spoken of merely as Lower and Upper Cretaceous.

The Lower Cretaceous of Eastern North America

New Jersey to Virginia (Potomac Group).—The Appalachian Mountains were again uplifted at the beginning of Early Cretaceous time and there was probably a sinking of the rocks underlying the present Coastal Plain and the continental shelf. The center of this "seesaw" may have been near the present "Fall Line," or contact between the Coastal Plain and the rocks of the Piedmont Plateau. In the uplifted regions, the stream velocity increased considerably and caused increased erosion of the land. The eroded material was carried by the rejuvenated rivers and spread out on the marshlands and swamps that were formed by the rivers and estuaries as they approached the Atlantic Ocean.

One such Cretaceous river apparently flowed across Maryland, approximately along the route of the present Potomac River to Washington and then flowed across the "Eastern Shore," following the Salisbury Embayment formed in Triassic or Jurassic time (see page 237). It reached the sea somewhere near the present site of Ocean City, Maryland. Deposits carried by this river, or possibly a series of rivers, make up the Potomac group of sediments which occur between southern New Jersey and Virginia. These deposits consist of alternating sands and varicolored clays, with frequent zones of lignite and other plant remains. A few fresh-water mollusks have been found, and the fragmental bones of some dinosaurs have been collected near Baltimore and Washington. These Lower Cretaceous sands and clays are well developed near Baltimore and can be seen in most of the cuts along the railroads between Baltimore and Washington, and again between Alexandria and Fredericksburg, Virginia. Near Baltimore the Potomac deposits are about 500 feet thick and have been subdivided into three formations, Patuxent, Arundel, and Patapsco (oldest to youngest). These three divisions, however, are not easy to observe and may be of merely local significance.

Thinner deposits of the Potomac group extend north into Delaware, near Wilmington, and have been found in a well at Salem, New Jersey. South of Virginia, the Potomac deposits become thin and apparently merge with those of the Tuscaloosa formation near the Virginia-North Carolina line. (The Tuscaloosa formation probably represents both Early and Late Cretaceous time.)

The Cretaceous (Upper and Lower) deposits thicken decidedly toward the east, in the Salisbury Embayment. At Meadows, Prince George County, Maryland, near Washington, D. C., they are about 1,500 feet thick, while near Salisbury, Maryland, the combined thickness of Upper and Lower Cretaceous beds is 3,980 feet. No marine fossils were found in the cores from the Lower Cretaceous section of the Salisbury well, although there were considerable swamp deposits containing lignite and fossil wood. Twelve miles east of Salisbury, near Berlin, a still greater thickness of 4,776 feet of Cretaceous sediments were penetrated. Here again, no definite marine fossils were found in the Lower Cretaceous section, although a few fragments of foraminifera at certain depths suggest that the ocean was not far away. Another well drilled near Ocean City, Maryland, did reveal some marine fossils, presumably of Early Cretaceous age. Evidently the shore line at that time lay close to the present one.

The dividing line between the Lower and Upper Cretaceous is very difficult to recognize on the Atlantic Coast. In fact, some recent workers, including Spangler, Peterson, and Anderson,[1] have placed part of the Potomac group in the Upper Cretaceous. However, this is refuted by the paleobotanical evidence.[2] (See Figure 187, page 254, for a cross section of the Salisbury Embayment from Washington, D. C., to Ocean City, Maryland, and Figure 198 for a cross section along the coast from Long Island, New York, to Fort Monroe, Virginia.)

North Carolina.—During Early Cretaceous time, sands and clays were washed down from the mountains of North Carolina, but rarely did they reach the thickness of those of the Potomac group farther north. At no place are they definitely known to occur on the surface in either North or South Carolina. However, the existence of Lower Cretaceous deposits under extreme eastern North Carolina has re-

---

[1] W. B. Spangler and J. J. Peterson, *Geology of the Atlantic Coastal Plain in New Jersey, Delaware, Maryland, and Virginia*, Bull. Amer. Assoc. Petrol. Geol., XXXIV (1950). J. L. Anderson, *et al.*, *Cretaceous and Tertiary Subsurface Geology of Maryland.* Maryland Dept. Geol., Mines and Water Resources Bull. 2 (1948).

[2] Personal communication from Professor Erling Dorf.

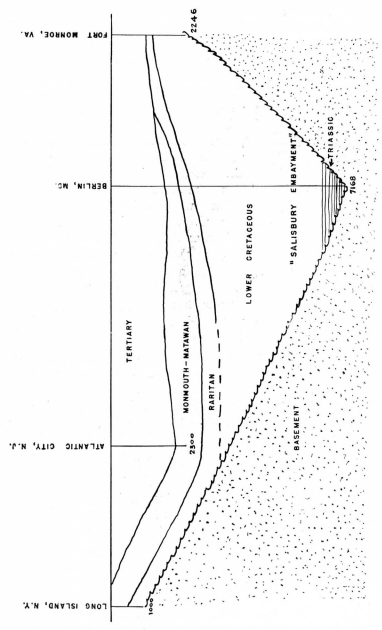

FIG. 198. Cross section from Long Island, New York, to Fort Monroe, Virginia, showing the Salisbury Embayment.

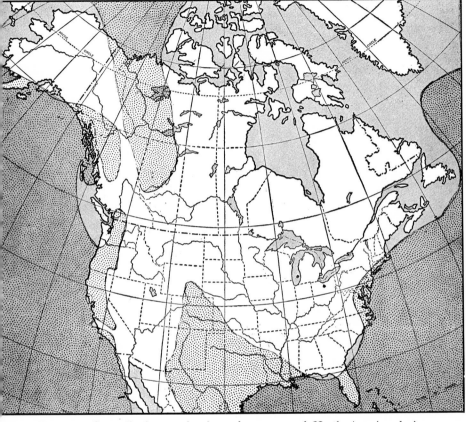

Fig. 199. Generalized map showing submergence of North America during
Early Cretaceous time.

cently been demonstrated by deep oil tests. The presence of Lower Cretaceous marine fossils in the cores of wells drilled near Morehead City, Beaufort, and Cape Hatteras show that this part of the state was under the sea during part of Early Cretaceous time (Figure 199). Near the Virginia-North Carolina line some of the sands and clays of the Tuscaloosa formation, usually regarded as Upper Cretaceous, may actually be Lower Cretaceous.

Gulf of Mexico Region.—The position of the Lower Cretaceous sea in the Gulf region was little different from what it had been during Jurassic time. It covered southeastern Texas, all of Louisiana, southern Arkansas, Mississippi, and Alabama, and southern Florida. Marine fossils have been found in Lower Cretaceous limestone at depths of about 11,000 feet in the Sunniland Oil Field in Collier County, Florida.

Along the margins of this sea, in Georgia and northern Florida, there were extensive alluvial deposits similar to those of the Potomac group farther north. Sands and clays tentatively correlated with the Lower Cretaceous have been found in deep wells in Alabama, Georgia, and northern Florida. Since no fossils have been found in these beds, their exact age is in doubt. As more wells are drilled in the Southeast we shall undoubtedly learn much more about Lower Cretaceous history, and may actually be able to draw the line between the marine and nonmarine phases, and thus map the extent of the seas more accurately.

The Lower Cretaceous sea extended over much of eastern Mexico and deposited extensive thicknesses of limestone. At least once during the Lower Cretaceous there was a seaway across Mexico connecting the Atlantic and Pacific Oceans, through the so-called "Balsas Portal."

The Lower Cretaceous of Western North America

Near the end of the Lower Cretaceous period (Washita time) the Gulf seas extended north into Kansas and Iowa and west into Colorado and Montana, where shales and sandstones were laid down in shallow seas and nearby marshes. At about the same time, the sea began to transgress southward from the Arctic Ocean down the Rocky Mountain geosyncline, but did not meet the invasion from the south until well into Late Cretaceous time.

To the west of this trough there was a mountainous land that extended approximately to the present Pacific coast. During part of

Early Cretaceous time, the sea encroached upon the extreme western margins of this continent, from Lower California to British Columbia.

THE UPPER CRETACEOUS

Lower-Upper Cretaceous Boundary.—It is not always easy to pick the dividing line between the deposits of the two halves of the Cretaceous. There is a rather significant stratigraphic break corresponding to the erosion interval which occurred when the seas, advancing southward from the Arctic Ocean and northward from the Gulf, temporarily retreated (Figure 200). This break is often spoken of as the Lower-Upper Cretaceous boundary. The break is much less distinct in eastern North America, and may not be recognizable there. However, it is convenient for purposes of discussion to divide the Cretaceous into the two parts.

Early Upper Cretaceous of the Atlantic Coastal Plain

Raritan Formation, New Jersey to Maryland.—It is especially difficult to draw the line between Lower and Upper Cretaceous along the Middle Atlantic coast; that is, between New Jersey and Virginia. Probably there was an increased tilting of the land and a consequent slight advance of the sea from the east. In the Salisbury Embayment, at any rate, there seems to have been continual deposition of deltaic and alluvial material with no conspicuous break between the Potomac group (Lower Cretaceous) and the Raritan (beginning of Upper Cretaceous).

On several occasions during Raritan time the sea advanced westward beyond the present shore line, with the result that the Salisbury Embayment and other coastal areas were covered with sea water. Shells and fossil remains of other animals that lived during these marine invasions have been found in wells at Salisbury, Berlin, and Ocean City, Maryland; Bridgeville, Delaware; Fort Dix, New Jersey, and in several excavations near Raritan Bay, notably at the Sayre and Fisher Pits at Sayreville, New Jersey. These marine invasions were of relatively short duration and it is probable that during most of Raritan time the sea lay some miles to the east of the present shore line, since most of the deposits of Raritan age in this region are sands and clays of nonmarine origin. The only fossils are plant remains, which are best preserved near Raritan Bay, New Jersey.

Raritan Formation of Long Island and New England.—Sands and clays of Raritan age are present on Long Island and probably on

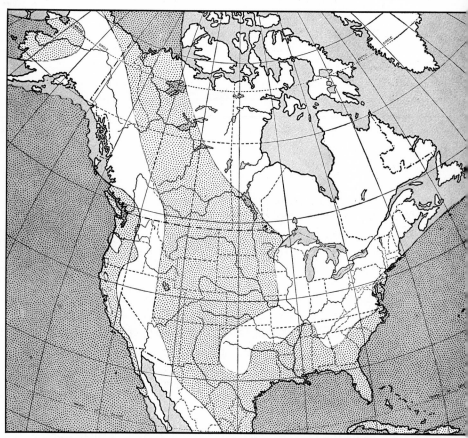

FIG. 200. Late Cretaceous. This map shows the approximate maximum submergence of Cretaceous time. For details of the Atlantic and Gulf Coastal Plain see Figure 203.

Cape Cod and Martha's Vineyard. Since the only fossils yet discovered in those areas are plant remains, we have no proof that the Raritan seas ever advanced over the present land north of New York harbor. A few years ago some Cretaceous fossils of Raritan aspect were dredged from the ocean floor at Banquereau, some 80 miles northeast of Sable Island, Nova Scotia. These were studied by L. W. Stephenson, who pointed out their relationship to fossils of the Raritan formation of New Jersey.

Raritan-Tuscaloosa of Virginia and the Carolinas.—That the Raritan seas covered the region in the vicinity of the Virginia Capes is shown by the presence of marine shells of this age in wells at Norfolk, Drivers, and Franklin, Virginia. As will be shown subsequently, no later Cretaceous deposits are known from Virginia, so the region may have been above water during the latter part of the Upper Cretaceous.

In North and South Carolina the sands and clays of the Tuscaloosa formation are probably equivalent in age to the Raritan formation although, as previously stated, some of them may be older. In North Carolina, the Tuscaloosa outcrops in a belt extending southwest across the state near the western margin of the Coastal Plain. It also extends southward through South Carolina and Georgia. At no place on the surface in either North or South Carolina have any marine fossils been found. A study of plant fossils obtained from South Carolina, especially near Middendorf, suggests a correlation with the Raritan of New Jersey.

While the outcrops of the Tuscaloosa formation seem to indicate swamp or estuarine conditions similar to those characteristic of the Potomac and Raritan formations farther north, the buried seaward extension of the Tuscaloosa ("down dip") definitely is marine. Characteristic Raritan-Tuscaloosa marine fossils have been found in deep wells near Morehead City, Beaufort, and Cape Hatteras, North Carolina and at Conway and Parris Island, South Carolina.

Magothy Deposition.—In some places, the Raritan formation was uplifted and slightly eroded before the overlying formation, the Magothy, was deposited. This unconformity is noticeable in the Raritan Bay region of New Jersey, but cannot be recognized in the subsurface in southern New Jersey, Delaware, and Maryland. Therefore, the erosion must have been local.

There must have been an oscillatory subsidence of the land and a consequent advance of the sea, a fluctuation that continued throughout the rest of Cretaceous time. In the Raritan Bay region the

Magothy is definitely marine and, as noted above, is separated from the Raritan by an erosion interval. Furthermore, the fauna of the Magothy is quite different from that of the Raritan, a fact which also suggests a considerable time difference. Farther south, however, there may have been continual deposition of alluvial or estuarine material, for it is practically impossible to pick the Raritan-Magothy contact in the deep wells in Delaware and Maryland.

Fig. 201. Silicified Cretaceous logs from the Peedee formation in South Carolina.

No deposits equivalent to those of the Magothy are known from Virginia, but in North and South Carolina, conditions were very much like those of New Jersey. The outcrops of the Magothy beds are continental and contain numerous plant fossils, including some well-preserved petrified wood, an example of which is shown in Figure 201. In the Carolinas, these deposits are mapped as part of the Black Creek formation. The buried portions of this formation "down dip," as shown by wells in the eastern part of those states, become marine and carry fossils suggestive of the Magothy of New Jersey and the Eutaw formation of the Gulf Coast. This indicates that the Magothy seas advanced only slightly farther over the Carolinas than those of Raritan time.

Late Upper Cretaceous of the Atlantic Coastal Plain

Matawan and Monmouth Formations of New Jersey.—The oscillatory subsidence of the land continued throughout Late Cretaceous time, as is shown by the beds of sands, clay, and glauconite (greensand marl) which cover the South Atlantic Coastal Plain. The oscillatory nature of the sinking is probably best demonstrated in New

Fig. 202. Graham Brickyard, Maple Shade, New Jersey. Some 75 species of Cretaceous invertebrate fossils have been found in the clay of the Merchantville formation at this site.

Jersey, where some eleven Upper Cretaceous formations have been named. These, together with their probable equivalents elsewhere, are shown on page 265. Some of the New Jersey formations are comparatively free from glauconite, while others are composed largely of this mineral. Since glauconite was believed to form only under fairly deep water, it was inferred that the Cretaceous seas were some 600 feet deep during parts of the period and that the shore line must have lain many miles northwest of the Delaware River. However, since no positive evidence of marine Cretaceous formations has ever been found in Pennsylvania, we cannot say for certain that the seas ever extended farther inland than the Delaware River. Furthermore, recent studies show that glauconite can form under water considerably shallower than was formerly believed. Therefore, the 600-foot minimum depth assigned to the greensand formations of New Jersey may be erroneous.

Nevertheless, the Upper Cretaceous seas along this part of the Atlantic Coast were certainly deeper during certain times than others. The Merchantville, Marshalltown, Navesink, and Mount Laurel formations, with their greensand marls and clays, probably represent the deeper phases, while the Woodbury, Englishtown, and Wenonah formations, with sand and less glauconite, probably represent the shallower phases.

Many Cretaceous fossils, both invertebrate and vertebrate, have been found in New Jersey. Unfortunately, because most of the old marl pits are now abandoned and filled with water or slumped material, collecting must be limited to relatively few localities. One of the best localities for fossils is the brickyard at Maple Shade, shown in Figure 202, where some seventy species have been collected.

Alternation of Faunas.—A fluctuation between shallow and deep water is also indicated by a careful analysis of the Cretaceous invertebrate fauna of New Jersey. This is well summarized by Lewis and Kummel:

> The strata, from the Magothy to the Tinton inclusive, contain a complex assemblage of organisms with two distinct facies. One of these, a *Cucullaea* fauna, characterizes the more glauconitic formations—the Merchantville, the Marshalltown, the Navesink, and the Tinton—and may be regarded as a deeper water fauna. The second fauna facies, characterized by *Lucina cretacea*[3] or its associates, occurs in the clay and clayey sand of the Magothy, the Woodbury, the Wenonah, and the Red Bank formations and was a shallower water fauna.
>
> Both of these facies probably lived side by side in their respective zones off the shore and migrated back and forth across the Coastal Plain region with the gradual advance and retreat of the sea [Figure 203]. During the periods of depression the deeper water, with the accompanying glauconitic sediments and the *Cucullaea* fauna, gradually entered this region from the southeast, and occupied a belt which had formerly been occupied by the shallower water fauna and in which chiefly land derived sediments had been deposited. With a later period of emergence both faunas shifted to the southeast and the shallow-water facies again occupied the region.[4]

Exogyra Zones.—Paleontologists have found it convenient to recognize certain zones within the Upper Cretaceous which are characterized by certain assemblages of fossils. Among the fossils most useful for this zoning are various species of the large oyster-like pelecypod *Exogyra*. These zones are shown on page 265. It seems significant

---

[3] Now called *Lucina glebula*.
[4] J. V. Lewis and H. B. Kummel, *The Geology of New Jersey,* New Jersey Geol. Surv. Bull. 50 (1940), pp. 121–22.

FIG. 203. Hypothetical shore lines during Cretaceous time of the Atlantic and eastern Gulf Coastal Plain.

that these zones can be traced for great distances. Thus the various species of *Exogyra,* together with their associated faunas, help determine the correlations of the various formations within the Upper Cretaceous of the Atlantic and Gulf Coastal Plain. The following zones may be recognized:

Exogyra costata Zone. This comprises the formations of the Monmouth group of New Jersey and the Peedee formation of the Carolinas. The zone may be traced as far as Texas, where it is partly equivalent to the Navarro group.

Exogyra cancellata Zone. This is a much thinner zone, and in fact forms the base of the *Exogyra costata* zone. Dr. L. W. Stephenson has recently pointed out that this zone can be traced for 2,500 miles from Atlantic Highlands, New Jersey, to Cárdenas in the State of

San Luis Potosí, Mexico. In New Jersey the zone is equivalent to the Mount Laurel formation, and in Delaware and Maryland it comprises part of the undifferentiated Monmouth formation. It is absent from southern Maryland to Pitt County, North Carolina, but forms part of the Peedee formation of the Carolinas as well as parts of the Ripley formation of Georgia, Alabama, and Mississippi. In Texas it forms the lowermost division of the Navarro group.

Fig. 204. Pen of *Belemnitella americana* showing the phragmocone, from Prairie Bluff, Alabama.

According to Dr. Stephenson, the following fossils of the *Exogyra cancellata* zone range from New Jersey to the Gulf region:

Ostrea tecticosta	*Anomia argentaria*
O. plumosa	*A. tellinoides*
O. falcata	*Paranomia scabra*
O. panda	*Veniella conradi*
Gryphaea mutabilis	*Cyprimeria depressa*
Exogyra cancellata	*Turritella trilira*
E. costata (Figure 229)	*Belemnitella americana* (Figure 204)
Pecten simplicius	

Exogyra ponderosa Zone. This zone comprises the formations of the Matawan group of New Jersey, the Black Creek formation of the Carolinas, and the Taylor formation of the Gulf Coast.

Exogyra upatoiensis Zone. This zone was first recognized by Stephenson from a well at Charleston, South Carolina. It is probably equivalent to the older, continental phase of the Black Creek formation of North Carolina, and the Magothy formation of New Jersey.

Exogyra woolmani Zone.   Another zone may possibly be indicated by the presence of *Exogyra woolmani* in the deposits of the Raritan and Tuscaloosa formations.   Another index fossil of this zone is the annelid *Hamulus protoonyx.*   *Exogyra woolmani* is closely related to *Exogyra columbella* from the Eagle Ford formation of Texas, which is of approximately the same age as the Raritan and Tuscaloosa formations.

Long Island and New England.—The Monmouth-Matawan seas extended across Long Island and eastern Massachusetts, and may possibly have advanced farther inland.   This is demonstrated by the finding of *Exogyra costata* and other marine fossils in wells on Long Island, and by the presence of other marine Cretaceous fossils on Martha's Vineyard.   To the northeast, Upper Cretaceous fossils have been dredged in about 260 fathoms of water on the Georges Bank, some 200 miles east of Cape Cod, and correlated with those of the Monmouth group of New Jersey.

Delaware, Maryland, and Virginia.—The deposits of the Monmouth-Matawan group apparently become thinner south of New Jersey and are completely absent from Virginia.   This probably indicates that the land was gradually rising out of the sea and that this elevation began in Virginia and gradually spread toward the north.

There are excellent exposures of Cretaceous sands and clays along the Chesapeake and Delaware Canal.   While it is not easy to recognize the individual formations, it is apparent that some of them are thinner than in New Jersey, and that the upper ones (Red Bank and Tinton) are absent.

Many fine fossils have been obtained from this canal, both in the banks of the canal and from dredgings beneath the water.   Some of the best localities have been destroyed by the sodding of the banks, but a few fossils, notably *Exogyra* and *Gryphaea,* can be obtained from the south bank just west of St. Georges, and some others from the spoil bank on the north side between Summit Bridge and the railroad crossing.   As is the case with all fossils secured by dredging, it is impossible to determine the exact depth from which they came, but the majority of the spoil bank fossils seem to be from the Merchantville formation.

Some interesting information on the Cretaceous history of Maryland was recently brought to light in the three oil wells in the Salisbury Embayment. The majority of the Cretaceous fossils recognized in the well samples are believed to be from the Raritan formation, or possibly the Magothy, while the Monmouth-Matawan deposits were thinner than in New Jersey and less fossiliferous. No traces of *Exogyra, Gryphaea, Belemnitella* or other characteristic New Jersey Upper Cretaceous fossils were found. In wells near Norfolk, Virginia, the entire Monmouth-Matawan section was found to be absent, the only Upper Cretaceous deposits being of Raritan age.

North and South Carolina.—The Cape Charles-Cape Henry area may have been in the nature of a promontory ("Fort Monroe High") during the latter part of Late Cretaceous time. We have just seen how the seas transgressed over the land north of these capes, and a similar inundation apparently occurred south of the capes. Thick deposits of Peedee (Monmouth) and Black Creek (Matawan) sediments are found in eastern North Carolina, becoming thin toward the Virginia line. There is no indication of any sharp break between the two formations in North Carolina. Deposition may have been more or less continuous during most of Black Creek and Peedee time. The older part of the Black Creek formation, as mapped in North and South Carolina, is of continental origin and contains numerous plant fossils. It is thought that this is equivalent to the Magothy formation of New Jersey and the Eutaw formation of the Gulf Coast.

In parts of South Carolina, the basal portion of the Peedee is missing, indicating an apparent temporary emergence. Furthermore, the upper part of the Peedee is apparently thin or missing in northeastern North Carolina. This may indicate that there was a cape or promontory in the vicinity of the mouth of Chesapeake Bay. Because of the thinness of the sediments in this region and because of the presence of basement rock at depths shallower than either to the north or south, this region is sometimes spoken of as the Fort Monroe High.

Many Cretaceous fossils have been obtained from North Carolina, and these have been studied and figured in a monograph by L. W. Stephenson. Unfortunately, the best of these fossils were collected many years ago from Snow Hill, Greene County, North Carolina, an outcrop, which time and a changing river have completely obliterated. There may have been another promontory in the vicinity of Cape Fear, North Carolina ("The Great Carolina Ridge"), although most geologists think that this ridge did not rise above sea level until Eocene time (see page 314).

Upper Cretaceous of the Gulf Coastal Plain

During the early part of Late Cretaceous time most of the Eastern Gulf Coastal Plain, like the Atlantic Coastal Plain, was covered with estuarine or alluvial deposits washed down from the mountains. The deposits of this age make up the Tuscaloosa formation, which is contemporary with the Raritan formation of New Jersey. At various times during this stage, the sea advanced over the plain, leaving marine or brackish-water fossils as proof of its existence. These advances were probably temporary and local, for the major part of the Tuscaloosa formation of Georgia, Alabama, and Mississippi is nonmarine; the best marine Tuscaloosa fossils come from wells such as those near Albany, Georgia, and Clayton, Alabama. True marine conditions probably existed in the western Gulf Region (Texas) at this time, where the Woodbine and Eagle Ford formations may be the approximate equivalent of the Tuscaloosa and Raritan formations.

As Cretaceous time continued, the sea advanced over most of the Gulf Coastal Plain. The geological history of this region is complex but has been fairly well worked out because of the importance of these Cretaceous deposits as source beds of petroleum and natural gas. At the climax of this Cretaceous advance, the salt waters of the Gulf of Mexico had moved up the Mississippi Valley to Cairo, Illinois, some 600 miles from the present coast.

Near Coon Creek, McNairy County, Tennessee, there is a deposit containing some 350 species of marine Cretaceous fossils. Many of these are completely unaltered and closely resemble modern sea shells. These fossils, as well as those from nearby localities, make up the fauna of the Ripley formation which is approximately equivalent in age to the Monmouth and Peedee formations of the Atlantic Coastal Plain. Another locality containing some beautifully preserved Cretaceous fossils was discovered a few years ago near Dumas, Tippah County, Mississippi.

In seas covering other parts of the Gulf region, chalk deposits were formed, the most important being the Selma chalk of Alabama and the Austin chalk of Texas. Southern Florida was probably under deep water during most of Late Cretaceous time, for a great thickness of Cretaceous limestone has been found in well cores in that region.

Upper Cretaceous of Western North America

Rocky Mountain Geosyncline.—We have seen on previous pages how, during Early Cretaceous time, the seas advanced from both the north and south along the Rocky Mountain Trough, without actually meeting. We also learned that the Lower-Upper Cretaceous boundary was determined by a retreat of the northern arm of this invasion. During the late Upper Cretaceous, the Arctic arm again advanced southward down the Mackenzie Valley and a western arm of the Gulf of Mexico again advanced northward. The two seas met and made a continuous seaway from the Gulf of Mexico to the Arctic Ocean by way of the present Rocky Mountains and the Great Plains. At the time of the greatest advance of the sea, approximately 50 per cent of the United States was under water.

Toward the end of Cretaceous time the arm of the Arctic Ocean retreated northward, owing to a rise of the land in the Canadian Arctic region. The southern arm also retreated toward the Gulf of Mexico because of the rapid filling of the sea by sediments poured into it from the recently risen land to the west. The trough was finally transformed into a low swampy region, suitable for the formation of coal. In these swamps were formed the Cretaceous coal beds of the Rocky Mountain area from Alberta to Mexico.

Pacific Coast Region.—West of the Rocky Mountain Trough were high mountains which had been uplifted at the close of the Jurassic. The sediments from these mountains that gradually filled the trough, just as the sediments from Appalachia filled the Appalachian Trough during Paleozoic time. To the west of these Jurassic mountains, the Cretaceous seas advanced over the Pacific margins of the continent. The land mass, Cascadia, had been eroded to or below sea level, as had its eastern counterpart, Appalachia. The seas filled the old Pacific Coast Trough, as they had during various earlier periods. In Early Cretaceous time, the seas were probably discontinuous, with bays that were separated by barriers. Cretaceous fossiliferous deposits can be found at numerous places along the Pacific coast, from Lower California to Alaska.

Laramide Revolution (Birth of the Rockies).—The end of the Cretaceous, and with it the end of the Mesozoic Era, was marked in western North America by a widespread period of mountain building known as the Laramide Revolution (from Laramie, Wyoming). In the Rocky Mountain Geosyncline the crust was uplifted, folded, and faulted over a length of 3,000 miles from southern Mexico to Alaska, to produce the present Rocky Mountains. The affected area had a maximum width of 500 miles in the United States, being somewhat narrower to both the north and south. The history of this mountain building is very complex and involved considerable thrust faulting on a very large scale. Because the Rocky Mountains are much younger than the Appalachians and other mountain chains thus far discussed, their history can be deciphered better. However, since the Rocky Mountain region is far afield from the area being emphasized in this book, they will not be further discussed here. While this great uplift probably began about the end of Cretaceous time, earth movements continued in this region well into the Tertiary.

Volcanic Activity.—Considerable volcanic activity accompanied the Laramide revolution. Several prominent batholiths were formed, one of the most conspicuous being the Boulder Batholith in southwestern Montana, a great mass of granitic rock more than 100 miles long and some 75 miles wide. The famous copper deposits at Butte and Anaconda, Montana, are associated with this batholith. Another great batholith was intruded at this time in central Idaho, the eroded remnants of which now cover some 16,000 square miles.

Thin layers of bentonite or volcanic ash are associated with Upper Cretaceous chalks and limestones in Nebraska and Kansas, and less abundantly in the Gulf of Mexico region (Mississippi, Arkansas, and Alabama). These thin layers are often very useful for correlation purposes, both on the surface and in wells. The bentonite in the plains states is thought to have come from volcanoes on the anticline west of the Rocky Mountain Geosyncline (the so-called Mesocordilleran anticline); the source of the ash in the Gulf region may have been some volcanoes which are believed to have existed in southwestern Arkansas and near Jackson, Mississippi.

Recently a 6-inch layer of bentonite was discovered in the Wenonah formation near Runnemede, Camden County, New Jersey. Since this is the only such deposit so far discovered in Cretaceous formations along the Atlantic Coastal Plain, and since no Cretaceous volcanoes were thought to have existed east of the Mississippi, it is very difficult to tell the source of this ash deposit. It may have blown from Arkansas or Mississippi, although the distance seems too great. A more probable explanation is that the ash blew from some oceanic volcano now beneath the sea, possibly in the vicinity of Bermuda.[5]

Cretaceous Life

Cretaceous marine life, even more than that of the Jurassic, had a modern aspect, most of the species belonging to present-day families. In fact, in some places where unaltered Cretaceous fossil shells are found such as Coon Creek, Tennessee, and Dumas, Mississippi, the

---

[5] Recent oceanographic studies of Dr. Maurice Ewing and others have shown the presence of probable extinct volcanoes on the sea floor between New York and Bermuda.

amateur collector might have some difficulty recognizing the shells as fossils because of their similarity to the shells of recent species.

Upper Cretaceous fossils are relatively abundant along the Atlantic and Gulf Coastal Plain, and consequently deserve special consideration in this book. Extensive faunas have been obtained from New Jersey, Maryland, North and South Carolina, and Tennessee. While many of the classic localities are no longer available, it is still possible to obtain fair collections from this region.

Foraminifera.—These shelled protozoa are abundant in almost every marine Cretaceous deposit. They are often used as index fossils in the oil fields of Texas, Mississippi, and elsewhere.

Sponges.—Sponges are not common in Cretaceous deposits of America, but a few examples of the boring type (*Cliona*) have been found in New Jersey and Texas (Figure 231). While the boring work of the sponge can be noted on many Cretaceous bivalve shells, the actual spicules of the sponge have been noted in only a few cases. In other parts of the world, notably England and Germany, Cretaceous sponges are extremely abundant.

Corals.—Apparently there were few if any extensive coral reefs in the Cretaceous seas of America, although some reefs existed in Europe. Individual corals (*Trochocyathus* sp., *Micrabacia americana*, etc.) are occasionally found in the Cretaceous formations of New Jersey and elsewhere in the Coastal Plain.

Echinoderms.—Echinoids or sea urchins, apparently not too different from those of the modern ocean, existed in the Cretaceous seas that covered what are now the Atlantic and Gulf Coastal Plains (Figure 232). Crinoids were also present but were rare; one characteristic form was the genus *Uintacrinus*, known from the Niobrara formation (Upper Cretaceous) of Kansas. The most common New Jersey echinoids are *Catopygus pusilus* from Maple Shade and *Cassidulus aequoreus* from Atlantic Highlands.

Brachiopods.—These formed only a minor part of the sea life of Cretaceous time. Only three species have been reported from the Cretaceous of the Atlantic Coastal Plain, the most common being *Chrystothyris* (*Terebratella*) *plicata* from the Navesink formation of New Jersey (Figure 207).

Annelida.—Worm burrows are common in many Cretaceous deposits. The tubes and fillings of *Hamulus, Diploconcha,* and *Longitubus* make excellent index fossils (Figures 217, 218, and 219).

CRETACEOUS FOSSILS FROM NEW JERSEY

FIG. 205. Cephalopoda, *Belemnitella*   FIG. 208. Pelecypoda, *Ostrea*
           americana.   *mesenterica.*
FIG. 206. Pelecypods, *Inoceramus*   FIG. 209. Pelecypoda, *Ostrea nasuta.*
           sagensis.   FIG. 210. Pelecypoda, *Pinna laqueata.*
FIG. 207. Brachiopoda, *Chrystothyris*   FIG. 211. Pelecypoda, *Neithea quin-*
           plicata.   *quescostata.*
                                                FIG. 212. Shark tooth.

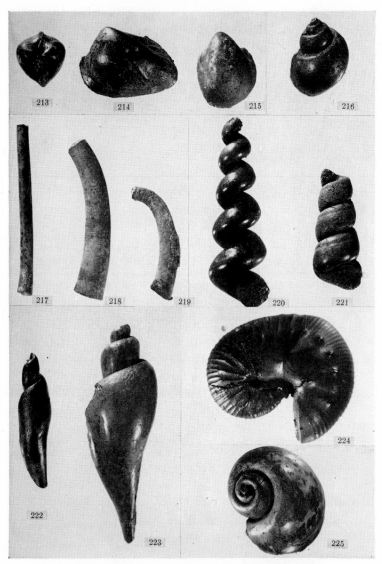

CRETACEOUS FOSSILS FROM NEW JERSEY

FIG. 213. Pelecypoda, *Cardium tenuistriatum.*
FIG. 214. Pelecypoda, *Ideonarca neglecta.*
FIG. 215. Pelecypoda, *Cardium tenuistriatum.*
FIG. 216. Gastropoda, *Lunatia halli.*
FIG. 217. Annelida, *Hamulus falcatus.*

FIG. 218. Annelida, *Hamulus lineatus.*
FIG. 219. Annelida, *Diploconcha cretacea.*
FIG. 220. Gastropoda, *Turritella vertebroides.*
FIG. 221. Gastropoda, *Turritella encrinoides.*

(Continued on opposite page.→)

Bryozoa.—These were present in the Cretaceous seas, but were not as abundant as they were to be in the Eocene.

Pelecypoda.—This group of mollusks became particularly numerous, certain species of *Ostrea, Exogyra, Gryphaea,* etc., forming extensive reefs. As was noted earlier in this chapter, certain species of the large clam *Exogyra* are used as index fossils of different phases of Late Cretaceous time. Other characteristic genera of the Upper Cretaceous deposits are *Pinna, Trigona, Pecten, Cucullaea,* and *Anomia* (Figures 210 and 211). Peculiar aberrant kinds of pelecypods, known as Rudistids, reached a length of 30 inches and more closely resembled corals than mollusks. These were especially abundant in the warm Cretaceous seas of Cuba.

Gastropoda.—Sea snails were almost as abundant as the clams in the Cretaceous seas of eastern America, although none of them reached the large size of the pelecypods *Inoceramus* (Figure 206) and *Exogyra.* Some of the genera still live today; others are extinct but have closely related living descendants. Among the most common genera from the Upper Cretaceous deposits of the Atlantic Coastal Plain are *Turritella, Gyrodes, Pyropsis, Anchura,* and *Volutomorpha* (Figures 220, 221, 222 and 225).

Cephalopoda.—The ammonites were on the decline during the Cretaceous, although many species persisted until the end of the period. Some of the forms were very large; for example, *Parapuzosia brady,* from Montana, reached a diameter of over three feet.[6] Only about a dozen species are known from the Atlantic Coastal Plain and a few more from the Gulf of Mexico region. One of the most characteristic ammonites is *Placenticeras placenta* (Figure 226), of which specimens up to one foot in diameter are frequently found at the brickyard at Maple Shade, New Jersey. Other ammonites include the coiled *Mortoniceras delawarensis* (Figure 228) and *Scaphites hippocrepis* (Figure 224), and the straight *Baculites ovatus* (Figure 233).

The nautiloids were much less conspicuous than the ammonites but were to become the dominant cephalopods of the next era (Cenozoic).

The belemnites resembled those of the Jurassic and were locally very abundant. Pens of the squid-like *Belemnitella americana* (Figures

---

[6] An ammonite more than eight feet in diameter has been reported from the Cretaceous rocks of Westphalia, Germany.

FIG. 222. Gastropoda, *Volutomorpha conradi.*

FIG. 223. Gastropoda, *Rostellites nasutus.*

FIG. 224. Cephalopoda, *Scaphites hippocrepis.*

FIG. 225. Gastropoda, *Gyrodes crenata.*

CRETACEOUS FOSSILS FROM NEW JERSEY

FIG. 226.   Ammonite, *Placenticeras placenta*.
FIG. 227.   Ammonite, *Mortoniceras delawarensis*.
FIG. 228.   Lobster, *Hoploparia gabbi*.

FIG. 229.   Pelecypoda, *Exogyra costata*.
FIG. 230.   Pelecypoda, *Exogyra ponderosa*.
FIG. 231.   Sponge, *Cliona cretacea*.

204 and 205) are very abundant in the Upper Cretaceous deposits at
Mullica Hill, Cream Ridge, and New Egypt, New Jersey, and at various localities in South Carolina, Alabama, and Mississippi.

Crustacea.—Crabs were numerous. Although perfect fossil specimens are rarely found in Cretaceous rocks, claws and fragments of the

Fig. 232. Cretaceous starfish, *Austinaster mccarteri*. (Texas Memorial Mus.)

carapace are not infrequently found at Maple Shade, along the Chesapeake and Delaware Canal, and elsewhere. A small but perfect crab, described as a new species, was recently discovered at Maple Shade by an amateur collector. Crawfish and lobsters were also present in

Fig. 233. The straight ammonite *Baculites,* common in the Merchantville formation of New Jersey.

the Cretaceous seas but, as in the case of the crabs, are usually represented in the fossil state merely by fragments. Again, one almost perfect specimen of *Hoploparia gabbi* (Figure 227) was recently discovered in the Maple Shade brickyard, also by an amateur collector.

Most of the claws found at Maple Shade, Beers Hill, and along the Chesapeake and Delaware Canal belong to the genus *Callianassa*.

Other crustacea included the minute ostracods (Figure 234) and the barnacles.

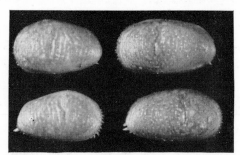

FIG. 234. Some Cretaceous ostracodes. (Ruth Schmidt.)

Fish.—The teleosts, or modern-type bony fish, were very conspicuous in the Cretaceous seas, while the ganoids had almost completely disappeared. Such modern types as the herring, cod, salmon, mullet, and catfish are represented as fossils in Cretaceous deposits. Sharks and rays related to modern genera were also abundant and their remains, especially their teeth, are found in most marine Cretaceous deposits (Figures 212 and 235). Other Cretaceous fish belonged to now-

FIG. 235. Dental plate of the Cretaceous ray *Myliobatis*.

extinct families, the most conspicuous being *Protheus*, a giant carnivorous fish which grew to 15 feet in length. Its fossils are frequently found in the chalk deposits of Kansas.

Fish fossils are not common in the Cretaceous deposits of the Atlantic Coastal Plain, although shark teeth are frequently found at Maple Shade, Mullica Hill, and Cream Ridge in New Jersey, as well as along the Chesapeake and Delaware Canal. A few vertebrae and jaw parts have also been found at Maple Shade.

Amphibia.—These were very rare in the Cretaceous, although a few fossil salamanders have been found.

Reptiles.—Gigantic dinosaurs continued to dominate the land until the end of the Cretaceous period. Among the most conspicuous of the Cretaceous dinosaurs were the following:

Tyrannosaurus. Nothing more frightful can be imagined than *Tyrannosaurus rex*, a carnivorous dinosaur which measured more than 50 feet from tip of nose to tip of tail and stood 18 feet high when erect. This animal must have weighed from eight to ten tons. Its front legs were greatly reduced in size and could not have been used for locomotion, but may have functioned as grasping organs. Fossil remains of this gigantic creature have been found in Montana, Alberta, and elsewhere in western North America.

Triceratops. This was the Great Horned dinosaur and was about 20 to 30 feet in length and about eight feet in height (Figure 236).

FIG. 236. A Cretaceous landscape. The armored dinosaur *Triceratops* in the foreground, with some flying reptiles, *Pteranodon,* flying overhead. (J. P. Cowan, Hughes Tool Co.)

It walked on all four legs and was characterized by its enormous head, which constituted about one third of the length of the animal. The head was equipped with strong horns, very suitable for fighting. Fossil remains of *Triceratops* have been found in western North America.

There were numerous other dinosaurs closely related to *Triceratops,* one of the most interesting being *Protoceratops,* a small animal about five to six feet in length which was probably a direct ancestor of the larger *Triceratops*. *Protoceratops* has been found only in the Upper Cretaceous deposits of Mongolia, but there is no reason why it might not be found in some of the Cretaceous deposits of the western United States. In spite of their large size and belligerent appearance, the Ceratopsia (*Triceratops*, etc.) were inoffensive plant eaters.

Trachodon or Hadrosaurus. These are the duck-billed dinosaurs, among the most common of Cretaceous reptiles. These animals walked

Fig. 237. Restoration of the duck-bill dinosaur (*Hadrosaurus* or *Trachodon*) at Rapid City, South Dakota.

on their hind legs, although they may at times also have used their smaller front legs for locomotion—particularly to escape from their feared contemporary, *Tyrannosaurus*.

The first dinosaur skeleton found in America was that of *Hadrosaurus foulkii*, found in a marl pit near Haddonfield, New Jersey. This was discovered in 1858 and was described in detail by Dr. Joseph Leidy. Other duck-billed dinosaurs have been found in the western part of America (South Dakota, Wyoming, Alberta, etc.) and have been described under the name *Trachodon* (Figure 237). Since the original skeleton of *Hadrosaurus* lacked a head, it never could be proved that these two duck-billed dinosaurs were one and the same, although it is now generally believed that the two genera are identical or very closely related.

The Eastern Cretaceous is not a favorable place for the preservation of dinosaur fossils. In the first place, most of the Coastal Plain Cretaceous is of marine origin, while dinosaur remains would be more likely to be found in nonmarine deposits. Furthermore, the type of rock or sand is not as suitable for preservation as the Cretaceous rocks of the West. Consequently, except for a few extremely fragmentary bones, no dinosaur skeletons were found in the Cretaceous rocks of the Atlantic Coastal Plain states until late in 1947, when another partial skeleton of a *Hadrosaurus* was found in a pit at Sewell, Gloucester County, New Jersey. This was apparently smaller than the original Haddonfield specimen, although closely related. It was assigned to the same genus but a different species, called *Hadrosaurus minor* (Figures 238 and 239).

The duck-billed dinosaurs probably lived in swamps and rivers. The two New Jersey specimens are found associated with marine fossils (mostly mollusks) and may have been bogged down in a coastal marsh, or perhaps carried down to the sea by an ancient river. A few fragmentary bones of duck-billed dinosaurs have been found at Barnsboro, Mullica Hill, Swedesboro, Matawan, and Keyport, New Jersey, but none are as complete as the specimens from Haddonfield and Sewell.

Not all Cretaceous dinosaurs were of great size. Some, such as *Ornitholestes* and *Struthiomimus* were about the size of ostriches and somewhat resembled them in appearance. Exceedingly fragmentary bones of another kind of dinosaur, probably a carnivore, have been found in New Jersey, but this identification has been questioned. A few partial skeletons of small dinosaurs have also been found in Lower Cretaceous rocks at Bladensburg and Muirkirk, Maryland, near Washington, D. C. The most complete specimen is that of *Pleurocolus nanus,* an animal probably about 15 feet in length and five feet in height. Other incomplete dinosaur bones have been found in the Cretaceous deposits of North Carolina, Georgia, and Alabama.

Dinosaurs, like many reptiles, reproduced by eggs. The eggs of *Protoceratops* have been found in the Gobi Desert. These eggs are similar in shape and in texture to those of modern turtles. In two of these eggs were found the bones of embryo dinosaurs. A few fragments of dinosaur eggs have been found in Upper Cretaceous beds

Fig. 238. The discovery of a leg bone of the dinosaur *Hadrosaurus* at a greensand pit at Sewell, New Jersey. (Paul Kornman.)

Fig. 239. The leg is removed after being coated with plaster and fastened to a plank.

FIG. 240. Cretaceous marine reptiles: Mosasaur (above) and Plesiosaur (below). (Colorado Mus. Nat. Hist.)

near Powell, Wyoming, and proof of their presence in other deposits
of similar age may be expected with further search.

Ichthyosaurs. These marine reptiles still lived in the seas, but their
fossils are not as numerous as in Jurassic rocks.

Fig. 241. Skull of Mosasaur from New Jersey. (Rutgers Univ.)

Plesiosaurs. The "sea serpents" of the Cretaceous seas were even
larger than those of the Jurassic. *Elasmosaurus* from Kansas was
over 40 feet in length, of which 22 feet was the slender neck. Fragmental remains of several plesiosaurs have been found in southern
New Jersey, but no perfect specimens have been obtained (Figure 240).

Fig. 242. Restoration of Mosasaur. (Rutgers Univ.)

Mosasaurs. These animals, known only from Cretaceous deposits,
comprised a group of marine reptiles related to the lizards. They
reached a length of 30 to 40 feet. Their limbs were converted into
flippers much like those of a whale. They were equipped with sharp
curved teeth and must have been formidable monsters of these ancient

seas. Incomplete mosasaur remains have been found in New Jersey on numerous occasions, 19 species in three genera having been recorded. Among the New Jersey localities where mosasaurs have been found are Red Bank, Sewell, Birmingham, Hornerstown, Swedesboro, and Barnsboro (Figures 241 and 242).

Pterosaurs. The pterosaurs or flying reptiles were abundant during Cretaceous time and were of immense size. Some of these creatures had a wing spread of 20 to 25 feet and were veritable flying dragons. Fossil remains of several of these pterosaurs have been found in the Cretaceous rocks of Kansas. (See Figure 236.)

Crocodiles. Animals very similar to our modern crocodiles swam in Cretaceous seas and fresh-water lakes. Remains have been found at various places in New Jersey, North Carolina, and on the Gulf Coastal Plain.

Turtles. Some very large sea turtles existed in the Cretaceous oceans, probably the largest being *Archelon,* known from the Cretaceous of Kansas. Turtle remains are also common in the Upper Cretaceous deposits of the Gulf Coastal Plain and a few are known from the Atlantic Coastal Plain. A few years ago, the fossil remains of an almost perfect turtle (*Podocdemis*) were found in the Merchantville formation at Maple Shade, New Jersey.

Lizards and Snakes. The earliest known lizards and snakes occurred in the Cretaceous period, but their fossils are rare, and little is known about them.

Extinction of the Dinosaurs and Other Large Reptiles.—The end of the Cretaceous period saw the complete extinction of the dinosaurs, ichthyosaurs, plesiosaurs, mosasaurs, and pterosaurs. On the other hand, the crocodiles, turtles, lizards, and snakes continued to exist into Cenozoic time, and have persisted to the present day.

The explanation of the extinction of these large reptiles is one of the many unsolved problems of paleontological science, and is possibly the one that has received the greatest amount of speculation, particularly among the general public. Let us examine a few of the proposed answers to this question.

1. The dinosaurs and other large reptiles began to die out because of "racial senescence," just as the trilobites had millions of years earlier. This is an evolutionary trend that may be hastened by overspecialization, such as the cumbersome and fantastic animal forms of the Jurassic and Cretaceous.

2. Perhaps they did not die out suddenly. In many places there is a conspicuous gap, or unconformity between the Cretaceous and Eocene deposits, and thus the extinction may have been more gradual than is indicated by the exposed rocks.
3. The exceedingly small brain may have been insufficient to permit the survival of such large creatures.
4. The mammals were beginning to appear in considerable numbers in Late Cretaceous time and, being more active and possessing larger brains, may have preyed upon the much larger dinosaurs.
5. The mammals may have devoured large numbers of the eggs of the dinosaurs and other reptiles.
6. Tremendous mountain building took place near the end of Cretaceous time. During this period of upheaval, the widespread warm climate of the Cretaceous in all probability gradually changed to the temperate and probably more seasonal climate of the Cenozoic era. Many of the large reptiles may have been unable to adapt themselves to this changing environment.

Some writers have depicted a sudden and drastic end of the race of dinosaurs and have spoken of the end of the Cretaceous as the "time of great dying." The transition between Cretaceous and Cenozoic time was very gradual, and changes in the fauna, such as the extinction of the dinosaurs, were probably very much slower than is suggested by the available paleontological record. Nevertheless, it is very remarkable that none of the dinosaurs, plesiosaurs, ichthyosaurs, mosasaurs, or pterosaurs managed to survive into Cenozoic time, while their generally smaller relatives such as the crocodiles, lizards, and snakes were able to survive to the present day.

Is it not possible that a few of the dinosaurs did manage to survive beyond the end of the Cretaceous? Sir Arthur Conan Doyle's *The Lost World* put forth the fantastic suggestion that some dinosaurs may have survived into the present time on an isolated plateau in South America. It is not inconceivable, however, that a few survived into Paleocene time in some favorable locality in the world and perhaps a Paleocene dinosaur will some day be discovered.

Birds.—Fossils of birds are extremely rare, the best Cretaceous fossils having been found in Kansas. One of these *Hesperornis* was six feet in height and had apparently completely lost the power of flight. Another of the Cretaceous birds, *Ichthyornis*, was much smaller and had powerful wings.

Mammals.—Although more numerous than in the Jurassic, mammals did not form a conspicuous feature of the fauna of Cretaceous time. They were, however, to become dominant during the Cenozoic era. A few of the primitive, and now extinct, types of the Jurassic continued into Cretaceous time. There were also some primitive marsupials and insectivores. The only Cretaceous mammal fossils found in North America have come from the Laramie group at the top of the Upper Cretaceous. The great development of mammals at the end of the Cretaceous and in Cenozoic time is correlated not only with the extinction of the dinosaurs but also with the spread of the grasses and other flowering plants.

Plants.—Our oldest fossils of angiosperms (flowering plants) date from the Cretaceous, although it is almost certain that they also existed during the Jurassic. Because of their high development in the Cretaceous, we must assume a long period of evolution prior to the beginning of the Cretaceous.

The flora of the Lower Cretaceous of the Atlantic Coastal Plain (Potomac group) is made up of ferns, cycads, and conifers, with a few species of flowering plants. The flowering plants become more conspicuous toward the end of Early Cretaceous time, and by the beginning of Upper Cretaceous time (Raritan) they formed the dominant element of the flora.

Seventy per cent of the flora of the Raritan formation is made up of angiosperms. Leaf impressions and pieces of lignitized or petrified wood are occasionally found in pits of the Raritan formation in Middlesex County, New Jersey. A similar flora has been described from the clays of the Tuscaloosa formation in South Carolina, which is thought to be of the same age as the Raritan (basal Upper Cretaceous).

Some fairly large trees of modern type apparently thrived during Upper Cretaceous time. Pieces of Upper Cretaceous wood, in excellent preservation, have been obtained from well borings in New Jersey. These are frequently difficult to distinguish from modern logs, although they crumble and crack when exposed to the air. Extensive collections of flowering plants have been obtained from the Dakota sandstones of the Great Plains and from similar Upper Cretaceous rocks of the western states. Evidence of a mild climate in the Arctic regions during Cretaceous time is afforded by the presence of sandstones with rich deposits of land plants in western Greenland, 300 miles north of the Arctic Circle, and by the presence of coal with an associated flora of Cretaceous age along the Arctic shores of Canada, from Coronation Gulf to the Alaska boundary.

Economic Resources of the Cretaceous

Coal.—This valuable mineral occurs in various deposits of Upper Cretaceous age throughout the Rocky Mountain area. As a rule, the coal is bituminous or subbituminous and is of considerably lower grade than the Carboniferous beds of the eastern part of the continent. However, where there has been sufficient local metamorphism, as in the Crested Butte field in central Colorado, a good grade of anthracite is mined. Most of the Cretaceous coal comes from formations of the Laramie group in Wyoming, Utah, Colorado, and Montana. In Alberta, Canada, coal also occurs in deposits of Lower Cretaceous age, and there are also extensive coal deposits throughout the Rocky Mountain area in rocks of Paleocene age (Fort Union). It has recently been estimated that 65 per cent of the coal reserves of the United States are in the western part of the country.

Petroleum.—Cretaceous rocks are among the most important source beds of petroleum in North America. Many of the rich oil fields of Texas, Mexico, Mississippi, and Wyoming produce from deeply buried Cretaceous sands. The East Texas Oil Field near Kilgore and Palestine has produced extensively from the Woodbine formation. The recent discovery of oil in the Cretaceous formations of Mississippi, and the less-important discoveries of oil in the Cretaceous of Alabama and Florida have given rise to the hope that buried formations of similar age along the Atlantic Coast between New Jersey and Georgia may also prove to be sources of petroleum.

Clay.—Clay suitable for bricks is found in deposits of most geologic ages. However, the Cretaceous clays of New Jersey deserve special consideration because of their use in the industrial region around Raritan Bay. The great clay industry of New Jersey exists in a belt extending across the state southwestward from Raritan Bay and down the Delaware River to Salem County. The clays are of various kinds, ranging from the nearly white or steel-blue fireclays through the stoneware and terra-cotta clays to black sandy clays containing considerable pyrite and marcasite. Most of these clays occur in the Raritan formation and are worked chiefly in the vicinity of Woodbridge, Sayreville, South River, Perth Amboy, South Amboy, and Cliffwood in Middlesex County.

Glauconite (Greensand).—This mineral, a hydrous silicate of potassium and iron, occurs in Cretaceous and Eocene formations from New Jersey southward. In New Jersey it occurs especially in the Marshalltown, Navesink, Hornerstown, and Manasquan formations.

Greensand marl from New Jersey and other coastal plain states was formerly dug extensively for fertilizer, but has been replaced to a large extent during recent years by artificial fertilizers. Many abandoned marl pits in New Jersey, Delaware, and North Carolina are still sources of vertebrate and invertebrate fossils.

During World War I, an investigation of these deposits was undertaken to determine if they could be used as a source of potash to replace the supply cut off from abroad. The results of the investigation showed a relatively high degree of concentration of potash and potassium in some New Jersey deposits and a somewhat lower concentration in greensand deposits farther south (5.84 per cent potassium and 7.07 per cent potash in New Jersey, as contrasted with 2.46 per cent and 2.96 per cent in North Carolina). However, the development of potash supplies from western United States has discouraged further development of the New Jersey sources.

During recent years greensand marl has been dug as a water softener; three such pits are now operating in New Jersey, at Sewell, Birmingham, and Medford. Most of this marl is of Eocene age (Hornerstown formation) although the deeper layers are undoubtedly of Cretaceous age (Navesink formation). Several unusual fossils including a dinosaur, a mosasaur, and a crocodile, were dug from the Cretaceous layer at the pit at Sewell.

FURTHER READING FOR CHAPTERS 17–19

ANDERSON, J. L., et al. Cretaceous and Tertiary Subsurface Geology of Maryland. Maryland Dept. Geol., Mines and Water Resources Bull. 2 (1948).

ASHLEY, GEORGE H. A Syllabus of Pennsylvania Geology and Mineral Resources. Pennsylvania Topog. and Geol. Surv. Bull. G-1 (1931).

BERRY, E. W. "The Upper Cretaceous Floras of the World," in Upper Cretaceous, Maryland Geol. Surv. (1919), pp. 183–313.

BOCK, WILLIAM. A New Small Reptile from the Triassic of Pennsylvania. Acad. Nat. Sci. Phila. Notulae Naturae, No. 154 (1945).

———. New Crustaceans from the Lockatong of the Newark Series. Ibid., No. 183 (1946).

CARTER, CHARLES W. "The Upper Cretaceous Deposits of the Chesapeake and Delaware Canal of Maryland and Delaware," Maryland Geol. Surv., XIII, Pt. 6 (1937), pp. 237–81.

CEDERSTROM, D. J. "Structural Geology of Southeastern Virginia," Bull. Amer. Assoc. Petrol. Geol., XXIX (1945), pp. 71–95.

CHAFFEE, ROBERT G. A New Jersey Mosasaur of the Subfamily Platecarpinae. Acad. Nat. Sci. Phila. Notulae Naturae, No. 37 (1939).

CLARK, W. B., and MILLER, B. L. The Physiography and Geology of the Coastal Plain Province of Virginia. Virginia Geol. Surv. Bull. 4 (1912).

CLARK, WILLIAM, et al. The Upper Cretaceous of Maryland. Maryland Geol. Surv. (1916).

COLBERT, E. H. "Hypsognathus, a Triassic Reptile from New Jersey," Bull. Amer. Mus. Nat. Hist., LXXXVI (1946), pp. 225–74.

COLBERT, E. H. "A Hydrosaurian Dinosaur from New Jersey," *Proc. Acad. Nat. Sci. Phila.,* C (1948), pp. 23–37.

———. *The Dinosaur Book.* New York: McGraw-Hill Book Co., Inc., 1951.

COOKE, C. WYTHE. *Geology of the Coastal Plain of South Carolina.* U.S. Geol. Surv. Bull. 867 (1936).

———. *Geology of the Coastal Plain of Georgia. Ibid.,* Bull. 941 (1943).

DUNBAR, CARL O. *Historical Geology.* New York: John Wiley & Sons, Inc., 1949, Chs. 14–16.

EARDLEY, A. J. *Structural Geology of North America.* New York: Harper & Bros., 1951.

HUSSEY, R. C. *Historical Geology.* New York: McGraw-Hill Book Co., Inc., 1948.

IMLAY, R. W. *Lower Cretaceous and Jurassic Formations of Southern Arkansas and Their Oil and Gas Possibilities.* Arkansas Geol. Surv. Inform. Cir. 12 (1940).

———. "Jurassic Formations of the Gulf Coast," *Bull. Amer. Assoc. Petrol. Geol.,* XXVII (1943).

JEPSEN, GLENN L. *A Natural Library.* New Jersey State Museum Bull. 3 (1949).

LEWIS, J. V., and KUMMEL, H. B. *The Geology of New Jersey.* New Jersey Geol. Surv. Bull. 50 (1940).

McGLOTHLIN, T. "General Geology of Mississippi," *Bull. Amer. Assoc. Petrol. Geol.,* XXVIII (1944), pp. 29–62.

McLAUGHLIN, DEAN, and WILLARD, BRADFORD. "Triassic Facies in the Delaware Valley," *Proc. Pennsylvania Acad. Sci.,* XXIII (1949), pp. 34–44.

MOORE, RAYMOND C. *An Introduction to Historical Geology.* New York: McGraw-Hill Book Co., Inc., 1949, Chs. 13–16.

RICHARDS, HORACE G. "Fauna of the Raritan Formation of New Jersey," *Proc. Acad. Nat. Sci. Phila.,* XCV (1943), pp. 15–32.

———. *Fossil Mollusks from the Triassic of Pennsylvania.* Acad. Nat. Sci. Phila. Notulae Naturae, No. 206 (1948).

———. "Studies on the Subsurface Geology and Paleontology of the Atlantic Coastal Plain," *Proc. Acad. Nat. Sci. Phila.,* C (1948), pp. 39–76.

———. *Geology of the Coastal Plain of North Carolina.* Trans. Amer. Philos. Soc., XL, Pt. 1 (1950).

SCHUCHERT, CHARLES. *Stratigraphy of the Eastern and Central United States.* New York: John Wiley & Sons, Inc., 1943.

SPANGLER, W. B., and PETERSON, J. J. "Geology of the Atlantic Coastal Plain in New Jersey, Delaware, Maryland and Virginia," *Bull. Amer. Assoc. Petrol. Geol.,* XXXIV (1950).

STEPHENSON, L. W. "Geology of Alabama (Mesozoic)," Geol. Surv. Alabama, *Special Report* 14 (1926), pp. 231–50.

STEPHENSON, L. W., *et al.* "Correlations of the Outcropping Cretaceous Formations of the Atlantic and Gulf Coastal Plain and Trans-Pecos Texas," *Bull. Geol. Soc. Amer.,* LIII (1942), pp. 435–48.

STEPHENSON, L. W., and RATHBUN, M. J. *Cretaceous Formations of North Carolina.* North Carolina Geol. and Econ. Surv., V (1923).

WADE, BRUCE. *The Fauna of the Ripley Formation on Coon Creek, Tennessee.* U.S. Geol. Surv. Prof. Paper 137 (1926).

WELLER, STUART. *A Report on the Cretaceous Paleontology of New Jersey.* New Jersey Geol. Surv. Paleontology, Series IV (1907).

WOODWORTH, J. B., and WIGGLESWORTH, E. *Geography and Geology of the Region Including Cape Cod, the Elizabeth Islands, Nantucket, Martha's Vineyard, No Man's Land, and Block Island.* Memoir Mus. Comp. Zool., LII (1934).

CHAPTER 20

THE CENOZOIC ERA

The Cenozoic era is the last major division of geologic time. Estimates based upon radioactive minerals suggest that the length of this era was about 60,000,000 years. Although the elapsed time of the Cenozoic is shorter than any major preceding era, some very important events took place during its several subdivisions. There were extensive episodes of mountain building, particularly in western North America, and one epoch, the Pleistocene, was marked by widespread advances of ice from the polar regions.

The Cenozoic era is usually divided into two periods, the Tertiary and the Quaternary. These periods, in turn, are subdivided into various epochs. The two terms, "Tertiary" and "Quaternary," although widely used in geologic literature, are actually relics of an obsolete system of classification (see page 26), and, in the opinion of many geologists, should be abandoned. Dr. R. F. Flint, in a book on the Pleistocene, points out that the break between the Pliocene and Pleistocene is not as great as was once supposed, and suggests that the Pleistocene can best be regarded as an epoch in the Cenozoic era, of the same rank as the Tertiary "periods" such as Eocene and Oligocene. He further believes that all the major subdivisions, from Paleocene to Recent, would constitute a single period divided in turn into the various epochs such as the Paleocene, Eocene, etc.

While, according to this logic, the term "Tertiary" should be abandoned, it is actually a very useful term. Since the term has been used so extensively in previous writings, we will continue to use it in this book, although an effort will be made to employ the more inclusive term "Cenozoic" or the various epoch names whenever possible. Also, as we shall see in Chapter 26, there is some difference of opinion in regard to the term "Recent." Many geologists use the term for the time following the end of the last (Wisconsin) glaciation. In other words, the term is practically synonymous with "post-glacial." Flint, on the other hand, points out that the dividing line between the Pleistocene and Recent varies throughout the world because the ice sheets retreated from different places at different times. He therefore proposes to use the terms "recent" and "post-glacial" in an informal sense, without exact stratigraphic definition.[1]

[1] Richard F. Flint, *Glacial Geology and the Pleistocene Epoch* (New York: John Wiley & Sons, Inc., 1947), p. 209.

Before passing on to a discussion of the geological history of the Cenozoic era it will be well to stress again the fact that this era is the shortest of the major eras, and that the various epochs into which it has been divided are very much shorter than the periods of Paleozoic or Mesozoic time. Since the epochs of the Cenozoic are much more recent and have been less obliterated by geologic time, we are able to decipher somewhat more of their history than we can of the earlier periods. For this reason, we are devoting individual chapters to the various epochs in spite of their relatively short duration.

Cenozoic history is of particular interest to the geologist from the Middle Atlantic States because much of the Atlantic Coastal Plain, from New Jersey to Florida, is covered with marine sediments deposited during the various stages of this era. Cenozoic deposits also occur along the coast of the Gulf of Mexico and southward into Mexico, where they are of great economic importance because they contain some of the richest oil reserves of America.

A few years ago it was commonly believed that the Cenozoic, as well as the Mesozoic history of the Atlantic and Gulf Coastal Plain was relatively simple, and that the "basement rock" was merely covered with horizontal, overlapping layers representing the major divisions of Cretaceous and Cenozoic time. However, since the discovery of oil in the formations underlying the Gulf Coast, a great deal of intensive geological work has been done in this region, and has shown that the history of the rocks is not nearly as simple as was once supposed. Even less was known about the geological history of the Atlantic Coastal Plain. The discovery of oil in Florida and Alabama has turned the attention of oil geologists to the Atlantic Coastal Plain, and some careful work has been done. Two interesting facts have been brought to light by this work: (1) the "basement" rock is buried deeper than was previously supposed, and (2) sediments representing certain formations or ages that are not present on the surface do exist underground. These studies have also produced evidence which indicates the existence of hitherto unsuspected faults and other structures. All this shows that the geological history of the Atlantic Coastal Plain, like that of the Coastal Plain of the Gulf of Mexico, is much more complex than was believed only a few years ago.

Much of the information on which the following chapters are based has been obtained during the past few years by petroleum geologists who are actively engaged in a detailed study of the surface and subsurface geology of the Atlantic and Gulf Coastal plains. Thus the economic needs of the world have given an incentive to the earth scientist to discover further details of geological history.

CHAPTER 21

THE EOCENE (INCLUDING PALEOCENE)

The term "Eocene," derived from the Greek *eo* meaning "dawn" and *kainos* meaning "recent," was originally used by Charles Lyell to designate the earliest division of the Cenozoic era. The term Paleocene, also taken from the Greek, *paleo* meaning "ancient" and *kainos*, was introduced in 1874 by Carl Schimper, as there seemed to be a well-marked division between the formations originally regarded as earliest Eocene and the later deposits of that epoch.

New Jersey	Virginia	North Carolina	South Carolina	Gulf Coast
(subsurface only)	Chickahominy (subsurface only)	Castle Hayne	Santee Cooper	JACKSON
Shark River-Manasquan	Nanjemoy	{"Middle Eocene"-	McBean	CLAIBORNE
Vincentown -Hornerstown-	-Aquia———		Black Mingo	WILCOX
		(subsurface only)	(subsurface only)	MIDWAY (Paleocene)

This separation can be demonstrated in the western part of the United States, where there was a more or less definite break in the fauna and flora at the end of Paleocene time. The separation is not nearly as obvious in the marine deposits of the Atlantic and Gulf Coasts and many geologists prefer to use the term Eocene for the entire interval between the Upper Cretaceous and the Oligocene. As will be pointed out later, the deposits of Paleocene age (= Midway) are very similar to those of the next younger formation (Wilcox) and, at least in some places along the Atlantic coast, are practically indistinguishable, the one grading into the other, a fact that can best be explained by continuity of deposition.

Because of the extensive geological work in the oil fields of the Gulf Coastal Plain, the major subdivisions of the Cenozoic of the region have become standard for all of eastern North America. For this reason, our discussion of the various stages of the Eocene will start in the better understood Gulf region and progress northward to the somewhat less studied Atlantic Coastal Plain. The major divisions of the Eocene are:

4. Jackson
3. Claiborne
2. Wilcox
1. Midway (Paleocene)

Interval between the Cretaceous and Eocene

Most geologists agree that there was a general uplift of the North American continent at the close of Upper Cretaceous time. This uplift caused the seas to withdraw from the Atlantic and Gulf Coastal plains as well as from the trough in the interior of the continent. As a whole, there is a tremendous difference between the faunas and floras of the Cretaceous and Eocene, a fact which points to a long period of erosion and nondeposition between these two periods. Changes in the fauna took place not only in the sea but also on land. We have just seen that the dinosaurs and other large Cretaceous reptiles became extinct at the end of the Cretaceous.

The widespread withdrawal of the sea may not have been complete, and the erosion interval may not have been as long, in some sections of the continent as in others. Evidence has recently come to light which suggests that southern Florida was submerged continuously from late Upper Cretaceous time far into the Eocene. Farther north, as revealed by a study of fossils obtained from wells along the New Jersey coast, it is very difficult to recognize a break between the highest Cretaceous level, such as the Red Bank and Tinton formations, and the lowest Eocene such as the Hornerstown formation.

Farther inland the break is more apparent, but it is possible that the erosion interval was not of great duration along the coast of New Jersey. Geologists have usually regarded the lowest Eocene formation of New Jersey, the Hornerstown formation, as equivalent to the Wilcox formation of the Gulf Coast. However, recent studies on the foraminifera obtained from well samples suggest that the lower part of the formation, which does not outcrop, dates from the Midway (Paleocene), thereby narrowing the time gap between the Cretaceous and the Eocene. It should be pointed out that the three lower Eocene formations of New Jersey, Hornerstown, Vincentown, and Manasquan were, until 1928, regarded as Upper Cretaceous. While careful studies of their faunas show them to be of Eocene age, they do possess a number of significant Cretaceous elements.

Midway Time (Paleocene)

Gulf Coast.—In no place did the Midway seas advance as far over the land as had those of the Upper Cretaceous. The seas of the in-

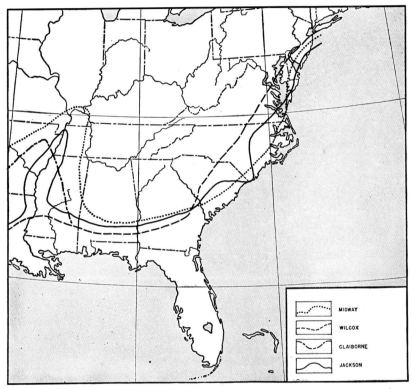

FIG. 243. Hypothetical shore lines during Paleocene and Eocene times along the Atlantic and eastern Gulf Coastal Plains.

terior of the continent were reduced to a narrow arm. Western Texas was dry land during this stage, although eastern Texas, Louisiana, Mississippi, and western Alabama were submerged. The Midway seas advanced up the Mississippi embayment as far as southern Illinois (Figure 243).

Atlantic Coast.—The Midway seas submerged all of Florida and southern Georgia almost to the inner edge of the Coastal Plain (Fall Line). South Carolina was less extensively covered and it is probable that there the shore line turned northeast. This is suggested by the fact that Midway fossils have been found only in wells in the extreme coastal regions of North and South Carolina. It is possible that the Midway seas extended farther inland and that the deposits laid down at that time have subsequently been eroded. However, it is more probable that the interval between the Cretaceous and the Eocene was prolonged in this region, and that extensive submergence of the Carolinas did not take place until Wilcox time.

Apparently the Midway seas did not extend very far inland over Virginia, Maryland, Delaware, and New Jersey. Until very recently, no deposits of this age were known north of Georgia. However, recent studies of deep wells have revealed the presence of Midway fossils, especially foraminifera, beneath the later Eocene deposits as far north as Asbury Park, New Jersey. In New Jersey these Midway fossils occur in the lower (subsurface) part of the Hornerstown formation, and in Maryland and Virginia they are in the basal (subsurface) part of the Aquia formation, both facts suggesting continuous deposition through Midway and Wilcox time. For this reason it does not seem practical to employ the term "Paleocene" along the Atlantic Coast for one of the major divisions of the Cenozoic.

Wilcox Time

Gulf Coast.—It is probable that there was a period of erosion between the deposition of the Midway and Wilcox formations along the Gulf Coastal Plain. However, as in the case of the Atlantic Coastal Plain, it is uncertain that this break was significant enough to mark the Midway as a definite major division of the Cenozoic (Paleocene).

The Wilcox seas did not cover the Gulf Coastal Plain as extensively as had those of the Midway. The shore line has been traced approximately 1,400 miles from the Rio Grande to a point near the boundary between North and South Carolina. Marine conditions existed in the southern parts of Texas, Louisiana, Mississippi, Alabama, and Georgia. North of the true marine deposits of Wilcox age, in northern Louisiana and Mississippi, and along the Mississippi embayment as far north as southern Illinois and Missouri, there were extensive lagoonal, estuarine, or flood-plain deposits that indicate a region at least partly covered with fresh water.

Atlantic Coast.—During Wilcox time, all of Florida and most of coastal-plain Georgia were submerged, as they had been during Midway time. The seas invaded South Carolina, reaching as far inland as Richland County. The sediments laid down by this sea make up the Black Mingo formation and consist chiefly of sand and a clay resembling Fuller's earth.

It is not possible to trace the Wilcox shore line north into North Carolina. Deposits, possibly of Wilcox age, occur near Lillington, Harnett County, North Carolina, so it is probable that the seas extended close to the Fall Line during Wilcox time and that the deposits left by this sea have been largely eroded away. The absence of Wilcox, as well as Claiborne deposits in northeastern North Carolina, may be explained by normal erosion, although it is also possible

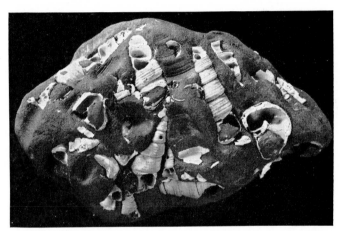

Fig. 244. Slab containing specimens of the Eocene gastropod *Turritella mortoni*, from Belvidere Beach, Virginia.

that a local uplift or warping caused the shore line to turn eastward to form a promontory somewhere between the present Cape Henry and Cape Hatteras.

In any case, deposits of Wilcox age are present in southern Virginia, where they form part of the Aquia formation, the lower part being of Midway age. The Aquia formation grades upward, apparently without an unconformity, into the Nanjemoy formation which is probably of Claiborne age. These two formations together constitute the Pamunkey group. The deposits of this group contain considerable glauconite ("greensand") with several intervening layers of limestone, the whole group having a maximum thickness of about 200 feet. Fossils, especially of the spiral snail *Turritella mortoni*, are abundant at the type locality of the Aquia formation, the junction of Aquia Creek and the Potomac River east of Fredericksburg, Virginia (Figure 244).

In New Jersey also there is no record of any major unconformity or erosion at either the beginning or the end of Wilcox time. The

Hornerstown formation, at least in its subsurface developments, represents both Midway and Wilcox time, and is apparently overlaid conformably by the Vincentown formation, which is also of Wilcox age. The Wilcox shore line apparently crossed New Jersey from near Salem to Keyport, although it may have extended farther westward. If it did extend farther west, the deposits have subsequently been removed by erosion.

One method of estimating the extent of the various Eocene seas is by a study of the distribution of glauconite. This mineral was formerly thought to form only in sea water of considerable depth. If, as some geologists believe, the water was 600 or more feet deep at the site of the present glauconite deposits in southern New Jersey, it is probable that the seas did extend across the present Delaware River into Pennsylvania. However, it is now known that glauconite can form in much shallower water than was originally supposed; in this case, the shore line may not have been very far west of the present outcrops of glauconite.

FIG. 245. The small coiled annelid worm *Spirulaea rotula,* from New Jersey. This is an important index fossil.

We have already learned that extensive beds of pure glauconite in the Hornerstown formation are dug at Sewell, Gloucester County, and near Birmingham and Medford, in Burlington County, New Jersey, for use in the manufacture of a water softener. In all of these pits the Eocene glauconite is underlain by similar deposits of Cretaceous age (Navesink formation), so it is difficult to determine the exact age of the various fossils dug from these pits. Definite Eocene species include the brachiopod *Oleneothyris (Terebratula) harlani* (Figure 248), the coral *Flabellum mortoni* (Figure 253), and the sponge *Eudea dichotoma.* The larger vertebrate fossils from the pits, especially the dinosaurs, are of Cretaceous age. (See page 293.)

Similar deposits of glauconite occur in New Castle County, Delaware, and it is probable that these can be correlated with the Hornerstown formation. Many years ago shell marl was dug for agricultural purposes near Middletown, Delaware. While all of these pits have been abandoned and filled, one locality containing good fossils can still be seen along the bank of Noxontown Pond, three miles south of Middletown.

In Delaware, it has been impossible to separate the Hornerstown from the overlying Vincentown formation, thereby affording further evidence that deposition was continuous. In fact, deposition may have been more or less continuous during Wilcox and Claiborne time along much of the Atlantic Coastal Plain north of South Carolina.

EOCENE FOSSILS

FIG. 246. Echinoid *Eupatagus mooreanus*, from Florida.

FIG. 247. Echinoid *Cardiaster cinctus*, from New Jersey.

FIG. 248. Brachiopod *Oleneothyris harlani*, from New Jersey.

FIG. 249. Coral *Dasmosmilia atlantica*, from New Jersey.

FIG. 250. Bryozoa from Vincentown, New Jersey.

FIG. 251. Gastropod *Fusus*, from New Jersey.

FIG. 252. Cephalopod *Aturia alabamensis*, from North Carolina.

FIG. 253. Coral *Flabellum mortoni*, from New Jersey.

The exact equivalence of these three deposits with those from the Gulf Coast has not been established and will require more field work and further analysis of the faunas.

The Vincentown formation of New Jersey (= Wilcox) has two facies, a limey phase and a slightly glauconitic one. The two occur in alternate layers, although the various layers in different parts of the state may not be continuous. Fossils are present in both phases, the limey phase containing many species of foraminifera and bryozoa, as well as echinoids, corals, and worms, especially *Spirulaea rotula* (Figure 245). The glauconitic phase is less fossiliferous, but contains a fairly rich fauna of foraminifera. The limey phase is very well exposed at the type locality of Vincentown in Burlington County and at various places in Salem County, while the greensand phase is best developed in Monmouth County.

Claiborne Time

Gulf Coast.—The deposition of Wilcox time ended with a tilting of the land in the Gulf region, followed by a period of erosion. Further sinking of the land permitted the seas to spread inland over the eroded surfaces of the Wilcox formation, and in this sea were deposited the sands and clays of the Claiborne group (or formation), named for Claiborne, Alabama. This sea was not as extensive as those of either Midway or Wilcox time. It advanced northward along the Mississippi-Tennessee border, thereby falling about 100 miles short of the two previous Eocene Mississippi embayments (Figure 243).

Atlantic Coast.—The Claiborne seas covered much of the Coastal Plain of Georgia and South Carolina, forming the McBean formation. The Claiborne history of North Carolina is very uncertain, no deposits of this age having been reported in that state until very recently when some quartzite and sandstone in the Piedmont region near Raleigh yielded some fossils tentatively identified as Claiborne in age. Furthermore, some fossils from wells in the eastern part of North Carolina have been correlated with the "Middle Eocene," probably Claiborne. Therefore it is highly probable that during part of Claiborne time the seas covered the Coastal Plain of North Carolina and extended for some fifty miles or more over the rocks of the Piedmont Plateau. This invasion may have been of relatively short duration, or else subsequent erosion has removed most traces of these deposits.

As suggested in the discussion of the Wilcox sea, it may be that a local uplift raised the land in northeastern North Carolina, which may account for the scarcity or lack of Wilcox and Claiborne fossils in that region. It has been observed that the Eocene deposits, as a whole, are considerably thicker north of the James River than they are south of that river. For example, at Newport News they are about 500 feet thick, whereas at Norfolk, 25 miles away, they are only 90 feet in thickness. D. J. Cederstrom of the United States Geological Survey has postulated a fault in this region to explain this difference. This fault, or a related one slightly farther south, may have caused the relative elevation of the land during part of Eocene time in southeastern Virginia and northeastern North Carolina. On the other hand, the variation in the thickness on the two sides of James River may indicate an ancient channel similar to the Salisbury embayment.

As we have seen, the fringes of the present coast between Virginia and New Jersey seem to have been covered continuously from Midway through Wilcox and Claiborne time. The Nanjemoy formation, named for the Nanjemoy River in Virginia, is probably equivalent to the Claiborne deposits farther south. The Claiborne seas covered about the same area in New Jersey as had those of Wilcox time, and, judging by a study of their fossils, the Manasquan and Shark River formations date from Claiborne time.

North of New Jersey the Eocene shore lines were probably all east of the present New England mainland, the only Eocene fossils in New England being some mollusks found on Martha's Vineyard. These are correlated with those of the Shark River formation (Claiborne). Some geologists believe that the Tertiary seas invaded much of the New England lowlands, but in the absence of any fossils such a hypothesis is far from proved.

Jackson Time

Gulf Coast.—At the close of Claiborne time there was a shoaling of the water, demonstrated by the presence of lignitic sands and clays containing plant remains at the top of the Claiborne formation. The seas then probably withdrew altogether from the Gulf Coastal Plain before the beginning of Jackson time. When the land again subsided and the seas advanced over the Gulf lowlands, they were less extensive than during any of the preceding Eocene invasions (Figure 243). The deposits of this sea are known as the Jackson formation (or group), named from Jackson, the capital city of Mississippi, where fossils of this age are relatively abundant.

Atlantic Coast.—All of Florida was submerged by the Jackson seas and during this submergence the Ocala limestone was deposited. This formation occurs on the surface of much of central Florida. The solution of this limestone by water has given rise to numerous lakes and sinkholes, including the famous Silver Springs near Ocala.

Until recently it was thought that all of the Eocene limestone of Florida belonged to the single Ocala formation. However, a recent discovery of some unusual fossils near Gulf Hammock in Levy and Citrus Counties suggests the presence of an older Eocene formation. One of the most interesting fossils found in this area is the large gastropod *Velates floridana,* a genus not hitherto known from eastern North America but which is characteristic of Middle Eocene deposits of Europe and other parts of the world. Whether this older formation (Gulf Hammock formation) be of Claiborne or lower Jackson age has not yet been determined.[1]

The Jackson (Ocala) seas deposited limestone in southeastern Georgia and South Carolina, the formations in the latter state being known as the Santee limestone and Cooper marl. Fossils are common at several places, an unusually rich fauna being obtained from excavations for the diversion canal of the Santee-Cooper power project near Moncks Corner, South Carolina.

"Great Carolina Ridge."—It is thought that there was a significant earth movement in early Jackson time that raised the region between the Cape Fear River in North Carolina and the Santee River in South Carolina, thus producing the "Great Carolina Ridge" or the "Cape Fear Uplift." This uplift apparently caused the shore line to turn to the east in northeastern South Carolina, forming a conspicuous promontory near the present Cape Fear. This "Carolina Ridge" is an important structural axis and may have existed during earlier periods. In fact, there is some slight evidence for its existence during Midway time and perhaps earlier.

North of the "ridge" the shore line again turned northwestward, and Jackson seas covered at least the eastern part of the Coastal Plain of North Carolina. Jackson sea deposits are known as the Castle Hayne formation, named for a small settlement near Wilmington, North Carolina. Fossils are present at many places in this formation, especially near Wilmington, Castle Hayne, and Dover, but as a rule are not well preserved.

The Jackson shore line may have turned eastward again near the suggested Cape Henry promontory ("Fort Monroe High"). At any rate, the Jackson seas did not transgress very extensively over the present land in northeastern North Carolina or in southern Virginia.

---

[1] An uplift (Ocala uplift) in north central Florida probably caused the appearance of these older Eocene deposits at the surface of this area. It also finds expression in all subsurface formations in the region and in many ways is comparable to the Great Carolina Ridge about to be discussed.

In fact, the only record of the former presence of Jackson seas in this region comes from some fossils recently obtained from wells in the Norfolk area, in a subsurface formation which D. J. Cederstrom has called the Chickahominy formation, from the well-known river of that name. Furthermore, the Jackson seas apparently transgressed inland only slightly beyond the present shore line of Maryland and Delaware. Fossils of this age are known only from wells near the coast at Salisbury and Berlin, Maryland, and Bridgeville, Delaware.

The Jackson seas probably crossed New Jersey from the site of Millville to a point a few miles north of Atlantic City. No Jackson fossils have been found in outcrops in New Jersey, although they have been found in several well borings between Cape May and Atlantic City.

Paleocene and Eocene of Central and Western North America

Paleocene.—The only marine deposit of either Paleocene or Eocene age in the Mid-Continent area is the Cannon Ball formation of North and South Dakota, where a fauna of marine mollusks, foraminifera, and sharks has been reported. No traces of the inlet to the sea have been found, but it is thought that a narrow seaway existed to the Gulf of Mexico. Elsewhere in the interior of North America there were extensive lowland plains, with sluggish streams and lakes. The Fort Union formation which covers a vast area in the Great Plains (North and South Dakota, Wyoming, Montana, and Alberta) dates from Paleocene time and is important because of its coal beds.

Eocene.—Nonmarine deposition continued throughout Eocene time, especially in the basins between the Laramide Ranges (Rockies). In order from oldest to youngest, the four most important Eocene formations of the Rocky Mountain area are as follows:

4. Wasatch Group. The erosion of these deposits formed Bryce Canyon. The Wasatch group is characterized by the fossils of the dawn horse (*Eohippus*).

3. Green River Group. Deposited in large shallow lakes in Wyoming and Colorado. Contains numerous fossils of fish, insects, and leaves.

2. Bridger Group. Shales and sands in southwestern Wyoming and southeastern Utah. Erosion of these deposits frequently forms "bad lands."

1. Uinta Group. These rest on the deposits of the Bridger group and are similar in character.

The Eocene seas covered the narrow western margins of the continent, but existed as bays and inlets caused by faulting of the rocks, rather than as conspicuous arms of the ocean.

Eocene Life

Foraminifera.—Very abundant, and valuable as index fossils. Some genera such as *Lepidocyclina* and *Discocyclina* reached the unusually large size (for foraminifera) of 80 mm., and are especially abundant in the Ocala limestone of Florida.

Sponges.—Apparently rare, very few having been described from the Eocene deposits of eastern North America. Several specimens, probably undescribed species, were recently collected from Eocene deposits in New Jersey and South Carolina.

Corals.—No reef corals are known from the Eocene of the Atlantic or Gulf Coast. A few solitary species such as *Flabellum mortoni* (Figure 253) and *Dasmosmilia atlantica* (Figure 249) are known from the Hornerstown and Vincentown formations of New Jersey and elsewhere along the Atlantic Coastal Plain. Sea pens (Penatulids) were recently described from the Vincentown formation.

Annelids.—Worm tubes are fairly common in Eocene deposits. One of the most useful as an index fossil is the small coiled genus *Spirulaea* (Figure 245).

Bryozoa.—These were very abundant throughout Eocene time. The Vincentown formation of New Jersey and the Castle Hayne formation of North Carolina contain a great number of species, most of which have been illustrated by Canu and Bassler (Figure 250).

Echinoderms.—Echinoids are fairly common in Eocene deposits of the Carolinas, Georgia, and Florida, and less frequent in New Jersey. *Eupatagus mooreanus* (Figure 246) is fairly common in the Middle Eocene(?) deposits near the Withlacoochee River, Florida, while characteristic species from the Castle Hayne formation of North Carolina are *Cidaris pratti* and *Cassidulus carolinensis*. Several species have been reported from the Vincentown formation of New Jersey, the most common being *Salenia belluta* and *Cardiaster cinctus* (Figure 247). Sand dollars were locally abundant. One species (*Periarchus lyelli*) was so abundant that certain Florida limestones contain countless masses of broken tests or shells of this fossil. This rock is designated as the *"Periarchus zone"* of the Ocala formation.

Brachiopoda.—Not many species of Brachiopoda are known from the American Eocene. One brachiopod *Oleneothyris (Terebratula) harlani* (Figure 248) is locally abundant in the Hornerstown formation of New Jersey and is occasionally present in the Aquia formation of Maryland and Virginia.

Pelecypoda.—Clams were very abundant in the Eocene deposits of the Gulf Coastal Plain, and only slightly less so along the Atlantic Coast. The four major divisions of the Eocene (Midway, Wilcox, Claiborne, and Jackson) all have characteristic species, although many other species persisted throughout the entire Eocene.

Oysters were locally very abundant and sometimes attained a very large size. The giant (12-inch) *Ostrea georgiana* apparently formed large reefs and its fossil remains can be found today in considerable numbers at Pollocksville, North Carolina, and at Shell Bluff, Georgia, on the Savannah River below Augusta.

Gastropods.—These were very abundant with definite index species for the various divisions of the Eocene (Figure 251). The spiral snail *Turritella mortoni* is especially characteristic of the Aquia formation of Virginia, and forms large slabs of rock exposed along the Potomac River, at the mouth of Aquia Creek, and near Belvidere Beach, Virginia (Figure 244).

Cephalopods.—While the ammonites and belemnites died out at the end of the Cretaceous period, their place was taken by the nautiloids, a group of animals which had previously been abundant in Paleozoic seas. Specimens are not common, but a few species have been described from the Eocene rocks of New Jersey, North Carolina, Florida, and the Gulf Coast (Figure 252).

Crustacea.—Although rarely found as fossils, crabs were present in Eocene seas, and were becoming more like those of the present time. Barnacles were present, but not as common as they were to be during the Miocene. There were also numerous minute ostracodes.

Fish.—Fish were very abundant in Eocene waters. A large fauna of beautifully preserved teleost fish has been obtained from the Green River Basin of southern Wyoming and northwestern Colorado (Figure 254). Sharks and rays (Figure 255) were also abundant and reached considerable size. Fish fossils from the Eocene of the Atlantic Coastal Plain are limited to shark teeth, which are very numerous at some localities, dental plates of rays, spines of a large fish known as *Cylin-*

FIG. 254. Caught in the act! The larger fish (a perch) was apparently trying to devour a herring when both were trapped and fossilized. From the Eocene Green River formation at Fossil, Wyoming. (Princeton University.)

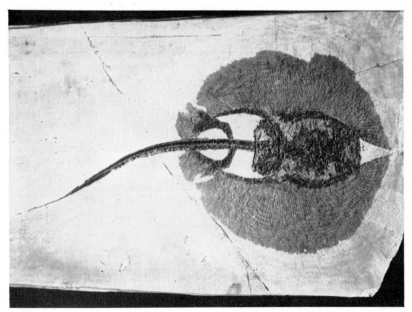

FIG. 255. An Eocene ray (*Palaeodasyphalis discus*), from the Green River formation of Wyoming.

FIG. 256. Children examining the jaw of an Eocene crocodile obtained from marl pits at Sewell, New Jersey. Actual length of jaw 31½ inches. In the background can be seen the reconstruction of the duck-bill dinosaur. (New Jersey State Mus.)

drocanthus (common in the Santee limestone of South Carolina), and numerous unidentified pieces of vertebra.

Amphibia.—Present, but rarely found as fossils.

Reptiles.—The immense reptiles of the Mesozoic completely disappeared by the beginning of the Cenozoic. Gone were the dinosaurs, ichthyosaurs, pterosaurs, plesiosaurs, and mosasaurs, although the crocodiles, turtles, lizards, and snakes had been able to survive. Croco-

FIG. 257. Fossil turtle (*Agomphus* sp.), from the Eocene Hornerstown formation at Sewell, New Jersey.

dile (Figure 256) and turtle fossils are not infrequently found in the Eocene deposits of the Atlantic Coastal Plain. A very fine specimen of the turtle *Agomphus* (Figure 257) was recently found at Sewell, New Jersey, in the same pit where the dinosaur *Hadrosaurus minor* was found. The turtle fossil was in the greensand of the Hornerstown formation (Lower Eocene or Paleocene) while the dinosaur was in the underlying Navesink formation of Upper Cretaceous age.

Birds.—Most of the existing orders of birds were present in the Eocene including the owls, eagles, vultures, gulls, waders, woodcock, quail, and pelicans. There were also a number of large flightless birds which are now extinct, the best example being *Diatryma* from the Wasatch beds of Wyoming. Bird bones resembling parts of our modern cormorants, snipe, and waders have been found in the greensand of the Hornerstown formation in New Jersey at Hornerstown, Birmingham, and Arneystown.

Mammals.—The mammals of Paleocene time were primitive and included survivals of some of the genera of the Cretaceous as well as a few new genera, which were to become larger and more conspicuous during the Eocene and later Tertiary. By Eocene time, mammals had increased in number and were an important feature of the life of the land. Extensive collections of Eocene mammals have been made

Fig. 258. Eocene palm (*Sabalites florissanti*) from Wyoming. (Princeton University.)

from Wyoming and other western states, and our knowledge of the life of the period is best obtained from these fossils. Among these Eocene mammals should be mentioned *Eohippus* ("dawn horse," no bigger than a cat), the camel, tapir, oreodont, rhinoceros, and hornless titanothere.

The Eocene deposits of eastern North America have yielded very few fossils of land mammals, probably largely because of the marine nature of the sediments. One tooth of a Tillodont (*Anehippodus ripatius*), an extinct order of mammals, was found many years ago near Shark River, New Jersey. The marine Upper Eocene deposits of Alabama, however, do contain the fossils of large whale-like mammals known as *Zeuglodon*, which reached a length of 60 feet.

Plants.—By Eocene time the land flora had assumed a truly modern aspect. Few species of Eocene plants are known from the Atlantic Coast, although floras of Wilcox, Claiborne, and Jackson age have been described from the Gulf Coastal Plain. In all cases, the Eocene plants afford evidence of a climate warmer than that now prevailing in the same latitudes. Conifers were inconspicuous, while tropical palms abounded. An unusually fine specimen of an Eocene palm is shown in Figure 258. A similar warm climate is indicated by the Eocene plants of the western part of North America, and even the Eocene flora of Greenland included many ferns, cypress, sequoia, magnolia, and other warm-climate plants.

*　*　*

The economic resources of the various epochs of the Tertiary will be discussed in the final section of Chapter 24, on the Pliocene.

<h2 style="text-align:center">FURTHER READING</h2>

The references for Chapters 20–24 will be found at the end of Chapter 24.

CHAPTER 22

THE OLIGOCENE

The term "Oligocene" is derived from the Greek *oligo*, "little" and *kainos*, "recent." The name was first proposed by E. von Beyrich, a German geologist, in 1854.

New Jersey to Virginia	North Carolina	South Carolina	Georgia and Florida	Gulf Coast
— —	— (subsurface only)	Flint River	Suwannee Byram	Chickasawhay Vicksburg

Oligocene History of the Gulf Coast.—Along the eastern part of the Gulf Coast, from Alabama to Louisiana, there was apparently little or no break or unconformity between the end of Late Eocene time (Jackson) and the beginning of the Oligocene. However, the Oligocene seas, as a rule, did not extend as far inland as had those of the previous epoch. Farther west, in Texas, it is probable that the Oligocene seas submerged the margins of the present land, but the deposits laid down at that time are covered by later sediments and it is consequently difficult to determine the actual shore lines. The Oligocene formations are best exposed near Vicksburg, Mississippi, a city which has given its name to the most important formation, or group, of that age.

Oligocene History of the Atlantic Coast.—Most of Florida was above water during the early and middle part of the Oligocene, with a narrow seaway connecting the Gulf of Mexico with the Atlantic Ocean across northern Florida and southern Georgia. Toward the end of Oligocene time, Florida began to subside, leaving only a large island in the northern part of the state—the so-called Ocala uplift. Eastern Georgia and extreme southeastern South Carolina were submerged by the Oligocene (Vicksburg) sea. North of the Savannah River, however, there are very few indications of the former presence of the Oligocene sea. In 1947, some microfossils were obtained from a well at Camp Lejeune, Onslow County, North Carolina, which suggest that the Oligocene sea submerged extreme eastern North Carolina. Apparently the present coast line was above water from Virginia northward, with the resulting erosion not only of many of the Eocene deposits but also of some of the underlying Upper Cretaceous strata (Figure 259).[1]

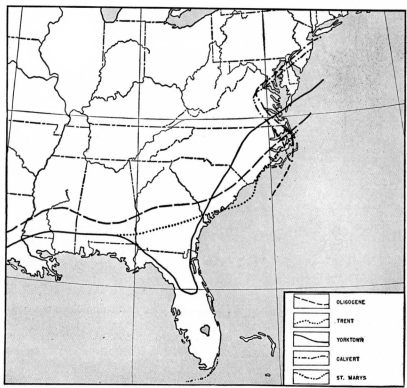

Fig. 259. Hypothetical shore lines during Oligocene and Miocene times along the Atlantic and eastern Gulf Coastal Plains.

Oligocene History of Central North America.—There are no traces of Oligocene seas along the western margins of the continent. In central North America, however, extensive quantities of clay and silt were carried eastward from the Rocky Mountains by streams which widened to form basins in Montana, Wyoming, North and South Dakota, and Nebraska. Some of these clay and silt beds were formed under fresh water, others in swamps or in great alluvial fans. The erosion of these beds formed the "Bad Lands" which are such a conspicuous feature of the landscape of western South Dakota today. A

[1] James D. McLean, Jr. *Oligocene and Lower Miocene Microfossils from Onslow County, North Carolina.* (Acad. Nat. Sci. Phila., Notulae Naturae No. 200, 1947.)

FIG. 260. The Bad Lands near Scenic, South Dakota. Fossil remains of many Oligocene mammals have been found in this region.

great many Oligocene mammals lived in this region, many of whom became bogged down in these swamps. Their bones are very abundant in these Oligocene formations. The most fossiliferous of these beds is known as the White River formation, which is best developed some 50 miles southeast of Rapid City (Figure 260). Volcanic activity took place during the Oligocene epoch, and is demonstrated by the deposits of ash interbedded with the silts and clays of the White River formation.

Oligocene Life

Marine Invertebrates.—Extensive faunas of marine invertebrates, especially mollusks, have been described from Vicksburg and Chicka-

sawhay, Mississippi, and elsewhere on the Gulf Coastal Plain. Many Eocene forms persisted into the Oligocene and it is often difficult to draw the line between the two periods. Other conspicuous Oligocene ma-

FIG. 261. Eocene foraminifera *Nodesaria zippei*, from
Salem County, New Jersey.

FIG. 262. Oligocene foraminifera *Orbitolites*
crustulum, from Vicksburg.

rine invertebrates were foraminifera, illustrated in Figures 261 and 262, and bryozoa.

Land Mollusks.—Fossil land snails are occasionally found associated with the mammalian fauna in the White River beds of the Bad Lands of South Dakota and Nebraska.

Fish, Amphibia, and Reptiles.—These animals differed little from those of the Eocene, although the lizards were becoming more varied. Fossil land tortoises are fairly common in the White River beds of South Dakota.

Birds.—Fossil birds are very rare in Oligocene deposits and are limited to a few scattered bones and some fossil eggs found in the Bad Lands of South Dakota.

Mammals.—The White River formation of the Bad Lands has yielded a great many species of Oligocene mammals. Fossil bones, teeth, and even perfect skeletons can be found with very little difficulty in this formation, especially near Scenic, South Dakota. The Oligocene fauna represents a great increase in the size of the carnivores and a great diversification of species. Among the most conspicuous Oligocene mammals are the ancestors of the wolves and foxes, the sabre-toothed cat, horses (*Mesohippus*), titanotheres, the giant pig (*Archaeotherium*), oreodont, rhinoceros, an ancestral camel (*Poebrotherium*), and peccaries.

Plants.—During Oligocene time the interior of the North American continent was probably uplifted. This created a cooler climate than that which had prevailed during the Eocene. Consequently, the palms and many other tropical plants of Eocene time disappeared from the land, their place being taken by flora of a somewhat cooler climate.

FURTHER READING

The references for Chapters 20–24 will be found at the end of Chapter 24.

CHAPTER 23

THE MIOCENE

The term "Miocene" is derived from the Greek *mio*, "less" and *kainos*, "recent." The name was proposed by Sir Charles Lyell in 1833.

	N. J.	Md.	Va.	N. C.	S. C.–Ga.	Fla.	Gulf Coast
UPPER	Cohansey	—	Chesapeake ⌈Yorktown	Duplin Yorktown	Duplin Rayson	Chocta-watchee	Pascagoula
MIDDLE	Kirkwood	Chesapeake ⌈St. Marys ⟨Choptank ⌊Calvert	Chesapeake ⟨St. Marys Choptank ⌊Calvert	— (subsurface only)	Hawthorne	Hawthorne Alum Bluff	Hattiesburg
LOWER	—	—	—	Trent	Tampa	Tampa	Catahoula

Miocene History of the Gulf Coast

Transition.—The deposition of the Oligocene Vicksburg formation was followed by an uplift or tilting of the land which caused the shore line to retreat toward the present Gulf of Mexico. This land movement, marking the transition from the Oligocene to the Miocene, was very gradual and it is difficult to draw a sharp boundary between the two periods. Consequently, certain deposits such as those near Chickasawhay, Mississippi, are regarded as Oligocene by some geologists and as Miocene by others.

Lower Miocene.—Along the Gulf Coast the deposits definitely assigned to the Lower Miocene are largely of nonmarine origin, indicating swamps or estuaries of the sea. A well-preserved fossil palm leaf, found in some Miocene sands near Waynesboro, Mississippi, is shown on Figure 56. The occurrence of the palm suggests a warm climate. Practically all of Florida and parts of southeastern Georgia were covered by the sea during Early Miocene time, during which the limestones of the Tampa formation were formed.

Middle and Upper Miocene.—The seas covered the lower margins of the Gulf Coastal Plain more or less continuously during Mid-

328

dle and Late Miocene time. The water was definitely salty in western
Florida and fossils are abundant at Alum Bluff on the Apalachicola
River and elsewhere in "panhandle Florida." Farther west, in Louisiana and Texas, the waters were brackish or fresh, except very close to
the present shore line, thus indicating only a slight submergence of
the land along the western Gulf coast.

Miocene History of the Atlantic Coast

Lower Miocene.—At the beginning of Miocene time both the "Great
Carolina Ridge" and the lands to the north and south of the Ridge
were above water. The first Miocene sea invasion of the Atlantic

Fig. 263. Internal case of *Panope intermedia*, a Miocene fossil from Belgrade,
North Carolina.

Coast was relatively slight and appears to have submerged only a
portion of eastern North Carolina, especially in Onslow and Jones
Counties. The deposits from this sea are known as the Trent formation and are regarded as of Early Miocene age, contemporaneous with
the Tampa limestone of Florida. The best fossil localities occur near
Belgrade and Silverdale, North Carolina. Many of the Belgrade fossils are internal casts of pelecypods, with details of the muscle scars
and other features clearly shown (Figure 263). Possibly the Trent
seas extended over the present land north of North Carolina; if so, the
deposits have long since been eroded and it appears more likely that
the invasion was more or less local. As far as can be determined from
the fossils that have been found, the climate was relatively warm.

Middle Miocene.—The next invasion of the land was in Calvert
time. The map (Figure 259) shows that the shore line probably extended across New Jersey from Asbury Park to near Salem, and then
across Delaware, Maryland, and Virginia to the vicinity of Petersburg.
This invasion by the sea probably did not extend far south of Peters-

burg, and consequently the shore line turned sharply to the east near the Virginia-North Carolina border. In North Carolina, the only fossils suggestive of Calvert age are some foraminifera that form a conspicuous ooze between the depths of 800 and 1,000 feet in the well at Cape Hatteras. Apparently the Calvert shore line existed somewhere in the vicinity of the western shore of Pamlico Sound. During Calvert time the "Carolina Ridge" probably extended far out into the sea as a cape, for the nearest counterpart of the Calvert formation to the south is thought to be the lower part of the Alum Bluff group of western Florida.

In New Jersey, the major part of the Kirkwood formation is thought to be equivalent to the Calvert formation of Maryland. Fossil mollusks, barnacles, and a few vertebrate remains have been found at Shiloh, Greenwich, Fairton, and in numerous wells along the New Jersey coast. Fossils are more abundant in Maryland, especially at the Calvert Cliffs, the type locality of the formation, which is near Chesapeake Beach and Plum Point on the western shore of Chesapeake Bay (Figure 264). Some 200 species of mollusks, as well as echinoids, corals, shark teeth, whale bones, and many other fossils have been collected from these cliffs. Judging by these fossils, the sea was warmer than during Early Miocene time.

The Choptank formation of Maryland was probably laid down at the close of Calvert time. Possibly there was a withdrawal of the sea and then a readvance to form the Choptank formation. It seems more likely, however, that the Choptank merely represents a late, sandy phase of the Calvert, possibly formed during a retreating phase of the sea. As evidenced by the Choptank fossils, the climate was slightly cooler. Fossils occur near Cambridge, Maryland, and along the Calvert Cliffs south of Parker Creek, where the Choptank overlies the Calvert formation.

Choptank time was followed by a period of uplift and erosion north of the "Carolina Ridge." During this interval some of the Choptank and Calvert deposits were eroded. The next advance of the sea (St. Marys) was probably initiated by a depression of the land which had its maximum a little farther south than the depression which caused the Calvert seas to invade the land. The St. Marys shore line probably crossed New Jersey from somewhere near Atlantic City to Millville, and then southeastward across Delaware, Maryland, and Virginia. Near Richmond, the St. Marys shore line overlapped the Calvert, thus indicating that the maximum advance of the sea was somewhere near that city. The sea extended south into North Carolina, although the deposits are buried and evidence is lacking to determine the exact position of the shore line. Just as in the case of the Calvert seas, the St. Marys shore line probably turned sharply eastward toward the present coast in central North Carolina. Southern North Carolina, including the "Carolina Ridge," was apparently above water. South of the "Ridge," the shore line again turned westward and submerged parts of southern Georgia and Florida.

Fig. 264.   Calvert Cliffs on the western shore of Chesapeake Bay, Maryland. An excellent source of Miocene fossils.

St. Marys fossils have been obtained from wells at Atlantic City, Wildwood, and Cape May where they occur on top of sediments containing Calvert fossils. In Maryland, they occur on the surface in St. Marys and southern Calvert Counties on the western shore of Chesapeake Bay, and in Dorchester County on the Eastern Shore. A study of the fossils indicated that the climate was slightly cooler than it had been during the deposition of the Calvert formation, although slightly warmer than that which prevails today.

Upper Miocene.—The withdrawal of the St. Marys sea was followed by further erosion. Then the land was depressed again and the Yorktown sea advanced. Although this sea did not extend as far north as New Jersey, it was continuous from Virginia to Florida. Its shore line crossed the present strand line not far north of Yorktown,

Virginia, as shown in Figure 259. It overlapped the Calvert and St. Marys shore lines near Richmond, extended inland a few miles over the Piedmont rocks, and then turned southeastward. The Yorktown sea covered the now submerged "Carolina Ridge." South of Cape Hatteras the climate was warm, as is shown by the fossils of the Duplin marl which represents a late phase of the Yorktown formation.

Fig. 265. Bluffs along the York River at Yorktown, Virginia. This is the type locality of the highly fossiliferous Yorktown formation of Miocene age.

Yorktown fossils are very abundant near the type locality at York-town (Figure 265), and elsewhere along the York and James Rivers. Similar fossils occur at many places in North Carolina, especially along the Meherrin, Chowan, and Roanoke Rivers. Farther south, extensive faunas characteristic of the Duplin marl have been obtained at the Natural Well near Magnolia, Duplin County, North Carolina, and from marl pits near Mayesville, Sumter County, South Carolina.

Since New Jersey was probably above water during Yorktown time, no marine fossils of this age are known from the state. It is highly possible that the sands and clays of the Cohansey formation represent deltas or estuaries equivalent in age to the Yorktown farther south. The presence of some warm-climate fossil plants near Bridgeton, New Jersey, suggests a late Miocene (Yorktown?) age for the Cohansey formation.

Miocene of New England

During part of Miocene time the shore line may have been slightly east and south of the present Massachusetts coast, for Miocene fossils similar to those from Maryland and New Jersey occur at Gay Head cliffs on the island of Martha's Vineyard (Figure 266). The fact that so much fossil wood occurs with the shells, shark teeth, and whale bones, suggests that the shore line was not far distant. It is possible that the Gay Head deposits represent a delta formed by a

FIG. 266. Gay Head on Martha's Vineyard, Massachusetts. Most of the varicolored clays are of Miocene age.

river flowing eastward toward the sea. A few Miocene mollusks have been dredged off Nova Scotia and from Georges Bank, but no outcrops are known from the New England mainland.

Miocene of Central and Western North America

Extensive deposits of sands and gravels were carried by streams flowing eastward from the Rocky Mountains over the Great Plains. Sandstones of this age near Agate, Nebraska, contain a great many fossil vertebrates, especially a rhinoceros-like animal, *Dineratherium*. These skeletons are so abundant that in places they form a bone conglomerate. Figure 267 shows a reconstruction of the Agate bone bed, while Figure 268 shows a restoration of the animals of that age.

Near Florissant, Colorado, a considerable amount of volcanic ash emitted from nearby volcanoes settled on the bottom of a lake, burying

Fig. 267. Fossil rhinoceros bones in Miocene sandstone at Agate, Nebraska. (Colorado Mus. Nat. Hist.)

FIG. 268. A North American Miocene landscape. The animals in the foreground are Elotheres, extinct pig-like mammals; to the right is *Moropus*, another grotesque extinct animal with no living descendants. In the background can be seen some primitive camels, rhinoceros, and horses. (Painting by Charles Knight. Chicago Nat. Hist. Mus.)

FIG. 269. Fossil leaf of *Fagopsis* (Beech) and a myriopod in volcanic ash at Florissant, Colorado. (Amer. Mus. Nat. Hist.)

FIG. 270. Fossil dragonfly (*Lipula macleuri*) from Florissant, Colorado. (Amer. Mus. Nat. Hist.)

thousands of insects and leaves. These are in an almost perfectly preserved condition (Figures 269 and 270). A few fossil fishes and birds
have also been found at this locality.

The Pacific coast of California was submerged during part of the
Miocene. The exact history is rather complicated because of the
numerous faults and structural features of the region. Many of the
important oil fields of the Los Angeles Basin produce from Miocene
sediments.

Miocene Life

Foraminifera.—These minute organisms were abundant in the
Miocene seas. Most of the larger types which were characteristic of
the Eocene had disappeared.

Porifera.—Indirect evidence for the presence of sponges in Miocene
seas is afforded by the holes in clam shells made by the boring sponge
Cliona.

Coelenterata.—Coral reefs were formed in tropical seas, while individual corals lived in semitropical and temperate waters. Characteristic genera are *Astraea, Astrangia,* and *Septastrea.*

Bryozoa.—These animals were not nearly as abundant as they
had been during Eocene time. However, encrusting forms are frequently found on shells and other objects in Miocene deposits.

Echinodermata.—Sand dollars and sea urchins were apparently
fairly numerous in Miocene seas, although perfect fossil specimens are
relatively rare. A large colony of the sea urchin *Echinocardium
orthornatum* has been found in the Calvert Cliffs along the west shore
of Chesapeake Bay. Sea urchin spines and fragments of tests of sea
urchins and sand dollars are present in many Miocene deposits.

Brachiopoda.—Rare and probably restricted to deep water. The
only important East Coast species is *Discinisca lugubris* from Shiloh,
New Jersey.

Mollusca.—These constitute the great bulk—probably 75 per cent
of the Miocene invertebrate fossils. Extensive faunas have been described from various Miocene deposits of New Jersey, Maryland, Virginia, the Carolinas, and Florida, some 500 species in all having been
listed. These faunas are relatively modern in aspect, most of the
genera and a few of the species still being found in present seas. Gastropods and pelecypods are equally numerous, while there are a few
species of nautiloids and scaphopods.

The most characteristic species of Pelecypoda from the Miocene of New Jersey (Kirkwood formation) are *Astarte distans, Eucrassatella melina,* and *Melina maxillata.* The characteristic Gastropoda species are *Turritella cumberlandia, Polinices hemicrypta* and *Nassarius trivitatoides.* The fauna of the Calvert Cliffs of Maryland is much more prolific and includes such characteristic Pelecypoda species as *Pecten madisonius, Astarte cuneiformis, Arca staminea,* and *Corbula inaequalis;* the characteristic Calvert Gastropoda are *Turritella plebia* and *Ecphora tricostata.* The Yorktown formation of Virginia and North Carolina is even more prolific, among which the following may be mentioned as typical Pelecypoda: *Pecten jeffersonius, Pecten madisonius, Glycymeris subovata, Plicatula marginata,* and *Arca incile;* while *Ecphora quadricostata* and *Turritella variabilis* are the two most typical species of Gastropoda.

Crustacea.—Crab claws occur in many Miocene deposits, while barnacles were more conspicuous than they had been during earlier periods. Fragments or plates of several species of *Balanus* are common at Shiloh, New Jersey; Chesapeake Beach, Maryland; Yorktown, Virginia; and elsewhere. Ostracodes, especially minute species, are present in many Miocene deposits and are used as index fossils by oil paleontologists.

Fish.—Few fish fossils are known from Miocene rocks of America, except for shark teeth. These are exceedingly abundant in Massachusetts, New Jersey, Maryland, Virginia, and the Carolinas, and are frequently so abundant along the Calvert Cliffs that it is possible to collect them by the basketful. The most common Miocene sharks belonged to the following genera: *Odontapsis, Notidanus, Carcharodon,* and *Oxyrhina.* Among the largest teeth is one of *Carcharodon megalodon,* eight inches in length, obtained from the cliffs at Gay Head, Martha's Vineyard, Massachusetts.

Amphibia, Reptiles, and Birds.—Large tortoises, some as much as three feet in length, have been found in the Miocene deposits of the Great Plains. In the East, reptiles are represented merely by a few fragments of turtles and crocodiles in Miocene formations of the Atlantic Coast. Miocene bird fossils have been found in the Florissant shales of Colorado, and a few bones have been collected from the Calvert Cliffs in Maryland, while an extensive fauna of birds has been collected at St. Gerand le Puy in France. Little is known about Miocene amphibia.

Mammals.—Prominent among the Miocene mammals were the horses, camels, rhinoceroses, peccaries, the first deer, oreodonts, and primitive mastodons (*Trilophodon*) which were no more than six feet in height. It is thought that many of the new elements of the Miocene mammal fauna reached America via a Siberia-Alaska land bridge. Whales were apparently abundant in the Miocene seas, for their fossil remains are frequently found in the deposits of the Chesapeake group in Maryland and Virginia. Several fine specimens of Miocene whales have been secured from the Calvert Cliffs.

Bones of *Dineratherium* (an ancient rhinoceros), *Desmathyus* (a peccary) and *Ammodon* (giant hog) have been found in the Kirkwood formation at Farmingdale, New Jersey, while a tooth of a fossil tapir (*Tapiravus vadidus*) was collected at Shiloh, New Jersey.

A restoration of a typical Miocene landscape with its characteristic animals is shown in Figure 269.

Plants.—The Miocene flora is definitely of modern aspect. Grassy plains occupied much of the land of western states, a fact revealed by the presence of fossil seeds and pollen. The best collection of Miocene plants comes from Florissant, Colorado, where an extensive flora of tropical affinities has been described. The Latch flora near Spokane, Washington, is also of considerable importance. Less is known about the Miocene plants of eastern North America, although a number of species have been described from the Gulf Coast and a few very poorly preserved plants have been found in the Cohansey formation near Bridgeton and Millville, New Jersey.

Diatoms abounded in the Miocene seas. In some places, as in Maryland and California, great masses of the skeletons of these microscopic plants occur in thick deposits known as diatomaceous earth or diatomite. This material is used for the manufacture of abrasives. Many diatoms are index fossils of certain zones or formations and are used to locate water or oil horizons. The important water-bearing "800-foot sand" of New Jersey coast lies directly beneath a recognizable diatom layer. While the majority of the Miocene diatoms were marine, some species, like their descendants today, lived in fresh water. A few characteristic Miocene marine diatoms are shown in Figure 52, page 83.

FURTHER READING

The references for Chapters 20–24 will be found at the end of Chapter **24**.

CHAPTER 24

THE PLIOCENE

The name "Pliocene" is derived from the Greek *plio*, "more" and *kainos*, "recent." Sir Charles Lyell also proposed this name in 1833.

	L. I.	N. J.	Pa.–Del.	Md.–Va.	N. C.–S. C.	Ga.–Fla.	Gulf Coast
UPPER	Manet o	Beacon Hill	B·yn Mawr	"Lafayette"	"Lafayette"	"Lafayette"	Goliad
LOWER	—	—	—	—	Croatan Waccamaw	Charlton (Ga) Caloosa- hatchee (Fla.)	Citronelle(?)

Pliocene History of the Gulf Coast and Florida

The seas advanced over the Gulf Coastal Plain during the Pliocene epoch, but nowhere did they reach as far inland as they had during earlier epochs of the Cenozoic. Very few marine outcrops of Pliocene age are found along the shores of the Gulf of Mexico from Alabama to Texas, but well borings have revealed a fauna of marine and brackish species, especially near the present coast. Farther inland, the Pliocene deposits of the Gulf Coastal Plain are largely sands and gravels of nonmarine origin. The stratigraphy of the Pliocene of the Gulf Coastal Plain is not well worked out, largely because of the lack of fossils. Two of the most important formations are the Goliad of Texas and the Citronelle of Alabama. A characteristic fossil of the marine phase of the Pliocene of the Gulf Coast is the pelecypod *Rangia johnsoni,* which has been found almost exclusively in wells.

There was apparently only a short time interval or erosional unconformity between the end of the Miocene and the beginning of the Pliocene along the south Atlantic Coastal Plain. This is demonstrated by the fact that the fauna of the Lower Pliocene is very similar to that of the Upper Miocene.

The Pliocene seas covered much of southern Florida. From the distribution of the Pliocene sediments it can be inferred that the Gulf of Mexico advanced farther north than at present and that the Atlantic Ocean extended some 50 miles inland from its present beach.

340

"The western shore of the peninsula north of Tampa, however, lay some distance seaward from its present location, though the southern end of the peninsula was submerged. This condition apparently had been brought about by a rise in sea level that flooded the lower parts of the late Miocene land but left the region of the Ocala uplift standing above water." [1]

Several marine Pliocene formations have been recognized in Florida, but these are probably of approximately the same age. The Caloosa-

FIG. 271. Caloosahatchee River near La Belle, Florida. Many Pliocene marine fossils have been obtained from the banks of this river.

hatchee formation of the southern part of the state is one of the most prolific fossiliferous formations of the North American Cenozoic, some 500 species having been reported. The best exposures are along the Caloosahatchee River near La Belle and Clewiston in Hendry County (Figure 271). Similar fossils have been dredged or dug from many shallow excavations in southern Florida.

Pliocene History of the Atlantic Coast

The Early Pliocene sea submerged the eastern part of Georgia and the Carolinas (Figure 272). The deposits of the Charlton formation along the St. Marys River, at the Georgia-Florida line, are probably

[1] C. Wythe Cooke, "Geology of Florida," Florida Geological Survey, Bull. 29 (1945), pp. 197-98.

contemporaneous with the Caloosahatchee formation of southern Florida. An interesting brackish-water fauna, probably of the same age, occurs along the Satilla River near Pearson in Atkinson County, Georgia.

The Early Pliocene shore line probably lay some 40 miles inland from its present position in South Carolina. It extended northeast-

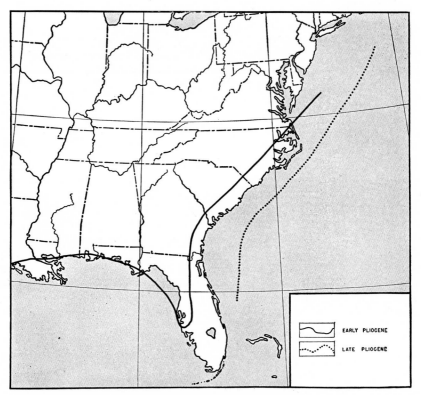

EARLY PLIOCENE

LATE PLIOCENE

Fig. 272. Hypothetical shore lines during Pliocene time along the Atlantic and eastern Gulf Coastal Plains.

ward across North Carolina and probably crossed the present shore line near the Virginia Capes (Figure 272). Two formations—the Waccamaw and the Croatan—have been described from this area, but are probably contemporaneous. Pliocene marine fossils have been obtained near Myrtle Beach, South Carolina, and from Wilmington, Lake Waccamaw, Silverdale, and New Bern, in North Carolina.

The only Pliocene fossils obtained from north of the Neuse River, North Carolina, are a few specimens of *Arca subsinuata* dredged from canals in the Dismal Swamp near the Virginia-North Carolina border. It is therefore thought that the Early Pliocene shore line crossed the present shore line near this point. North of the Virginia Capes the land was probably above water throughout the Pliocene. While the sand and shell marls were accumulating in the shallow seas of the Waccamaw formation of the Carolinas, the land in the northern part of the Coastal Plain stood high and was being actively eroded. Chesapeake Bay and Delaware Bay were probably river valleys at this time, and the Hudson River was cutting a gorge across the emerged Continental Shelf.

The rise of the land from Virginia to New Jersey may have had some connection with a renewed uplift of the Appalachian Mountains. At any rate, this uplift brought about a rejuvenation of the streams, causing them to carry increased amounts of gravel, which in turn was spread out near the seaward edge of the Coastal Plain. With continued uplift, these gravel deposits were in turn eroded and the zone of deposition extended still farther seaward. The gravel which caps some of the highest hills of the New Jersey Coastal Plain (Beacon Hill formation) is thought to be a remnant of stream deposits made during the Pliocene.

Beacon Hill gravel is present on the tops of such New Jersey hills as Beacon Hill (the type locality), Hominy Hill, and the Clarksburg Hills in Monmouth County, Old Half Way and Forked River Mountains in Ocean County, and Apple Pie Hill in Burlington County. These widely spaced gravel-capped hills are eloquent witnesses of the widespread erosion of post-Beacon Hill time. Similar isolated patches of gravel cap some of the hills in Pennsylvania west of Philadelphia, especially near Newtown Square and Bryn Mawr, and constitute the Bryn Mawr formation.

Farther south similar gravel occurs on some of the hills near the landward margin of the Coastal Plain (Fall Line). These were originally mapped as the "Lafayette formation," but this name must be discarded because it was originally used for deposits of another age. The exact age of these gravels is uncertain. Some of them may be contemporaneous with the Waccamaw marine deposits, while others are undoubtedly later. C. Wythe Cooke, of the United States Geological Survey, believes that many of the gravels originally assigned to the "Lafayette formation" are actually of Pleistocene age. In the absence of fossils, in place in the gravel, the exact age cannot be determined, although it may be said that the evidence favors a late Pliocene age for the majority of the gravels of the "Lafayette," Bryn Mawr, and Beacon Hill formations.

Paleozoic corals, bryozoa, brachiopods, and other fossils are frequently found in the chert pebbles of the Beacon Hill formation. These, of course, have no bearing on the age of the gravels, but show that the gravels were transported by streams, probably the ancestors of the Delaware and other rivers, from the Paleozoic rocks of northern New Jersey, Pennsylvania, and New York. Similar fossiliferous pebbles are found in the Pleistocene gravels of New Jersey and adjacent states.

Pliocene History of Long Island and New England

Certain gravels (the Manetto formation) of Long Island and the Cape Cod region of Massachusetts have been dated as Pliocene by some geologists, while others prefer to regard them as Early Pleistocene. In any case, the Pliocene shore line probably lay far beyond the present New England coast, since no marine fossils of this age have been found.

Pliocene History of the Mid-Continent and Pacific Coast

Extensive nonmarine deposits of sand and gravel were formed during Pliocene time in the Great Plains area and scattered remnants

Fig. 273. Pacific Beach, California. A well-known locality for collecting Pliocene invertebrates.

can be found today from Nebraska to Texas (Ogallala formation). Other nonmarine Pliocene deposits were formed in Arizona, New Mexico, Nevada, Idaho, and Southeastern California.

The margins of the present Pacific coast were submerged during part of the Pliocene epoch. Excellent Pliocene marine fossils can be collected today along the sea bluff at Pacific Beach (Figure 273), a few miles north of San Diego, and elsewhere in that vicinity. The Gulf of California was much larger than at present and extended northward into the present Imperial Valley of California. Good fossil localities occur at Coyote Wells and Carizzo Creek, California, as well as near Santa Rosalia, Baja California, Mexico.

Pliocene Life

Marine Invertebrates.—A large percentage of the fauna of Pliocene seas is still living in modern oceans. Mollusks, corals, echinoderms, and bryozoa are abundant in the Lower Pliocene deposits of the Atlantic Coastal Plain, while crabs and barnacles are present, although less conspicuous. The Waccamaw formation of the Carolinas is characterized by the following mollusks: pelecypods, *Pecten eboreus, Arca limula, Crassatellites gibbesii,* and *Ostrea sculpturata;* gastropods, *Fasciolaria apicina, Oliva sayana, Fulgur maximus,* and *Vermetus graniferus.* Included in the extensive fauna of the Caloosahatchee beds of Florida are the following: pelecypods, *Cardium emmonsi, Arca rustica,* and *Arca wagneriana;* gastropods, *Scaphella floridana, Fasciolaria apicina, Turritella perattenuata,* and *Strombus leidyi.* Related forms lived in the Pliocene seas in other parts of the world, an especially rich Pliocene marine fauna being known from Sicily and southern Italy.

Fresh-Water Mollusks.—Fresh-water gastropods and a few pelecypods are present in some Pliocene deposits, especially in the western part of the United States, although a few are known from Florida.

Fish, Amphibia, and Reptiles.—Apparently these groups were very little different from those of the Miocene epoch. Pliocene fossils of these groups from America are very rare.

Mammals.—Mammal remains are fairly abundant in the terrestrial deposits of the Great Plains and elsewhere in the western part of the continent. Among the mammals conspicuous for the first time during the Pliocene were the giant ground sloths (*Glyptodon*), which reached North America over a land bridge from South America. The Pliocene mammal fauna also includes a horse (*Pliohippus*), several species of mastodon, sabre-tooth tigers, and many other species.

Plants.—The Pliocene flora is essentially similar to that of the present day. Very little is known of the American plants of this period, since only about 50 species have been recorded, mostly from the Citronelle formation of Alabama. The only Citronelle genus not known from North America today is *Trapa*, the water chestnut.

Tertiary History of the Appalachian Mountains

It will be remembered that the Appalachian Mountains had been formed by uplift and folding during Permian time. At the time of their birth they were probably very high, possibly as much as 20,000 feet, rivaling the present-day Himalayas. Gradually, however, the Appalachians were eroded and the region became a surface or peneplane sloping toward the east. Certain high peaks of more resistant rock rose above this peneplain, including the White Mountains of New Hampshire, the Adirondacks of New York, Mount Katahdin of Maine, and the Great Smokies of North Carolina and Tennessee. This ancient surface, of which remnants can still be seen, is called the Schooley Peneplain. The exact age of the formation of this peneplain is uncertain, but it is generally thought to date from the early Tertiary.

Later during the Tertiary period, a renewed uplift took place in the Appalachian region. As this uplift took place, the rivers began to entrench themselves and cut into the underlying rocks. These streams formed water gaps where they cut through the hard upturned rocks and "wind gaps" where the channels were started but later abandoned. Wind Gap in Northampton County, Pennsylvania, is an excellent example of an abandoned channel of an ancient river.

A pause in the uplift of the Appalachian region allowed the formation of a new erosional surface, which has been termed the Harrisburg Peneplain. Uplift started again, and the Harrisburg Peneplain was dissected and more water gaps and wind gaps were created. The erosion of the softer elements of the uplifted mountains and the resistance of the harder rocks account for the present contours of the Appalachian Mountains and their present-day scenery.

Economic Resources of the Tertiary

Coal.—The Fort Union formation (Paleocene) in Montana and Wyoming contains commercial bituminous coal, and there are Eocene subbituminous coal beds in Washington and Oregon. Lignite occurs in some Eocene formations in the Gulf Coast and in North Dakota, but is chiefly of potential rather than actual economic value. Small quantities of anthracite occur in King County, Washington.

Petroleum.—The oil fields of coastal Louisiana and southeastern Texas produce mainly from deeply buried Miocene deposits. These fields are frequently associated with salt domes (Jurassic?) that have pushed upward into Tertiary deposits. The oil fields of the Los Angeles basin (California) produce largely from Miocene and Pliocene formations. Most Tertiary marine formations are potential sources of petroleum.

Gold.—As noted under the discussion of the Jurassic, most of the placer gold of California was carried by Tertiary streams from the Mother Lode of the Sierra Nevada. Smaller quantities of gold have been found in Tertiary (and Pleistocene) gravels along the Atlantic seaboard. At one time, considerable gold was obtained near Dahlonega, Georgia, the gold presumably having been concentrated in gravels from older rocks to the west. Smaller and rather unprofitable gold mining enterprises were undertaken many years ago near Middletown, Delaware, and Washington, D. C.

Sand.—Southern New Jersey, especially near Glassboro, Millville, and Vineland, saw the development of the early American glass industry. The Cohansey formation (Miocene) of this region is still an important source of glass sand. Quartz sand of varying quality occurs extensively along the Atlantic Coastal Plain and is used for many purposes, such as building, paving, molding, and other commercial needs. Sand deposits, of course, are not limited to Tertiary formations, but occur throughout the geologic column, from the Cambrian to the Pleistocene.

Glauconite (Greensand).—Most of the glauconite now being dug in New Jersey for a water softener comes from the Hornerstown formation (Eocene). The deeper parts of some pits are in the Cretaceous, and it is probable that much of the Eocene glauconite was reworked from similar material deposited during Late Cretaceous time.

Shell Marl.—Some fifty years ago or more, shell marl was dug extensively from Tertiary deposits between New Jersey and Florida. The scarcity of labor, together with the use of commercial lime and fertilizer has resulted in the abandonment of most of these pits. A few are still in operation in eastern North Carolina.

Cement.—Investigations during the past two or three years have disclosed the fact that some of the Miocene and Eocene limestones from North Carolina are suitable for the manufacture of cement.

Operations are now under way near New Bern, Belgrade, and Wilmington.

Bauxite.—Supplies of this mineral (source of aluminum) were formerly almost exclusively obtained from Surinam (Dutch Guiana) and British Guiana, although some deposits were known to exist in Arkansas. The great need for aluminum during World War II and the difficulty of transport from South America caused an intensive search for new supplies of bauxite in the United States. According to a recent survey by the United States Bureau of Mines, there are numerous deposits of bauxite on the Gulf Coastal Plain at the contact of the Paleocene Midway (Paleocene) and Wilcox (Eocene) groups. Near this contact the bauxite is found in Arkansas, Mississippi, Alabama, and Georgia. Not only is the bauxite found in the deposits laid down at the time of the transition between these two formations, but it also occurs in formations exposed at the surface at that particular time. Under such circumstances it occurs in the Tuscaloosa (Upper Cretaceous) formation of northwestern Alabama. It is also thought that the bauxite deposits of the Appalachian region (Alabama, Georgia, Tennessee, and Virginia) were formed during Eocene time.

Phosphate.—Phosphate rock is now being mined in Florida near Lakeland and Bartow, and is primarily used for agricultural fertilizer. This material is from the Bone Valley formation of Pliocene age. Other phosphate rock is obtained from Eocene and Miocene formations in Florida. Many years ago phosphate mining was an important industry in coastal South Carolina, but at present all such pits have been abandoned.

Diatomaceous Earth.—Pure diatom deposits quarried from Miocene rocks at Lompoc, California, are used as insulating material and as a base of certain commercial scouring powders. Deposits of diatomaceous earth occur near Chesapeake Bay in Maryland and Virginia and are of potential economic importance.

FURTHER READING FOR CHAPTERS 21–24

ANDERSON, J. L., et al. *Cretaceous and Tertiary Subsurface Geology of Maryland.* Maryland Dept. Geol., Mines and Water Resources, Bull. 2 (1948).

ASHLEY, GEORGE H. "Studies in Appalachian Mountain Sculpture," *Bull. Geol. Soc. Amer.,* XLVI (1935), pp. 1395–1436.

CANU, F., and BASSLER, R. S. *The Bryozoan Fauna of the Vincentown Limesand.* U.S. Nat. Mus. Bull. 165 (1933).

CEDERSTROM, D. J. "Structural Geology of Southeastern Virginia," *Bull. Amer. Assoc. Petrol. Geol.,* XXIX (1945), pp. 71–95.

CLARK, W. B., et al. *The Eocene Deposits of Maryland*. Maryland Geol. Surv., 1901.

———. *The Miocene Deposits of Maryland*. Maryland Geol. Surv., 1904.

CLARK, W. B., and MILLER, B. L. The Physiography and Geology of the Coastal Plain of Virginia. Virginia Geol. Surv. Bull. 4 (1912).

COOKE, C. WYTHE. "Geology of Alabama (Cenozoic)," Alabama Geol. Surv. *Special Rept.* 14 (1926), pp. 251–97.

———. *Geology of the Coastal Plain of South Carolina*. U.S. Geol. Surv. Bull. 867 (1936).

———. *Geology of the Coastal Plain of Georgia*. U.S. Geol. Surv. Bull. 941 (1943).

———. *Geology of Florida*. Florida Geol. Surv. Bull. 29 (1945).

COOKE, C. WYTHE, GARDNER, JULIA, and WOODRING, W. P. "Correlation of the Cenozoic Formations of the Atlantic and Gulf Coastal Plain and the Caribbean Region," *Bull. Geol. Soc. Amer.*, LIV (1943), pp. 1713–23.

COOKE, C. WYTHE, and STEPHENSON, L. W. "The Eocene Age of the Supposed Upper Cretaceous Greensand Marls of New Jersey," *Jour. Geol.*, XXXVI (1928), pp. 139–48.

DALL, W. H. *Contributions to the Tertiary Fauna of Florida*. Trans. Wagner Free Inst. Sci., III (1890–1905).

DUNBAR, CARL O. *Historical Geology*. New York: John Wiley & Sons, Inc., 1949, Chs. 17 and 19.

EARDLEY, A. J. *Structural Geology of North America*. New York: Harper & Bros., 1951.

GARDNER, JULIA. *Mollusca from the Miocene and Lower Pliocene of Virginia and North Carolina*. U.S. Geol. Surv. Prof. Paper 199-A (1943).

GREACEN, KATHERINE. *The Stratigraphy, Fauna and Correlation of the Vincentown Formation*. New Jersey Geol. Surv. Bull. 52 (1941).

KING, PHILIP B. *The Tectonics of Middle North America*. Princeton: Princeton University Press, 1951.

LEWIS, J. V., and KUMMEL, H. B. *The Geology of New Jersey*. New Jersey Geol. Surv. Bull. 50 (1940).

MANSFIELD, W. C. "Stratigraphic Significance of Miocene, Pliocene and Pleistocene Pectinidae in the Southeastern United States," *Jour. Paleont.*, X (1936), pp. 168–92.

McGLOTHLIN, T. "General Geology of Mississippi," *Bull. Amer. Assoc. Petrol. Geol.*, XXVIII (1944), pp. 29–62.

MOORE, RAYMOND C. *An Introduction to Historical Geology*. New York: McGraw-Hill Book Co., Inc., 1949, Chs. 17 and 19.

OSBORN, HENRY F. *The Age of Mammals*. New York: The Macmillan Co., 1921.

RICHARDS, HORACE G. "Correlation of Atlantic Coastal Plain Formations: A Discussion," *Bull. Geol. Soc. Amer.*, LVI (1943), pp. 401–8.

———. "Subsurface Stratigraphy of Atlantic Coastal Plain between New Jersey and Georgia," *Bull. Amer. Assoc. Petrol. Geol.*, XXIX (1945), pp. 885–955.

———. *Geology of the Coastal Plain of North Carolina*. Trans. Amer. Philos. Soc., XL, Pt. 1 (1950).

RICHARDS, HORACE G., and HARBISON, ANNE. "Miocene Invertebrate Fauna of New Jersey," *Proc. Acad. Nat. Sci. Phila.*, XCIV (1942), pp. 167–250.

ROBERTS, J. K. *The Lower York James Peninsula*. Virginia Geol. Surv. Bull. 37 (1932).

SCHUCHERT, CHARLES. *Stratigraphy of the Eastern and Central United States*. New York: John Wiley & Sons, Inc., 1943.

SCOTT, W. B. *A History of Land Mammals in the Western Hemisphere*. New York: The Macmillan Co., 1937.

SPANGLER, W. B., and PETERSON, J. J. *Geology of Atlantic Coastal Plain in New Jersey, Delaware, Maryland and Virginia.* Bull. Amer. Assoc. Petrol. Geol., XXXIV (1950).

STEPHENSON, L. W. "Major Marine Transgressions and Regressions and Structural Features of the Gulf Coastal Plain," *Amer. Jour. Sci.* Ser. 5, XVI (1928), pp. 281–98.

WELLER, STUART. *A Report on the Cretaceous Paleontology of New Jersey.* New Jersey Geol. Surv. Paleontology, IV (1907). (Includes fossils now referred to the Eocene.)

CHAPTER 25

THE PLEISTOCENE

Quaternary Period—General Discussion

The term "Pleistocene" is derived from the Greek *pleistos*, "most" and *kainos*, "recent." Post-Tertiary time is generally spoken of as the Quaternary, the fourth major division of time in the earth's history, according to the older classification. Some writers use the term to include the Pleistocene and Recent, while others restrict it to the Pleistocene alone. Dr. R. F. Flint has recently proposed the abandonment of the term altogether, along with the term "Tertiary," and prefers to regard all epochs from Eocene (Paleocene) to Recent as a single period within the Cenozoic era.

"The Ice Age."—The Pleistocene, or Quaternary, is the most recent episode in geologic chronology. Although very brief in comparison with the older periods, it was one of the critical times in the history of the earth. Despite the fact that the Pleistocene is often spoken of as the "Great Ice Age," we know that its climate was not always severe. Immense ice sheets did cover the northern part of the United States and most of Canada, as well as other parts of the world. There were several advances of the ice, probably four major ones, but they were separated by periods of interglacial time, probably longer than the glacial stages, when the climate was at least as mild as at the present time, and probably somewhat milder.

The following table shows the most generally accepted classification of the Pleistocene of North America, together with the probable correlations with the stages of the Alps of Europe, where a chronology of the Pleistocene was originally worked out:

NORTH AMERICA	ALPS	NUMBER OF YEARS SINCE BEGINNING OF STAGE [1]
4. Wisconsin glacial stage (including Iowan and Peorian)	Würm	55,000
3. Sangamon interglacial stage	Riss/Würm	190,000
3. Illinoian glacial stage	Riss	290,000
2. Yarmouth interglacial stage	Mindel/Riss	600,000
2. Kansan glacial stage	Mindel	700,000
1. Aftonian interglacial stage	Gunz/Mindel	900,000
1. Nebraskan glacial stage	Gunz	1,000,000

[1] Time estimate after Flint.

Source of Ice.—The Pleistocene glaciers were vast in extent, in some places a mile thick. One will readily agree that this is a tremendous amount of ice. Where did all the water that formed this ice come from? Originally, of course, it must have come from the sea. One can figure out, if one is adept in mathematics, how much ice there

Mississippi Valley (standard terminology)		Long Island and New England	Northern New Jersey	Southern New Jersey	Maryland– Carolinas
Post-Wisconsin		"Saxicava sand" "Leda clay"	—	—	—
Wisconsin	Mankato Cary Tazewell Peorian Iowan	Wisconsin (various phases) Jacob sand	Wisconsin	—	—
Sangamon		Gardiners	—	Cape May	Pamlico = Suffolk scarp
Illinoian		—	Illinoian	Pennsauken and Bridgeton	—
Yarmouth		—	—		"Higher terraces" = Surry scarp
Kansan		Jameco?	Jerseyan?		
Aftonian		—	—		"Higher terraces"
Nebraskan		—	Jerseyan?		—

was on North America and on other parts of the world which were glaciated at that time, for we know approximately how thick the ice was. We can determine how much salt water is required to make a given volume of ice, and therefore can make a rough estimate of the amount of the water taken from the sea to produce the land ice. The removal of the water from the sea caused the sea level to fall some 300 feet. Along the New Jersey part of the Atlantic Coastal Plain, for instance, the Pleistocene shore line during the last glacial stage was some 80 miles beyond the present shore line. In other words, the site of Atlantic City or Cape May, instead of being on the coast, would have been some 80 miles inland.

Conversely, during the last major interglacial stage, perhaps, 100,000 years ago, the climate was warm and there was less ice on the land. The sea would have been higher by something like 25 feet. As we shall see later in this chapter, we find evidence for this interglacial high level of the sea all the way from Long Island to Florida and along the Gulf of Mexico.

This warm, high-water interglacial sea undoubtedly extended north of Long Island. However, this region has been glaciated, and most of the records of the earlier interglacial sea have been destroyed by the ice. There are, however, a few traces still visible, for instance on Nantucket Island off the Massachusetts mainland. The relationship of glaciation to sea level is called "glacial control" and has been extensively studied by Antevs, Daly, Cooke, and many other geologists.

Weight of the Ice.—There is another way in which these great glaciers produced changes in the earth, particularly along the shore of the ocean. The stupendous amount of ice was a great weight on the earth's crust. The crust, being somewhat elastic, felt the strain of this weight, and was depressed. This depression was probably greater in the north where the thickness of the ice was greater. The amount of depression diminished toward the south and there is little or no evidence of any depression south of the terminal moraine, or furthest advance of the ice.

The combined effect of the sinking of the land and the lowering of sea level, for instance, caused the Late Pleistocene New England shore line to be somewhere in the vicinity of the present shore line, whereas farther south, where there was no weight of the ice, it was far to the east. Figure 274 shows the last interglacial shore line (Cape May-Gardiners) submerging the margins of the present strand of New Jersey and Long Island, and the glacial (Jacob) shore line far east of the present New Jersey beach (where there was no depression of the land caused by the ice) and crossing Long Island, where the land was pushed down by the ice.

As the ice withdrew, the sea rose and flooded the land before the latter had a chance to recover from the effect of the great weight of the ice. The land later rose to something near its present position, and the sea withdrew once more.

We will return to these changes in shore line later in this chapter, when we attempt to trace the Pleistocene history of eastern North America. Fossil evidence will be cited to show the effect of the Pleistocene glaciers on the relative position of sea and land.

The preceding remarks apply primarily to the last interglacial and glacial stages (Sangamon and Wisconsin). The same two phenomena, removal of sea water to form the ice, and the depression of the land by the ice, undoubtedly took place during the earlier stages of the Pleistocene. However, the records of these earlier stages are much more difficult to decipher from the rocks of the Atlantic Coast of the United States because in many cases these records have been completely obliterated by later advances of the ice or by other geological events. On the other hand, in some parts of the world elevated beaches

FIG. 274.   Late Pleistocene shore lines of New Jersey and Long Island.

dating from the early interglacial stages are known to exist. Examples are found on the shores of the Mediterranean Sea, in Scandinavia, and on the island of Jersey in the English Channel.

Atlantic Coastal Terraces.—Along the Atlantic Coastal Plain, from New Jersey southward, there is a series of deposits, frequently called terraces, occurring at various elevations from 25 to 300 (or more) feet above sea level. The lowest terrace deposit, the Pamlico formation, contains abundant marine fossils and is therefore clearly of marine origin. Because of the warm-water character of the fossils, it is believed that the Pamlico formation dates from an interglacial stage, and because of the youthful nature of the "terrace" it is believed that it represents the last major (Sangamon) interglacial stage.

The origin of the higher (older) terraces is not obvious. Dr. C. W. Cooke, of the United States Geological Survey, believes that these terraces represent the various older interglacial stages, when the sea level was higher than today. The intermediate terraces then could represent temporary stands of the sea. Dr. R. F. Flint questions this interpretation and points out the lack of marine features of the "higher terraces." Paleontological evidence does not support the view of the marine origin of the higher terraces. While marine fossils are abundant in the Pamlico formation, they are entirely absent—except for a record in South Carolina which may be of Pliocene age—from the Pleistocene formations higher than 25 feet above present sea level. The presence of fossil plants and vertebrate animals in these "higher terraces" is an argument against their marine origin and is in favor of an origin by fresh-water rivers.

If these older Pleistocene deposits are not marine, why do we not find older marine Pleistocene deposits along the East Coast? That question remains unanswered. Possibly a sinking of the land has obliterated the traces of the early interglacial marine advances.

Pleistocene History of Glaciated Eastern North America

Nebraskan Glacial Stage.—The first of the Pleistocene glaciers advanced from the northwest. It is difficult to trace the exact distribution of this ice sheet because, in many places, the till and boulders were covered by one or more subsequent ice sheets. However, deeply weathered till and other deposits left by the Nebraskan glaciers have been recognized in Nebraska, which gives the stage its name, in Minnesota, Iowa, northern Missouri, and Kansas. If the Nebraskan glaciers did cover eastern North America, all traces have long since been obliterated.

Aftonian Interglacial Stage.—The Nebraskan glaciers retreated and there was a long period of time when the climate was mild and the ice sheets were limited to the true Arctic regions. This was the Aftonian Interglacial stage. The Nebraskan till was deeply weathered during this stage and all of the soluble carbonates disappeared from the soil.

Fossil pollen is present in many of the Aftonian deposits, especially in Iowa and Nebraska. Studies of this pollen indicate that during the early part of the stage Iowa was largely covered by conifers. As the climate became milder, the conifers gave way to grasslands and then to oak trees. Finally, the conifers returned as the climate became cooler, owing to the approaching Kansan glaciers.

Kansan Glacial Stage.—The ice sheets again came down from the north and reached as far south as Kansas City and St. Louis, slightly south of the terminal moraines left by the Nebraskan glaciers. Kansan till is exposed in Illinois, Iowa, Kansas, Nebraska, and Missouri.

The Jerseyan drift of Pennsylvania and New Jersey, while not continuous with that of the Kansan stage, is thought to be of the same age. In New Jersey, the Jerseyan drift occurs in discontinuous patches south of the later Wisconsin terminal moraine, to a maximum distance of 24 miles. In the Delaware Valley it reached a point below Riegelsville, Bucks County, Pennsylvania, where obscure glacial scratches have been observed on a ledge of gneiss.

The till left by the Jerseyan glaciers is much more deeply weathered than that of the later Wisconsin age and can therefore be easily distinguished from it. However, the exact age is uncertain because it cannot be traced westward to the Mississippi Valley. It is probable that many deposits of Jerseyan age were covered by later glacial deposits. Possibly the deposits termed Jerseyan may actually represent two glaciations, the Nebraskan and the Kansan, although a Kansan age seems more probable. Some workers have attempted to trace the Jerseyan deposits eastward to Long Island and Massachusetts, but it is more probable that these latter deposits date from the Wisconsin glacial stage.

Yarmouth Interglacial Stage.—The Kansan ice finally retreated and was followed by another mild interglacial stage, termed the Yarmouth. Peat beds, 15 feet thick, deposited during this stage have been found in Iowa. The plant fossils in this peat indicate a climate not very different from that in the Central Plains states today. Mollusk shells are also present in some Yarmouth deposits, while the vertebrate fossils include giant ground sloths, peccaries, horses, elephants, and many other varieties of animals.

Not many deposits of proved Yarmouth age are known from eastern North America. Extensive fossiliferous deposits along Lake Ontario at Scarborough Bluffs, near Toronto, are probably partly of Yarmouth age. Many fossil fresh-water mollusks and plants have been reported from this locality.

Illinoian Glacial Stage.—The next glacial advance was one of the most extensive. The ice sheets extended southward to the Ohio River and westward across Illinois to Iowa and Missouri. An eastward extension of this sheet extended across New York State, northern Pennsylvania, and northern New Jersey. According to Frank Leverett, who has done extensive work on the Illinoian deposits in the eastern states, the Illinoian sheets border those of the Wisconsin in a narrow

FIG. 275. Scarborough Bluffs near Toronto, Ontario. These deposits are
thought to date from the Yarmouth and Sangamon interglacial stages.

zone between Dover and Hackettstown, New Jersey, and cover much of the lowland areas on both sides of Schooley Mountain.

The Illinoian deposits are frequently difficult to distinguish from the older Jerseyan drift and the younger Wisconsin. In general, however, they represent an intermediate stage in weathering.

Sangamon Interglacial Stage.—The Illinoian glaciers retreated to the north and there followed a long interglacial stage, when the climate was at least as mild as that of today and probably slightly milder. This was the Sangamon interglacial stage. The till of the Illinoian glaciers was weathered to a depth of four to six feet. The ice sheets must have retreated beyond their present limits, for there is evidence that the sea was some 25 feet higher during this stage than at present, as indicated by the marine fossils of the Pamlico and Cape May formations. Some of the fossiliferous clays along Lake Ontario at Scarborough Bluffs near Toronto are probably of Sangamon age (Figure 275). Wings and other fragments of insects as well as plant fossils are present in Sangamon deposits in some localities, notably in Iowa. Vertebrate fossils are rarely found.

Iowan Substage.—Geologists formerly recognized the Iowan as a separate glacial stage which was separated from the Illinoian by the Peorian interglacial stage. According to the more recently accepted classification, especially the work of Marshall Kay, the Peorian and Iowan are regarded as early phases of the Wisconsin glacial stage. These deposits are best represented in Iowa and Illinois.

Wisconsin Glacial Stage.—Because of its later age, more is known about the history of the Wisconsin glacial stage than about any of the previous stages of the Pleistocene (Figure 276). The glacial deposits grouped together as of Wisconsin age include four main stages which probably represent four advances and retreats of a single great ice sheet. The time intervals between the stages are known as interstadials, but little is known about any except the Peorian. The Wisconsin is thus subdivided as follows:

1. Iowan substage
2. Peorian interstadial (loess)
3. Tazewell substage [2]
4. Cary substage
5. Mankato substage

The glaciers of Wisconsin age covered practically all of Canada and much of northern United States (Figure 277). Certain areas, how-

[2] Sometimes used as adjectives: "Tazewellian," "Caryan," and "Mankatoan."

Fig. 276. Pleistocene (Wisconsin) till on the north shore of Long Island.

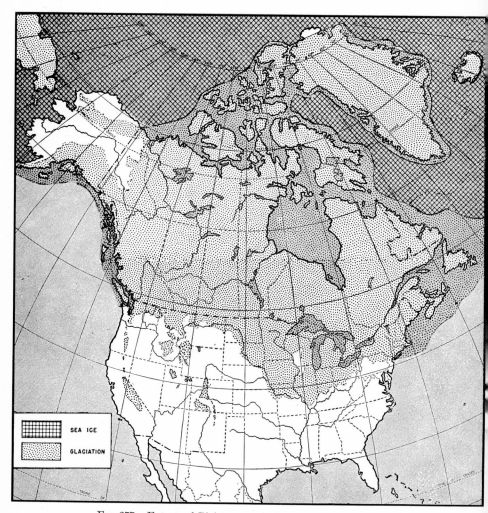

FIG. 277.   Extent of Pleistocene glaciation in North America.

ever, were not covered by the glaciers. For example, parts of Alaska, as well as eastern Siberia, were unglaciated probably because of insufficient snowfall. Furthermore, there was a large area in southwestern Wisconsin, known as the Driftless Area, which apparently lay between two lobes of Wisconsin glaciers. Various scientists have advanced the theory that other areas of the United States and Canada were also untouched by the Wisconsin ice sheets. The late M. L. Fernald, after studying the living flora of North America, came to the belief that the plants of some localities are of ancient stock and therefore antedate the Wisconsin glacial stage. Thus, he believed that during Wisconsin time certain mountains of Newfoundland, the Shickshock Mountains of Quebec, and other places in eastern North America remained above the ice, as nunataks. A few geologists have followed Dr. Fernald's interpretation of glacial history; however, most recent workers are very skeptical, and it is generally believed that most of eastern North America, as shown in Figure 277, was covered by the Wisconsin ice. The peculiar plant distribution is explained in part by postglacial migration.[3]

Post-Wisconsin Time.—According to many geologists, the Pleistocene came to an end with the retreat of the Wisconsin glaciers, and the time following this was called the Late Glacial and Recent. There can be no exact boundary line because the glaciers retreated from different places at different times. According to the latest estimates, based on radioactive carbon (see page 28), the ice began to retreat from the terminal moraine on Long Island about 12,000 years ago,[4] while the northern shores of Hudson Bay were not freed from ice until only a few thousand years ago. According to this same interpretation, Greenland with its thick ice cap is still in the Pleistocene.

As the ice began to melt and retreat, water poured back into the sea, gradually causing the sea level to rise. The land had not yet recovered from the weight of the ice; consequently, much of the terrain along the coast of New England and eastern Canada was flooded by this rising sea. This sea flooded the Gulf of St. Lawrence embayment, spilling over the present lowlands. Arms of this sea—sometimes called the "Champlain Sea"—extended up the Saguenay River to Lake St. John, up the Ottawa River to Ottawa, and south over the lowlands now separating the St. Lawrence River from Lake Champlain (Figure 278). Hudson Bay and James Bay were more extensive

---

[3] Edward S. Deevey, "Biogeography of the Pleistocene," *Bull. Geol. Soc. Amer.*, LX (1949), pp. 1378–82.
[4] Earlier estimates based on the measurement of varves suggested a figure nearer 25,000 years.

than at present and parts of the Arctic Archipelago of Canada were submerged by this sea.

The land gradually recovered from the effect of the weight of the ice and began to rise. This caused the sea to retreat, leaving behind

FIG. 278. Pleistocene fossiliferous gravel deposit left by the "Champlain Sea" at Isle La Motte, Vermont.

it abandoned shore lines and fossil deposits. The rise was greater where the weight of the ice had been heavier. Consequently, these abandoned shore lines are found high above present sea level in the Canadian Arctic and Labrador, and at decreasing elevations south along the New England coast. Somewhere near New York City there was a "hinge line," south of which there was no noticeable movement of the land caused by the weight of the ice.

The accompanying table shows the elevation of Post-Wisconsin beaches, as determined by the finding of fossil shells or other marine animals. Some workers, basing their studies on physiographic studies of terraces and strand lines, without fossil evidence, have postulated a considerably higher rise of the Post-Wisconsin sea. However, since many of these ancient beaches may actually have been made by fresh-water lakes, only those raised beaches that can definitely be demonstrated by fossil evidence are considered in this table.

Point Shirley, Massachusetts	50 feet
Belfast, Maine	250
Mount Desert, Maine	210
St. Albans, Vermont	300
Montreal, Quebec	500
Ottawa, Ontario	380
Venosta, Ontario	540
Rivière du Loup, Quebec	300
Coral Rapids, Ontario	250
(50 miles north of James Bay)	
Curling, Newfoundland	140
50 miles inland from Churchill, Manitoba	450
Wolstenholm, Quebec	548
Hudson Strait	898

Pleistocene History South of the Terminal Moraine

Early Pleistocene.—Little is known about the detailed history of the Early Pleistocene south of the glaciated area. As mentioned earlier, the so-called "terraces" of the South Atlantic Coastal Plain are sometimes thought to be of marine origin, but it is probable that the higher (older) ones are of fresh-water origin. Fossils are rare, and the few that are known are of plants or land animals.

In New Jersey, the Bridgeton and Pennsauken formations are thought to be of Early Pleistocene age, but their exact correlations with the glacial timetable is uncertain. It seems legitimate to consider these gravels as either a single formation with many and complex parts at different levels, or as a series of many formations. They are considered to date largely from one or more of the interglacial stages, although part of them may date from the glacial stages. The presence of Paleozoic fossils in the chert pebbles of these formations has already been mentioned (page 179). These, of course, are not in place and tell little about the age of the gravels.

Sangamon Time.—As mentioned earlier in this chapter, the terrace deposits along the Atlantic Coastal Plain are thought to have formed during the last major interglacial stage. These deposits are called the

Cape May formation in New Jersey and the Pamlico formation farther south. In most cases the fossils of these formations indicate a climate slightly warmer than that prevailing in the same latitude today. For example, coquina rock, somewhat similar to that now forming off the coast of Florida, was found in the Cape May formation in excavations for a tunnel under the Hudson River between New York and New Jersey

Fig. 279. Pleistocene coquina from beneath the Hudson River at New York. This type of rock is now forming off the coast of Florida and its presence under New York is evidence of a mild interglacial stage.

(Figure 279). An extensive fauna containing many warm-water species was obtained by dredgings from beneath the bottom of the channels and inlets in Cape May County, New Jersey, especially at Two Mile Beach and more recently in the excavations for the Cape May Canal. Farther south, evidence for this warm climate can be found from fossils obtained from many localities in Maryland, Virginia, and the Carolinas. The best collections were obtained from the following:

Cornfield Harbor, Maryland (near the mouth of the Potomac River).

Dismal Swamp Canal, Virginia and North Carolina (excavations).

10 miles below New Bern, North Carolina (bluffs on the Neuse River).

Intracoastal Canal in Hyde County, North Carolina (excavations).

Near Myrtle Beach, South Carolina.

In Florida, the warming effect of the interglacial sea is less apparent. However, the reef coral of the Key Largo formation (= Pamlico) has been found at Pompano, slightly north of existing coral reefs, and some

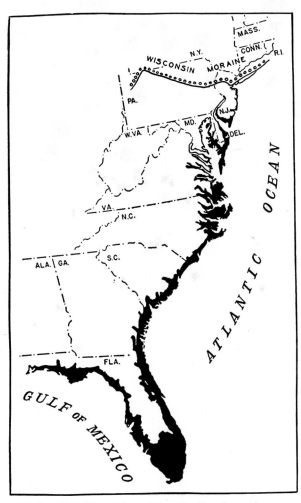

FIG. 280. Shore line of the Pamlico formation.

West Indian species of mollusks were obtained from a well at Delray near Palm Beach.

Figure 274 showed the probable position of the interglacial (Cape May) shore line in New Jersey, while Figure 280 shows the submergence during Cape May–Pamlico time, from New Jersey to Florida. This interglacial shore line has been traced along the coast of the Gulf of Mexico from Florida to Louisiana. However, as the Mississippi River is approached, the effect of the weight of the sediments carried down this river is noticed. A tremendous sinking of the land in the region of the Mississippi Delta has taken place since the Pleistocene—and is still taking place. The result is that Pleistocene marine deposits are more than 2,000 feet thick in the "Deep Delta" south of New Orleans, whereas to the east and west of the delta, the Pleistocene deposits are only about 100 feet in thickness.

Wisconsin Time.—How far south the cooling effects of the Wisconsin ice were felt is a matter of speculation. According to the glacial control hypothesis, the glacial shore line from New Jersey southward was some 80 miles east of the present strand. Consequently, any fossils from this stage would have been deposited far from the present shore. Farther north, for instance on Long Island, the land was pushed down by the weight of the ice, causing a partial cancellation of the lowered sea level. The position of this shore line, called the Jacob shore line from the Jacob sand of Long Island, is shown on Figure 274. It probably dates from early Wisconsin time at a time when the sea was becoming cold owing to the advancing ice. The Jacob sand overlies the Gardiners clay (Sangamon age) on Gardiners Island, Robins Island, and elsewhere in the Long Island region. Certain cold-water mollusks, especially *Neptunia stonei*

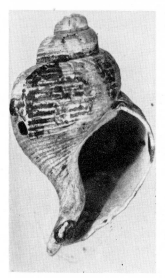

Fig. 281. *Neptunea stonei*, an extinct gastropod indicating a cold glacial climate.

(Figure 281), are found in the Jacob sand on parts of Long Island, Martha's Vineyard, and Nantucket. These same species are occasionally washed onto the beaches of New Jersey after heavy storms, and it seems highly probable that they came from the glacial shore line some miles off the present shore. A large number of these cold-water mollusks, especially *N. stonei*, were dredged from the excavations for the Cape

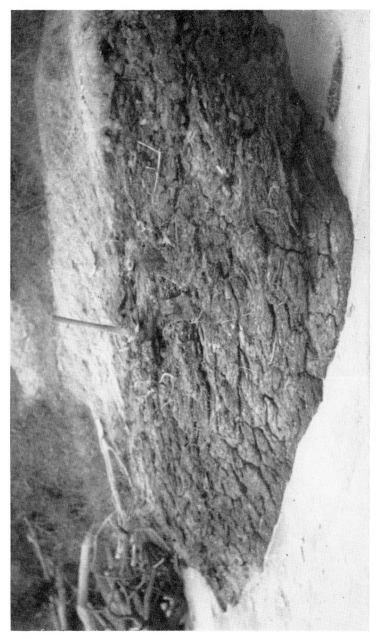

FIG. 282. Pleistocene peat along the Rappahannock River, Taft, Virginia.

May Canal in southern New Jersey, together with some other fossils that indicate a warm climate. The cold-water fauna may indicate an ancient (glacial) estuary of the Delaware River which would have permitted the mollusks to live closer to the present beach than along the Jacob shore line as shown in Figure 274. Recently *N. stonei* has been found in excavations at Manteo, North Carolina, possibly suggesting a similar estuary of the glacial sea in this region.

Most of the Pleistocene plant fossils from south of the glaciated area indicate temperatures similar to those of today in the same regions. Numerous plant fossils have been found in the Pleistocene of North Carolina, but no species can be interpreted as northern elements. The only suggestions of a cool glacial climate in the south come from Georgia and Florida. Near Dahlonega, Lumpkin County, Georgia, there is a deposit containing fossil plants which are presumably of early Pleistocene age. The flora is characterized by the presence of the tamarack larch (*Larix laricina*), not known today south of the Maryland-West Virginia line, near Cranesville, West Virginia. The cool climate indicated by this plant suggests that the deposit was formed during a glacial stage. In various parts of Florida, extensive peat deposits carry a cold-water flora of diatoms; in some places these are underlaid by a brackish water flora (diatoms). This brackish water flora has been correlated with the Pamlico formation (interglacial), while the overlying fresh-water peat (Figure 282) with the cool-water diatoms was probably deposited during part of the Wisconsin stage.

Some recent studies by the Woods Hole Oceanographic Institute have demonstrated the presence of sub-Arctic foraminifera in borings from the floor of the Gulf of Mexico, thus suggesting a cooling considerably south of the glaciated area.

Pleistocene History of the Interior of North America

During the Pliocene period it is probable that the region of the present Great Lakes was a broad lowland. Little is known about the region of the lakes during the early Pleistocene because most of the evidence has been destroyed by the subsequent Wisconsin ice sheets. During Wisconsin time the region was covered and scoured by the ice. The terminal moraine, or farthest stand of the ice, was many miles to the south.

As the glaciers began to melt at the end of Wisconsin time, great quantities of melt water accumulated in the lowlands and valleys now occupied by the Great Lakes. The history of these lakes is very complicated. At some stages, they were much more extensive than at present, a fact that can be demonstrated by the "fossil beaches" high above the present water level and the fossil fresh-water shells therein. These various stages have been given names such as Glacial Lake Chicago, Lake Algonquin, and Nipissing Great Lakes.

Changes in Drainage.—As the ice retreated and new outlets were created for these glacial lakes, their levels fell and they approached their present-day positions. Furthermore, the land rose, having recovered from the effect of the load of the ice. In some places it is probably still rising. The courses of many preglacial rivers were changed by the southward advancing ice sheets. North-flowing streams were reversed because their seaward paths to the north was blocked by the ice, and they consequently had to find new outlets to the south. Other drainage changes took place during Pleistocene time. Some geologists think that the Delaware River flowed southward from Port Jervis through Culvers Gap (instead of the Delaware Water Gap) to the vicinity of Bound Brook, and then eastward to the present channel of the Delaware near Trenton. It has also been suggested that the Hudson River flowed westward across New Jersey, joining the ancient Delaware near New Brunswick or Bound Brook.

Varves.—It has been observed that there is an alternation of deposition in glacial lakes. Silt was deposited during the summers, when the ice was melting, while during the winter the finer clays settled at the bottom. Thus, the combination of the clay and silt layers represents a year of deposition. If this correlation is carried back to the Pleistocene it should be possible to estimate the age of certain deposits. The alternating silts and clays of these glacial lakes are called "varve clays." These have been studied extensively in both Europe and America to attempt to date the retreat of the last glaciation. While no section can represent a full time-scale of varves, a comparison of a great many sections will frequently show overlappings and thereby establish a complete time scale. This is very similar to the study of dendrochronology, in which tree rings are studied to determine a time scale. Dr. Antevs has studied the varves of eastern North America from Long Island to James Bay, and while it has not been possible to establish a continuous record of the overlapping varves, it has been established by this method that the Wisconsin glaciers began to retreat from the Long Island moraine about 25,000 years ago. It will be noted that this figure is quite different from the estimate of 12,000 years reached by studies of radioactive carbon (see page 28). To date, no satisfactory explanation of this discrepancy has been suggested.

Other Glacial Lakes.—Many other glacial lakes were formed during the retreat of the Wisconsin glacial stage. One of the largest was Lake Agassiz, which covered an area of about 110,000 square miles in North Dakota, Minnesota, Manitoba, and Saskatchewan. Lakes Winnipeg and Winnipegosis are remnants of this once immense body of water.

Pluvial Time.—While the glaciers covered the northern part of North America there was a period of unusually heavy rainfall in other parts of the continent, especially in the West and Southwest. This period is sometimes spoken of as Pluvial time. During this stage several large lakes came into existence. One of these, Lake Bonneville in Utah, was the ancestor of Great Salt Lake. Lake Bonneville was originally fresh water, as is indicated by deposits of fresh-water mollusk shells along its ancient beaches. The salt of the present Great Salt Lake was derived from nearby salt deposits and transported to the lake by streams. Similar lakes of Pluvial time existed in New Mexico, Arizona, and California.

Loess.—At various times during the Pleistocene, especially at stages of maximum glaciation, extensive deposits of wind-blown silt or loess accumulated near the edge of the ice sheets.[5] These deposits can be seen in many places along the Mississippi Valley from northern Louisiana north into Canada, frequently in the form of river bluffs. The most southern deposit of loess occurs at Tunica, Louisiana, and is shown in Figure 283. Less conspicuous deposits of loess accumulated elsewhere in North America, but in the eastern part of the continent climatic and other conditions did not favor the formation of loess deposits. Detailed studies have been made to correlate the loess of the Mississippi Valley with the various stages of the Pleistocene. In many places the loess contains large numbers of land snails and occasional bones of mammals. The particular species of snails, together with the remains of musk ox, mammoth, and bison, can be taken as an indication of a somewhat cooler climate at the time of the formation of most loess deposits.

Loess deposits are conspicuous in other parts of the world, being notably associated with the Seine, Rhine, Danube, Bug, and Volga Rivers in Europe. Extensive deposits of loess are found in north-central China; in this case, the material is thought to have been blown from the vast deserts of Central Asia and hence has no connection with Pleistocene glaciation.

[5] A few geologists, notably Dr. R. J. Russell, of Louisiana State University, believe that loess was formed under water rather than by wind action. See Richard J. Russell, "Lower Mississippi Valley Loess," *Bull. Geol. Soc. Amer.*, LV (1944), pp. 1–40.

Fig. 283. Pleistocene loess at Tunica, Louisiana.

Causes of Glaciation

Various attempts have been made to explain the series of glacial advances during the Pleistocene. Among the various theories and combinations of theories are: (1) a shift of the earth's poles; (2) the passing of the solar system through "cold regions of space"; (3) an unusual amount of volcanic dust and carbon dioxide in the earth's atmosphere, which prevented part of the sun's heat from reaching the earth; (4) variations in the earth's internal heat; (5) pronounced elevation of the land, causing mountains and consequent lowering of temperatures; (6) periodic changes in the motion of the earth, which would affect the distribution of solar heat to various parts of the earth; (7) variations in the amount of solar heat.

Most of these theories, while satisfying many of the known conditions, do not fully explain the complex glacial cycles. Among the facts which have to be considered are the following:

1. Glaciation not only took place during the Pleistocene, but on numerous other occasions throughout geologic time, notably in the Pre-Cambrian and the Permian.
2. The glaciations of the Pleistocene were apparently synchronous in all parts of the world.
3. A drop in the mean annual temperature of only about three degrees Centigrade would probably cause the ice sheets to advance again from the polar regions.

4. The advance and retreat of the Pleistocene glaciers were accompanied by the lowering and rising of the snow line in mountainous areas.

5. The climatic belts of the world maintained their relative positions; in other words, there was no major shift of the poles.

Solar-Topographic Hypothesis.—The first three explanations set forth above are no longer tenable. There are, however, arguments both pro and con for the remaining hypotheses. In 1947, Flint, in his work on the Pleistocene, proposed a combination of theories 5 and 7, which he called the Solar-Topographic Hypothesis. Briefly stated, it holds that the pronounced uplift of the land which took place at the end of Tertiary time in various parts of the world, together with variations in the solar intensity, may have combined to bring about the glaciations of the Pleistocene. He cites the numerous mountains which were uplifted at this time, notably the Himalayas, the Coast Range in California, as well as a renewed uplift of the Alps and the Andes. He also cites the work of Abbot on the sun to support the solar part of the hypothesis. Possibly the earlier glaciations can also be explained by this hypothesis. The topographic element of the hypothesis could explain the glaciation of Permian time, which might have been connected with the uplift of the Appalachian Mountains. While the Solar-Topographic Hypothesis seems to best fit the known facts, it does not necessarily follow that all the glaciations of the world during geologic time were brought about by the same causes. The problem is by no means solved.

Life of the Pleistocene

Marine Invertebrates.—Practically all of the species found in marine Pleistocene deposits are known to be living today in the ocean. On the other hand, not all present-day species are living in the same latitudes today as they did during the Pleistocene. We have already seen how these Pleistocene fossils indicate fluctuations in climate. For example, the deposits of the Cape May formation of New Jersey contain a number of mollusks that are now known to be living only farther south. Among the most characteristic of these are: *Terebra dislocata, Terebra concava, Thais floridana, Nassarius vibex, Nassarius acuta, Arca ponderosa,* and unusually heavy shells of *Venus campechiensis.* In North Carolina the warm-water element of the fauna is more pronounced and the fossils from excavations in Hyde County include such species as *Rangia cuneata* and *Cantharus cancellaria.*

As mentioned earlier in this chapter, the glacial shore line from New Jersey southward was probably many miles east of the present beach. Consequently, fossils are only rarely found, either by being washed up on the beaches or by being dug from near the present strand. Among the characteristic cold-water species are *Neptunea decemcostata, Colus simpsoni, Buccinum undatum,* and the extinct *Neptunea stonei.*

Many of the mollusks of the Post-Wisconsin sea of New England and eastern Canada indicate a cooler climate than that which prevails today. Among the characteristic species of these deposits are: *Saxivava arctica, Leda glacialis, Macoma balthica, Mya arenaria,* and *Mytilus edulis.* The abundance of the first two species is sometimes so great as to give rise to the terms "Saxicava sand" and "Leda clay" for these deposits.

A few Pleistocene marine mollusks are apparently entirely extinct, although their climatic significance can frequently be determined by a study of closely related species. One of the most interesting of these extinct species is *Neptunea stonei* (Figure 281), a gastropod of northern affinities, originally described as a fossil of unknown age, which was washed up on the beaches of New Jersey in 1893. (See page 366.)

Land Mollusks.—The majority of the land snails found in Pleistocene loess deposits of North America belong to living species, although a few are represented in the fossil stage by extinct varieties.

Fresh-Water Mollusks.—Dry-lake beds such as those formed in the American West and Southwest during the Pluvial stage (contemporaneous with the Wisconsin glaciation) frequently contain fossil fresh-water snails. Again, the majority of these species are still to be found living in the region, although a few indicate a cooler climate. For example, some found near Clovis, New Mexico, and at Keet Seel and Cochise in Arizona, indicate a slightly cooler as well as a moister climate. Human artifacts have also been found at some of these sites, indicating that man may have reached North America during the latter part of the Wisconsin glacial stage. (See Chapter 26.)

Mammals.—The mammal fauna of North America during the Pleistocene was very impressive; in fact, it was rather similar to that of Africa today. At various times during the Pleistocene there was a land bridge connecting North America with Asia, via Siberia and Alaska, and many animals undoubtedly found their way to the New World over that bridge.

The Pleistocene fauna of North America included the mammoth and mastodon (Figures 284 and 285), various species of bison, horses, camels, peccaries, the sabre-toothed tiger as well as many animals similar to those living here today. Not all of these animals reached America via the Pleistocene land bridge. Many had been here throughout Tertiary time or had evolved from Tertiary ancestors.

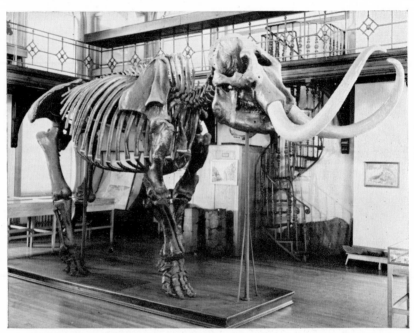

FIG. 284. Skeleton of mastodon from Salem, New Jersey. (Rutgers University.)

In addition to the land bridge to Asia, there was also a land bridge connecting North and South America, which apparently afforded a two-way route of migration. Mastodons, horses, camels, and peccaries migrated from North to South America, while the ground sloths, armadillos and glyptodonts migrated northward. Fossil remains of giant ground sloths, animals of truly South American affinity, have been found in many parts of the United States. The first to record this fossil was Thomas Jefferson who, as long ago as 1797, described in the *Transactions of the American Philosophical Society* what he thought was the claw of a giant lion from a cave in Greenbrier County, West Virginia (then Virginia). The further studies of Dr. Caspar Wistar in 1799, reported in the *Transactions*, showed its true relationship to the present-day South American sloths. The fossil still goes by the name *Megalonyx jeffersonii*. Subsequent to Jefferson's day, the re-

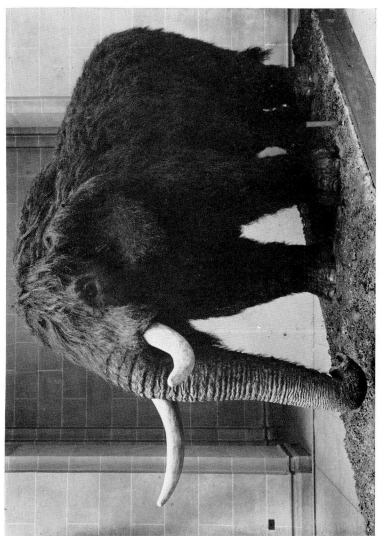

FIG. 285. Restoration of mastodon from Cohoes, New York. (New York State Mus.)

mains of *Megalonyx* as well as other giant sloths have been found in many localities, especially in California. The most recent discovery was made in 1950 by a young amateur from excavations for the New Jersey Turnpike near Moorestown, New Jersey (Figure 286).

The climatic fluctuations during the Pleistocene apparently had their effect on the land life as well as that in the seas. Until a few years ago it was believed that the ground sloths did not migrate north

FIG. 286. The giant ground sloth *Megalonyx jeffersonii*.

of the present United States–Canadian boundary, the northernmost record being from Washington state. However, in 1941, Otto Geist, working for the American Museum of Natural History, found part of a claw of a *Megalonyx* in frozen muck near Fairbanks, Alaska. Still more recently, an amateur collector brought to the Academy of Natural Sciences of Philadelphia a tooth of a *Megalonyx* which he had collected near Yellowknife, Northwest Territories, Canada.[6] Both of these records mark a considerable extension of the range of this animal and suggest that there must have been considerable deglaciation and amelioration of the climate in northern Canada and Alaska to permit these animals to migrate that far north.

[6] Chester Stock and Horace G. Richards, "A Megalonyx Tooth from the Northwest Territories, Canada," *Science*, CX (1949), pp. 709–10.

In addition to the northward migration of southern animals during the warmer interglacial stages, many Arctic animals migrated considerably to the south during the cold glacial advances. These migrations are witnessed by the finding of the fossil remains of the musk ox in Arkansas and Utah, the mammoth in the Carolinas and Florida, and the walrus in New Jersey and North Carolina.

No primates have been found in the Pleistocene deposits of North America. Although human remains have been found in deposits of Early and Middle Pleistocene age in Europe, Asia, and Africa, none that can be positively proved to antedate the Wisconsin glaciation have been discovered in North America. (See Chapter 26 for a discussion of Pleistocene man.)

Collecting Localities.—Perhaps the best collection of Pleistocene mammals has come from the tar pits at Rancho La Brea in Los Angeles, California, where a great many species have been recorded. Many years ago, a cave (unfortunately, no longer accessible) along the Schuylkill River at Port Kennedy, Pennsylvania, was a prolific source of Pleistocene vertebrate fossils. In this cave were found fossils of the mastodon, extinct tapir, sabre-toothed tiger, bison, ground sloth, peccary, a giant bear related to a South American species, as well as numerous animals still living in the region. It is thought that these fossils date from the Early Pleistocene. Another cave, thought to be somewhat younger than the one at Port Kennedy, was excavated a number of years ago near Cumberland, Maryland. The fossil remains of some fifty species of mammals have been identified.

Pleistocene vertebrate animals are not infrequently found in the surface deposits of eastern North America. Probably the most spectacular accounts which frequently reach the newspapers are those of the mastodons and mammoths. Skeletons or teeth of mastodons have been found at Salem, Woodbury, and Trenton, New Jersey; Port Kennedy and Reading, Pennsylvania; St. Marys, Maryland; Wilmington, North Carolina; and many other places. Mammoth remains have been found at Trenton, North Plainfield, Lumberton, and Blackwood, New Jersey; Chadds Ford, Pennsylvania; Oxford, Maryland; and elsewhere.

Several mastodon teeth have been dredged from the ocean some 20 miles off the New Jersey coast, and on one occasion part of a skeleton of a large walrus tusk was obtained in this way. Perhaps the shore line was this far east of the present strand at the time the mastodons lived—or perhaps the teeth were carried out to sea on ice. Another extinct mammal, known as a fossil from New Jersey, is a genus of moose known as *Cervacales* (Figure 287).

Plants.—The flora of the Pleistocene is essentially similar to that of today except with respect to migrations caused by climatic changes. During the glacial stages certain northern plants moved southward; for example, fossil remains of the larch were found in Georgia. Conversely, during the mild interglacial stages, the southern flora migrated northward. During recent years considerable information on the floral and climatic fluctuations of the Pleistocene has been ob-

Fig. 287. *Cervacales scotti*, an extinct moose from Mount Hermon, New Jersey. (New Jersey State Mus.)

tained by a study of fossil pollen and spores. A statistical study of these microfossils obtained from borings in bogs and marshes will frequently yield much information on the climatic history of the region, including such factors as temperature, moisture, and plant associations.

Relatively few plant fossils (other than microfossils) have been found in the pleistocene deposits of eastern North America. A flora indicating slightly warmer climate was found in the Pensauken formation near Dunhams Corner, New Jersey, and a few cypress stumps have been found in the Cape May formation, possibly indicating a slightly milder climate than prevailing today. One rather spectacular cypress stump was found in the excavation for a subway in Philadelphia in 1931 and was popularly known as the "Subway Tree." A few leaves and seeds have been found in Pleistocene deposits of North and South Carolina, but as a rule are rather poorly preserved.

Economic Resources of the Pleistocene

Sand and Gravel.—Since many of the glacial deposits consist of unconsolidated sand and gravel, they are dug extensively for construction work and other uses. Some Pleistocene sand is used for glass making, while the unusually pure deposits of sand near Cape May Point, New Jersey, are used primarily for filter sand.

Clay.—Brick clay was formerly extensively dug from post-glacial clays in New England. Although this industry has declined considerably in recent years, Pleistocene brick clays are commercially important in the Hudson and Delaware River valleys.

FURTHER READING

The references for Chapters 25–26 will be found at the end of Chapter 26.

CHAPTER 26

THE RECENT

Post-Wisconsin Time

Pleistocene-Recent Boundary.—As was pointed out earlier, there is no exact boundary between the Pleistocene and the Recent. In the present chapter we will use the word "Recent" to designate the time since the retreat of the Wisconsin glaciers. Thus, the transition from Pleistocene to Recent took place at different times in different parts of the world. The period during and immediately following the retreat of the last glaciation is often called "Late Glacial."

Post-Wisconsin Warm Stage (Climatic Optimum).—It was once thought that the climate has gradually become warmer since the end of the Wisconsin glacial stage. Modern research, however, especially the studies of pollen found in ancient peat bogs, has demonstrated that the climate gradually became warmer from the end of Wisconsin time up to a period between 6,000 and 4,000 years ago. Following that warm stage, the climate became cooler and more moist down almost to the present time and is now probably becoming warmer again. This Post-Wisconsin warm stage has been called the "climatic optimum" or, especially in Europe, Atlantic time.

Evidence for this climatic optimum is most complete from studies in Europe, especially in Scandinavia. It has been demonstrated that during this period the snow line in the Alps was about 1,000 feet higher than today. The marine deposits of the Littorina sea of Norway are also referred to the Post-Wisconsin warm stage, and are believed to indicate a water temperature approximately 2.5° C. higher than today.

Research work on ancient pollens of North America has not yet developed to a stage comparable to that of Europe. However, there are certain indications, particularly from the work of Sears, Deevey, and Hansen, that the climatic optimum also existed in North America. A slight cooling since the optimum is best demonstrated by a study of pollen from ancient bogs in eastern Canada, parts of New England, and the Pacific Northwest.

Subway excavations in Boston have yielded invertebrate shells suggesting a slightly warmer climate than that which prevails north of Cape Cod today. The shells were associated with a fish weir and have been dated from the warm climatic optimum. Shells of the salt-marsh periwinkle (*Littorina irrorata*) were found in an old peat deposit at Branford, Connecticut. This species is very rare north of New Jersey. It is possible that these shells lived during the climatic optimum, although it is equally possible that they merely indicate a sheltered cove where the water temperature was slightly higher than in surrounding areas.

It has not been demonstrated whether there was enough recession of the ice to cause a significant rise in sea level. Certainly there is little or no evidence of an extensive submergence of the Atlantic Coast of North America as recently as 4,000 or 6,000 years ago. It is true that some attempts have been made to correlate the fossiliferous deposits along the Atlantic Coast (such as the Cape May and Pamlico formations) with the Post-Wisconsin warm stage, but the majority of geologists believe that these are considerably older. On the other hand, the shells associated with the Boston fish weir may indicate a slight rise of sea level that can be correlated with the post-glacial temperature maximum.

Recent Extinction.—A few animals have become extinct in North America within historic times, or at least within the record of Indian habitation. Among these is the giant beaver (*Casteroides*) whose bones or teeth are occasionally found in camp sites or caves associated with Indian artifacts or skeletal remains; for example, at Stroudsburg, Pennsylvania, and at Faery Hole Rock Shelter near Johnsonsburg, Sussex County, New Jersey. Indian caves such as these as well as one near Reading, Pennsylvania, contain bones of animals no longer living in the immediate vicinity, such as the porcupine, bobcat, and timber wolf.

In other cases, animals which were formerly widespread are now more limited in distribution. Early accounts of Pennsylvania and New Jersey contain mention of elk, bison, and other animals no longer to be found in this region. Skeletal remains or teeth of bison have been found at various places in Pennsylvania and near Woodstown, Walnford, and Trenton, New Jersey. A striking example of recent extinction—although in this case entirely caused by man—is that of the passenger pigeon. It was formerly very abundant in eastern North America, and became extinct in 1914.

Early Man in the Old World

Human remains and artifacts have been found throughout the Pleistocene deposits of Europe, Asia, and Africa. The oldest traces of human habitation are some crude implements called "eoliths," supposedly (but not positively) made by humans in early Pleistocene (first glacial) deposits near Ipswich, England,[1] and in North Africa.[2] The accompanying table (Figure 288) shows a chronology of the prin-

American Chronology	European (Alpine) Chronology	Early Man	Flake or Blade Industry
RECENT	RECENT		Neolithic Mesolithic
WISCONSIN	WÜRM	Cro-Magnon (France) Rhodesian (Africa)	Magdalenian Solutrean Aurignacian Mousterian
SANGAMON	RISS/WÜRM	Neanderthal (Europe) Piltdown (England) Mt. Carmel (Palestine) Fontechevade (France) ?	Late Acheulean Upper Acheulean
ILLINOIAN	RISS	*Homo soloensis* (Java) Steinheim (Germany) ?	Middle Acheulean
YARMOUTH	MINDEL/RISS	Swanscombe (England) *Pithecanthropus* (Java) *Sinanthropus* (China)	Old Acheulean Chellean
KANSAN	MINDEL	Heidelberg (Germany) ?	Pre-Chellean (= Abbevillian)
AFTONIAN	GÜNZ/MINDEL	?	
NEBRASKAN	GÜNZ	Australopithecinae (Man Apes)?	Eoliths (England; North Africa) (Villafranchian)

FIG. 288. Chronology of Early Man in the Old World.

cipal types of fossil man from the Old World. There is not absolute agreement on the dating of several of these finds, and further work will undoubtedly refine the correlation. Recent investigations have produced evidence to suggest that several types of fossil man of totally different character may have lived at the same time in certain areas

[1] Until 1948 the gravels containing the "eoliths" were regarded as Pliocene.
[2] C. Arambourg, "Traces possibles d'une industrie primitive dans un niveau Villafranchien de l'Afrique du Nord," *Société Préhistorique de la France*, Nos. 6–8 (1950), pp. 348–50.

of the Old World. For example, investigations in France have suggested the contemporaneity of a Neanderthal type man with a more modern *Homo sapiens* type (Fontechevade), both dating from the last interglacial stage.

Early Man in America

It has been rather generally agreed that man reached North America by way of Siberia and Alaska. However, the exact time of this migration has been a matter of controversy for many years. Most scientists believed that man did not reach the Western Hemisphere until late in post-glacial time, probably as recently as only a few thousand years ago. It is true that there was evidence for Pleistocene man in the New World, but many of the data seemed inconclusive, and the apparent antiquity could frequently be explained by other interpretations. During the past 20 years, however, evidence has been accumulating to show that man did reach the New World much earlier than had previously been supposed, probably about the time of the climax, or retreat of the Wisconsin glaciation. Among the evidences for late glacial or early post-glacial man in America is the finding of extinct animals associated with human skeleton remains or artifacts, as well as skeletal and archaeological material in deposits of almost unquestionable geologic antiquity.

It is now believed that man crossed from Siberia to Alaska as the Wisconsin glaciers were beginning to withdraw, probably about 10,000 to 15,000 years ago. Sea level was probably low, causing a land connection to exist between western Alaska and East Cape, Siberia. Parts of Alaska, as well as parts of eastern Siberia, were unglaciated. Consequently, it would have been relatively easy for man to have migrated east along the Arctic coast of Alaska and then southward along the Mackenzie River to the eastern slope of the Rockies. When this route was opened, the temperature in Arctic Canada was probably lower than it is today. Most of the country was tundra, and these early immigrants experienced difficulties in obtaining food. As early man migrated southward, the climate became gradually more favorable, partly because of the more southerly latitudes, and partly because of a general increase in temperature. In the forests of the Mackenzie Valley (Figure 289) game probably became more plentiful, the chief animals being moose, caribou, bear, and bison. As man progressed farther south, into the Great Plains, bison became the chief game animal. It is probable that man reached the Southwest at the time of the transition between the Pluvial and Post-Pluvial epochs, or roughly 12,000 years ago.

Fig. 289. Air view of the Mackenzie Delta, Arctic Canada. This region may have been on the migration route of early man from Asia to America.

It is significant that all human skeletal remains found in North or South America are of modern types, closely resembling living Indians and Eskimos. This fact caused the late Dr. Aleš Hrdlička, one of the foremost physical anthropologists of his day, to argue strongly in favor of a very recent migration to the New World.

On the other hand, a few thousand years scarcely seem sufficient to allow for the migration of man to all parts of North and South America and to permit the diversification of the various tribes and languages of the Indians. (It is generally accepted that the Eskimos are very recent migrants, probably having come from Asia no earlier than about the beginning of the Christian era.)

Folsom Man.—In 1926, some crude stone implements were found near Folsom, New Mexico, in the same deposits as the extinct *Bison taylori*. This type of implement was characterized by fluting on one or both sides, and has been called the "Folsom Point." A small percentage of the points found at this site were long and narrow, with sides practically parallel, with parallel flaking extending across the blades at a slight angle, and with no fluting. These are called "Yuma points."

The Folsom culture has also been found at Clovis and Portales, New Mexico; Plainview, Texas; Fort Collins, Colorado ("Lindenmayer site"); and elsewhere in the West and Southwest. Among the extinct animals associated with this culture, in addition to the bison, are the camel, elephant, mastodon, horse, and ground sloth. No human skeletal remains have been found.

Although the first Folsom points have been found in the same deposits as the fossils of the extinct animals, the exact association of man and these extinct animals was not positively established. However, in 1927, some scientists from the Colorado Museum of Natural History, working near Folsom, found a Folsom point actually embedded in the bones of the extinct *Bison taylori*, this establishing the contemporaneity of man with this extinct animal (Figure 290). Further evidence was found at Clovis, New Mexico, by a party from the Academy of Natural Sciences which found a spear point embedded within the leg bone of a mammoth. A similar find was made near Miami, Roberts County, Texas, where an artifact was found in the bone of an extinct elephant. Radiocarbon studies on carbonaceous material associated with Folsom artifacts, suggest an age of between 8,000 and 12,000 years for Folsom man.

Folsom points have been found at Mortlach, Saskatchewan, associated with bison remains. This site may have been on the early route of migration. In 1948 and 1949, excavations made by J. L. Giddings, Jr., at Cape Denbigh on the north Bering Sea coast of Alaska revealed a culture considerably older than that of the Eskimo and con-

FIG. 290. Folsom point and associated fossil bison ribs, Folsom, New Mexico. (Colorado Mus. Nat. Hist.)

taining Folsom-like implements suggesting the American Southwest, as well as some implements (burins) not hitherto known from America but which are characteristic of the Aurignacian and Magdalenian of Europe and possibly Asia.[3] The exact age of the Cape Denbigh site

[3] J. L. Giddings, Jr., "The Denbigh Flint Complex," *American Antiquity,* XVI (1951), pp. 193–203.

has not been determined, but it is at least suggestive as a connecting link between the cultures of the Old and the New World.

It is worthy of note that in 1935, the late Dr. Edgar B. Howard of the University Museum in Philadelphia visited the museums of Leningrad for the purpose of studying Siberian archaeological material. He reported that "nothing was found in any of the collections, nor had any of the scientists of whom I inquired ever seen anything comparable to our Folsom points." [4]

In 1946, an expedition led by Dr. Helmut de Terra discovered a human skeleton with associated artifacts as well as skeletal remains of numerous extinct animals, in excavations at the village of Tepexpan, near Mexico City. Preliminary reports suggested that this skeleton might be the long-sought Folsom Man; however, considerable doubt has recently been shed on the antiquity of this find.

Sandia Culture.—Most archaeologists today are of the opinion that the oldest known human culture in North America is that found in Sandia Cave, New Mexico, by Frank C. Hibben in 1936. Beneath the remains of the Pueblo Indians, Hibben found a layer of stalagmatic travertine, a material that forms under moist conditions; beneath this travertine he found some Folsom points, together with the bones of some extinct animals. Next below these points and bones he found a layer of yellow ochre made from the remains of fir and spruce, trees that require a colder and moister climate than that prevailing in the vicinity of Sandia today. Beneath this ochre layer, Hibben found what is now called the Sandia point, a crude stone implement that, at least superficially, resembles the Solutrean points of Europe. Because of its deeper position in the cave it is believed that the Sandia point is definitely older than the Folsom, but its exact age is uncertain. Some believe that the Sandia culture is at least 25,000 years old, dating from an interstadial within the Wisconsin. Others believe that it only slightly antedates the Folsom culture, and dates from the Pluvial period, about 12,000 years ago.

Other Ancient Cultures of the Southwest.—Many other sites found in the Southwest have been assigned considerable antiquity. Some, in the vicinity of Abilene, Texas, have been regarded as considerably older than either Folsom or Sandia, but the evidence is not convincing. Others, of approximately the same age as the Folsom culture, or younger, are the Gypsum Cave culture of Nevada and the Cochise culture of Arizona.

---

[4] Edgar Howard, "Early Man in America," *Proc. Amer. Philos. Soc.,* LXXVI (1936), pp. 327–33.

The transition from the primitive Folsom and related cultures to the early Indian cultures, such as the Basket Maker and the Pueblo, is very indistinct and cannot be completely traced. Fortunately, however, there are a few suggestions of cultural links. The Ventana Cave in southern Arizona, for example, contains various layers of archaeological material that tell a reasonably complete story: from a Folsom culture at the base through the Cochise culture, to several pre-pottery and pre-agricultural layers to a pottery layer which apparently dates from about the beginning of the Christian era. The Basket Maker civilization of the Southwest is thought to have flourished from about 100 B.C. to A.D. 700. The early Basket Makers did not know the art of making pottery, although they wove excellent baskets. Pottery was apparently adopted by the Basket Makers about A.D. 500 and was used by them as well as by the succeeding Pueblo Indians. Further attempts at dating by means of radioactive carbon will probably result in the clarification of the prehistory of the Southwest.

"Minnesota Girl."—In 1931, the skeleton of a young woman was found in varved clay near Pelican Rapids, Minnesota, at a depth of 9 feet, 9 inches. Considerable argument arose as to whether the find indicated drowning in a glacial lake, perhaps 10,000 years ago, or whether it represents burial by human agencies or by slope wash. The argument is still unsettled, although the evidence seems to be in favor of a considerable antiquity.

Vero, Florida.—During the construction of a drainage ditch at Vero, Florida, in 1916, fragments of a human skeleton were found at a depth of less than four feet. It was associated with numerous extinct animals such as the giant ground sloth (*Megalonyx jeffersonii*), two extinct species of the horse, the mastodon, mammoth, and sabretoothed tiger. This bone deposit, known as the Melbourne Bone bed, occurs elsewhere in Florida and is generally regarded as of early Post-Wisconsin age. Considerable argument has arisen as to whether the human bones were deposited "in place" and were consequently contemporaneous with the extinct animals, or whether they indicated burial or a disturbance of the ground. These finds, like that of the "Minnesota Girl," are still a matter of some controversy although the majority of geologists and anthropologists believe that Vero Man did live at the same time as the extinct animals found in the deposit.

The finding of human remains associated with these extinct animals in Florida does not necessarily imply a tremendous antiquity. It is possible that many of the Pleistocene animals such as the mammoth and sabre-toothed tiger were driven south to Florida because of unfavorable climatic conditions in the north, and that they persisted in the warm Florida climate much longer than elsewhere in North America.

Natchez, Mississippi.—In 1846, the pelvic bone of a man (Figure 291) was found at Natchez, Mississippi, associated with the mastodon, the Pleistocene horse, several species of sloth, and the bison. The material came from 30 feet beneath the surface of the ground, and about 170 feet above the level of the Mississippi River. The English geologist Sir Charles Lyell, who examined the bones, stated that the human bone appeared to have the same preservation and the same

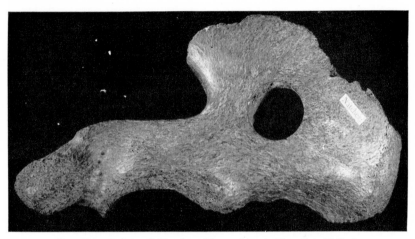

Fig. 291.   Pelvis of Natchez Man.   (Acad. Nat. Sci. Phila.)

black color as the other fossils. Later studies on the fluorine content of the bones also favored a contemporaneity of "Natchez Man" with the extinct animals, thereby implying a considerable antiquity.

Abbott Farm, Trenton, New Jersey.—For more than 50 years the Abbott Farm site on the Delaware River, about two miles south of Trenton, New Jersey, was one of the most controversial of all American archaeological sites. It was for a long time regarded as the best or only proof of Paleolithic man in the New World, and was widely discussed in the scientific literature both in this country and abroad.

The discoveries were made in 1872 by Dr. Charles G. Abbott, a Trenton physician and author. It was largely because of the writings of Dr. Abbott that the site achieved such publicity. Dr. Abbott described three cultural levels: first and oldest, a Paleolithic culture in the so-called "Trenton gravels," an outwash deposit of the Wisconsin glaciation; second, and overlying the first, the "Argillite culture," a rather rude culture of chipped implements, largely argillite, containing no pottery, and regarded as of considerable antiquity; third, the culture of the historic Delaware Indians in the black soil. It was with the first of these layers—the Paleolithic culture—that most of the controversy was concerned.

In spite of considerable excavating at the Farm, no conclusive proof of the Paleolithic culture has been discovered. Many of the so-called "paleoliths" appear to be blanks or incomplete implements of more recent age, or else natural river pebbles without signs of use. The real implements found in the gravel may have reached their position by the slumping of the bluff.

The antiquity of the "Argillite culture" has also been questioned. Excavations undertaken by the New Jersey State Museum showed no stratification between this culture and that of the Delaware Indians. It is significant that pottery was found to be associated with the other artifacts at all depths throughout the site. The fact that some of the artifacts, as well as the associated pebbles, have been found at considerable depths can possibly be explained by postulating the former existence of gullies and consequent slopewash. There is, therefore, no reason to believe that any of the material found at the Abbott Farm site antedates the culture of the Delaware Indians, or dates back more than 1,000 years.

Boston, Massachusetts.—We have mentioned that excavations for a subway at Boylston Street in Boston revealed an ancient fish weir associated with mollusks indicating a slightly warmer water temperature than that existing in the Boston area today. These specimens have been correlated with the Post-Wisconsin climatic optimum, which suggests the existence of man in the Boston area some 4,000 to 6,000 years ago.

Other Cultures of Eastern North America.—Little is known about the migration of primitive man to the eastern part of the North American continent. It has been suggested that during the warm and dry period, 6,000 to 4,000 years ago, possibly equivalent to Atlantic time, Folsom man migrated eastward from the Great Plains to regions with heavier rainfall and thus reached what is now the eastern states. However, the presence of skeletal material, presumably of considerable antiquity, in Florida, Mississippi, and Minnesota suggests that some migration may have taken place considerably earlier. Folsom or Folsom-like ("Folsomoid") points have been found in most parts of the United States, including the Atlantic seaboard. None of the finds in the East can be proved to be of great antiquity, and many of them are associated with material of definitely younger age. The

widespread distribution of these points may indicate trading, imita-
tion, or a more general distribution of the Folsom culture.

Recent excavations in New York State, together with radiocarbon
studies, have suggested an Archaic Indian culture of about five thousand years ago.[5] A direct sequence has been established between this

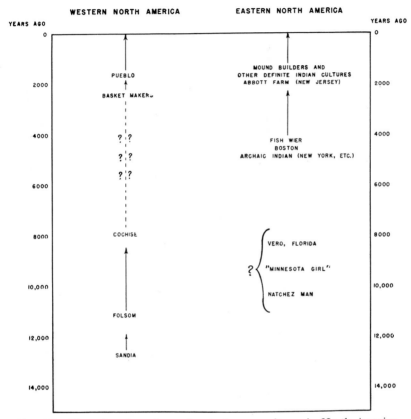

Fig. 292.   Tentative chronology of early human cultures in North America.

and the definite Indian cultures of the region. Indications of cultures
of similar antiquity may be looked for elsewhere in the eastern states.
The later development of the Indian cultures, including the Mound
Builders of Ohio, West Virginia, Georgia, etc., is fairly well known
and need not concern us here. What we would like to find in the East
is a connecting link between the Archaic or some other definite Indian
culture and the Folsom or other prehistoric cultures of the West and
Southwest. Perhaps we will not have to wait too long for such a

[5] William A. Ritchie, "A Current Synthesis of New York Prehistory," *American
Antiquity,* XVII (1951), pp. 130–36.

discovery. The table (Figure 292) gives an approximate chronology of the various American cultures mentioned in this chapter.

What Is Happening Today?

Rise of Sea Level.—According to the glacial control hypothesis, the retreat of the glaciers should be accompanied by a rise in sea level. If, as suggested in the preceding chapter, the sea level was about 300 feet lower during Wisconsin time than at present, it must have risen that much since the glacial climax. Since the glaciers of Greenland and many other parts of the world are slowly melting and pouring water back into the sea, it is probable that sea level is still rising, although the rise is so slow that it has been almost imperceptible within recorded historic time.

Sinking of the Land.—Some fifty years ago it was generally accepted that the coast of New Jersey was sinking at a rate of about a quarter of an inch per year, or two feet a century. The evidence seemed undeniable, especially to anyone who had witnessed the tremendous loss of land that had occurred at many places along the coast. Later investigations have shed considerable doubt on this theory of coastal subsidence. A careful study of the New Jersey coast line by the Department of Commerce and Navigation showed that land had undeniably been washed away in many places, but that in others it had been added by the sea. It was shown that 5,220 acres had been lost and that 3,025 had been added (to 1920). While the loss was considerably greater than the gain, it did not indicate a general subsidence. The same situation holds true in other regions along the east coast. For example, it is well known that Cape Hatteras is washing away, having lost more than a mile within the past hundred years, but it is also true that Cape Lookout is gaining land because of the considerable amounts of sand added by the sea.

It is now generally believed by geologists that most of the loss of land along the Atlantic Coast is primarily caused by waves and currents rather than by a sinking of the land. The slight rise in sea level caused by the melting ice may also have some slight effect, but it is of very minor consequence. This interpretation does not rule out local subsidence or elevation of the land, but does not regard these as the main cause of the coastal changes.

Some of the changes in the position of the shore line in the vicinity of Cape May, New Jersey, were discussed in Chapter 4 (page 45), in connection with the "fossil" footprints found in buried peat or meadow

FIG. 293. Traces of an ancient log road uncovered by a heavy storm. This road once extended from the vicinity of the present shore line at Cape May Point, New Jersey, to what is now a submerged bar, which a hundred years ago was farm land. Footprints of horses and cattle were preserved in the peat along the side of the road. The thin layer of overlying sand which protected the road and footprints was washed away by the storm.

sod extending out beyond the present tide line. Figure 293 shows the remains of a log road extending from the present beach in the direction of Prissy Wick Shoal, now beneath the water but probably once meadowland. Figure 294 illustrates even more recent erosion, being a former street corner in the now almost completely destroyed town of South Cape May.

Fig. 294. Evidence of changes in the position of the New Jersey shore line. The fire plug stood on a street corner in South Cape May.

Shore Processes.—Existing shore lines show evidence of pronounced changes in the relative level of sea and land. Some, generally spoken of as *shore lines of submergence,* indicate that the coast line has been depressed by diastrophic movements or that the sea level has risen. Such shore lines usually have wide bays (which can frequently be interpreted as drowned river valleys) as well as vertical sea cliffs and bold headlands. This kind of shore line occurs generally in northeastern North America and Western Europe.

The South Atlantic and Gulf Coasts are usually regarded as *shore lines of emergence.* Such shore lines produce barrier beaches (or offshore bars) such as those along the New Jersey and North Carolina coasts, bays or lagoons such as Barnegat Bay in New Jersey, Pamlico Sound in North Carolina, Laguna Madre in Texas, as well as sand spits such as Sandy Hook in New Jersey.

It should be borne in mind that most shore lines possess features of both submergence and emergence and should be regarded as *compound shore lines*. The terms "submergence" and "emergence" usually refer to the dominant features of the shore line. New Jersey and Maryland, with their bays, barrier beaches, and gently sloping shores, are usually regarded as having shore lines of emergence. However, Delaware and Chesapeake Bays are drowned river valleys, which are features of shore lines of emergence; hence, these shores should be regarded as compound.

Present-Day Sedimentation.—The processes of sedimentation did not stop with the transition from Pleistocene to Recent time. They have been continuous, thereby usually making it impossible to draw a sharp line between Pleistocene and Recent deposits. In Chapter 1, we learned of the deposits of aeolian limestone in the Bahamas containing "fossil" coins and broken bottles, obviously no more than one or two hundred years old (Figure 1, page 9). Sand dunes, also of aeolian origin, may be of considerable thickness and may move rapidly across the landscape, covering and then uncovering trees, old ships, roads, and even houses. Dunes along the Atlantic coast of North Carolina near Kitty Hawk and Nags Head, as well as those along Lake Michigan near Chicago, are especially striking.

Marine sedimentation is going on actively today, but most of the deposits are inconspicuous because they lie beneath the waters of the ocean. However, marine deposits such as the coquina (shell-limestone) now forming along the coast of Florida, have occasionally been exposed by recent withdrawals of the sea. A peculiar type of limestone is now being deposited in the shallow waters near Andros Island in the Bahamas, giving the ocean an almost milky appearance. Some geologists think that this limestone is largely of nonorganic origin and has precipitated directly from the sea water. Others believe that it forms from detrital waste washed from the nearby limestone islands.

Present-Day Diastrophism.—That the world is still in the process of geologic change is shown by the diastrophism going on at the present time. Some of this is so slow that it cannot be observed or recorded, but if the present can be judged in any way by the past, it is certain that some regions of the earth are sinking, while others are rising. Not all present-day diastrophism is slow. We frequently read in the paper of earthquakes and volcanoes that radically change the configuration of the earth. As a rule, both volcanoes and earthquakes are limited to certain belts or arcs of structural weakness in the earth's crust. For example, a very definite earthquake-volcano arc extends along the west coast of South, Central, and North America, to the Aleutians, then southward through the Kurils and Japan along the eastern coast of Asia into Indonesia. Another, smaller arc, occurs in the islands of the West Indies.

However, not all earthquakes are limited to definite zones of activity. As we read in Chapter 4, the major quakes at New Madrid, Missouri (1811–12), and Charleston, South Carolina (1886), were far removed from the major earthquake belts and are thought to have been caused by movements along deep-seated faults. The occasional minor quakes felt along the east coast of North America are probably caused by either deep-seated faults (possibly Triassic) or by slight readjustments of the earth's crust as an aftermath of its release from the load of the Pleistocene glaciers.

What of the Future?—It is not the province of the geologist to predict the future. However, it is obvious that the factors which have controlled the geological history of the earth for countless millions of years are at work today, and will continue to have their effect in the years to come. Sea level will rise and fall, and there will be uplift and depression of the land. Sediments will accumulate in geosynclines, and after they reach considerable thickness, diastrophism will produce new mountain ranges. It will be recalled that some geologists think a geosyncline is now forming beneath the Gulf of Mexico, caused by the tremendous quantities of sediments brought down by the Mississippi River. If this is true, perhaps a mountain range may be uplifted in that area in some future geological period.

We have seen in this chapter that the trend is for a slow rise of sea level, caused by the melting of the Arctic ice sheets. If this continues for many thousands of years, much of the lowlands along the present seacoast will be submerged. Many of the important cities and harbors of the world would thus be inundated.

Some scientists think that in spite of the minor fluctuations in climate we are approaching an interglacial stage, and that the climate will continue to become generally warmer for thousands of years and then become colder again as new glaciers advance from the poles. Whether or not this will actually take place, we will leave to the future.

FURTHER READING FOR CHAPTERS 25 AND 26

ANTEVS, ERNST. *The Last Glaciation.* New York: Amer. Geographic Soc., Research Series **17**, 1928.

———. "Maps of the Pleistocene Glaciation," *Bull. Geol. Soc. Amer.,* XL (1929), pp. 631–720.

BAKER, FRANK C. *The Life of the Pleistocene or Glacial Period.* Urbana: University of Illinois, Vol. 17, No. 41, 1920.

COLEMAN, A. P. *Ice Ages, Recent and Ancient.* New York: The Macmillan Co., 1929, pp. 3–73.

———. *The Last Million Years.* Toronto: University of Toronto Press, 1941.

COOKE, C. WYTHE, GARDNER, JULIA, and WOODRING, W. P. "Correlation of the Cenozoic Formations of the Atlantic and Gulf Coastal Plain and the Caribbean Region," *Bull. Geol. Soc. Amer.,* LIV (1943), pp. 1713–23.

DALY, R. A. *The Changing World of the Ice Age.* New Haven: Yale University Press, 1934.

DEEVEY, EDWARD S. "Biogeography of the Pleistocene," *Bull. Geol. Soc. Amer.,* LX (1949), pp. 1315–1416.

DUNBAR, CARL O. *Historical Geology.* New York: John Wiley & Sons, Inc., 1949, ch. 18.

FERNALD, M. L. "Persistence of Plants in Unglaciated Portions of Boreal America," Amer. Acad. Arts and Sci. *Memoirs,* XV (1925), pp. 237–342.

FLINT, RICHARD F. *Glacial Geology and the Pleistocene Epoch.* New York: John Wiley & Sons, Inc., 1947.

FULLER, M. L. *The Geology of Long Island.* U.S. Geol. Surv. Prof. Paper 82 (1914).

GIDLEY, J. W., and GAZIN, C. L. *The Pleistocene Fauna from Cumberland Caves, Maryland.* U.S. Nat. Mus. Bull. 171 (1938).

HANSEN, HENRY P. "Postglacial Forest Succession, Climate and Chronology in the Pacific Northwest," *Trans. Amer. Philos. Soc.,* XXXVII, Pt. 1 (1947), pp. 1–130.

HAY, O. P. *The Pleistocene of North America and Its Vertebrated Animals.* Carnegie Inst. Wash. Pub. 322 (three parts), 1922–27.

HOWELLS, WILLIAM. *Mankind So Far.* New York: Doubleday & Co., Inc., 1944.

LEWIS, J. V., and KUMMEL, H. B. *The Geology of New Jersey.* New Jersey Geol. Surv. Bull. 50 (1940).

MARTIN, PAUL S., QUIMBY, GEORGE I., and COLLIER, DONALD. *Indians Before Columbus.* Chicago: University of Chicago Press, 1947.

MACGOWAN, KENNETH. *Early Man in the New World.* New York: The Macmillan Co., 1950.

MCCLINTOCK, PAUL, and RICHARDS, HORACE G. "Correlation of Late Pleistocene and Glacial Deposits of New Jersey and New York," *Bull. Geol. Soc. Amer.,* XLVII (1936), pp. 289–338.

MOORE, RAYMOND C. *An Introduction to Historical Geology.* New York: McGraw-Hill Book Co., Inc., 1949, ch. 18.

OSBORN, HENRY F. *The Age of Mammals.* New York: The Macmillan Co., 1921.

RICHARDS, HORACE G. "Correlation of Atlantic Coastal Plain Formations: A Discussion," *Bull. Geol. Soc. Amer.,* LVI (1943), pp. 401–8.

———. "Fauna of the Pleistocene Pamlico Formation of the Southern Atlantic Coastal Plain," *Bull. Geol. Soc. Amer.,* XLVII (1936), pp. 1611–56.

———. "Geology of the Coastal Plain of North Carolina," *Trans. Amer. Philos. Soc.,* XL, Pt. 1 (1950), pp. 1–83.

RUSSELL, RICHARD J. "Quaternary History of Louisiana," *Bull. Geol. Soc. Amer.,* LI (1940), pp. 1199–1234.

SCOTT, W. B. *A History of the Land Mammals in the Western Hemisphere.* New York: The Macmillan Co., 1937.

SELLARDS, E. H. "Early Man in America," *Bull. Geol. Soc. Amer.,* LVIII (1947), pp. 955–78.

SHATTUCK, G. B. *The Pliocene and Pleistocene Deposits of Maryland.* Maryland Geol. Surv., 1906.

WOODWORTH, J. B., and WIGGLESWORTH, E. *Geography and Geology of the Region Including Cape Cod, the Elizabeth Islands, Nantucket, Martha's Vineyard, No Man's Land, and Block Island.* Memoirs, Mus. Comp. Zool., LII (1934).

WORMINGTON, H. M. *Ancient Man in North America.* Denver Mus. Nat. Hist., Popular Series 4 (1944).

ZEUNER, FREDERICK. *Dating the Past.* London: Methuen & Co., Ltd., 1951.

———. *The Pleistocene Period.* London: Bernard Quaritch, Ltd., 1945.

INDEX OF NAMES

INDEX OF SUBJECTS